Libraries in the United Kingdom and the Republic of Ireland 2000

LIBRARY ASSOCIATION PUBLISHING
LONDON

7 Ridgmount Street
London
WC1E 7AE

Library Association Publishing is wholly owned by The Library Association.

First edition	private circulation	Fourteenth edition	1988
Second edition	1960	Fifteenth edition	1989
Third edition	1966	Sixteenth edition	1990
Fourth edition	1969	Reprinted	1990
Fourth edition	(revised) 1971	Seventeenth edition	1991
Fifth edition	1974	Eighteenth edition	1991
Sixth edition	1975	Nineteenth edition	1992
Seventh edition	1977	Twentieth edition	1993
Eighth edition	1979	Twenty-first edition	1994
Ninth edition	1981	Twenty-second edition	1995
Tenth edition	1983	Twenty-third edition	1996
Eleventh edition	1985	Reprinted	1997
Reprinted	1985	Twenty-fourth edition	1997
Twelfth edition	1985	Twenty-fifth edition	1999
Thirteenth edition	1986	Twenty-sixth edition	1999

ISBN 1-85604-342-8
ISSN 1369-9687

Whilst every effort has been made to ensure accuracy, the publishers cannot be held responsible for any errors or omissions.

This twenty-sixth edition has been compiled by Lin Franklin and June York.

Typeset in 8/10pt Switzerland by Library Association Publishing.
Printed and bound in Great Britain by MPG Books Ltd, Bodmin, Cornwall.

Contents

Preface

How this book is organized

Libraries in the United Kingdom and the Republic of Ireland is published annually, and is a listing of libraries falling into the four categories below.

1 Public library authorities

■ All public library authorities in the UK and the Republic of Ireland, arranged under home countries
- Public Libraries in England, Northern Ireland, Scotland, Wales and Crown Dependencies
- Public Libraries in the Republic of Ireland

It is clearly impossible to list all branch libraries, mobile bases and so on, so each entry includes headquarters/central library details, together with major branches and area/ regional/ group libraries in that authority. Libraries in this section are arranged by name of authority. This edition contains complete details of all the new unitary authorities.

■ Children's, Youth and Schools Library Services

This section gives you more specific information about what services for children and young people are available within the public library authorities, and how you can contact them.

2 Academic libraries (arranged by name of institution)

■ University libraries in the UK and the Republic of Ireland, together with major department and site/campus libraries
■ College libraries at the universities of Oxford, Cambridge and London

Please note: potential users of the Oxford and Cambridge libraries should be aware that their use is restricted to members of the college, and to bona fide scholars on application to the Librarian; any additional information about their use is given with each entry.

■ Scottish central institutions
■ The university-equivalent colleges in the Republic of Ireland
■ Other degree-awarding institutions in the UK

This edition features all colleges of higher education funded by HEFCE, SHEFC and HEFCW.

3 Selected government, national and special libraries in the UK and the Republic of Ireland

■ Entries for government departments include at least the main library for the department, together with any specialist libraries. For example, the entry for the Health and Safety Executive includes the Nuclear Safety Division.

■ Special libraries are included if they are one of the main libraries or organizations in their subject field. For example, the Royal Photographic Society is included for photography, the Institution of Civil Engineers for civil engineering. *Many of the libraries in this section require a prior appointment to be made before visiting.*

4 Schools and departments of information and library studies

■ Each academic institution offering courses in information and library studies, with full contact details of the departments concerned.

Indexes

Again this year we have produced separate name and subject indexes to the book. We hope this will further assist you in finding the information you are looking for.

Updating *Libraries in the UK*

The directory is compiled by mailing questionnaires or entries for updating to libraries already listed in this book, and to others that have been suggested for inclusion. We would like to thank them all for taking the time to reply to yet another mailing. With their assistance we received a 100% return rate. This means that every entry has been approved by the institution concerned.

We are dependent upon libraries to keep us informed of changes throughout the year. In this way we shall be able to ensure that our mailing label service is as current as possible. Libraries will, of course, be contacted afresh for the preparation of the next edition.

Mailing labels

The *Directory* is also available in the form of continually updated laser-quality mailing labels, with the option of either the named Chief Librarian or the Acquisitions Librarian as addressee. They are available in the following sets from Bookpoint Ltd, 39 Milton Park, Abingdon, Oxon OX14 4TD. (Tel: 01235 827794. Fax: 01235 400454):

Full set
Named Chief Librarian   ISBN 1 85604 026 7
Acquisitions Librarian   ISBN 1 85604 198 0

Public libraries (main headquarters)
Named Chief Librarian   ISBN 0 85365 587 1
Acquisitions Librarian   ISBN 1 85604 199 9

Public libraries (main headquarters and branches)
Named Chief Librarian   ISBN 1 85604 025 9

Academic and special libraries
Named Chief Librarian   ISBN 0 85365 959 1
Acquisitions Librarian   ISBN 1 85604 201 4

Children's, youth and schools library services
Named Children's/Schools Officer   ISBN 1 85604 247 2

Please help us to improve this directory

Any comments about additions or other changes to *Libraries in the United Kingdom and the Republic of Ireland* will be welcomed. Please address them to:

The Editor
Libraries in the UK
Library Association Publishing
7 Ridgmount Street
London WC1E 7AE

Tel: 020 7636 7543 (from 1 October 1999: 020 7255 0590)
e-mail: lapublishing@la-hq.org.uk

Public Libraries in the United Kingdom, the Channel Islands and the Isle of Man

England
Northern Ireland
Scotland
Wales
Crown Dependencies

ENGLAND

BARKING AND DAGENHAM

Headquarters London Borough of Barking and Dagenham, Central Library, Barking, Essex
IG11 7NB
☎020 8517 8666 (enquiries); 020 8252 8310 (administration)
Fax 020 8594 1156
Borough Librarian Vacant
Head of Library Resources and Development T R Brown ALA
Community & Education Services Manager Mrs S Leighton ALA
Departmental IT Officer A Clifford ALA (e-mail: fm019@viscount.org.uk)
Support Services Manager D W Bailey ALA (020 8252 8310)
Central Library Manager Miss S Currie ALA

Central/largest library
As above

Community libraries
A   Marks Gate Library, Rose Lane, Chadwell Heath, Essex RM6 5NJ
      ☎020 8599 9953
      Senior Library Assistant Mrs B Mortimer
B   Markyate Library, Markyate Road, Dagenham, Essex RM8 2LD
      ☎020 8592 1309
      Senior Library Assistant Mrs K Avagah
C   Rush Green Library, Dagenham Road, Rush Green, Essex RM7 0TL
      ☎(01708) 744795
      Senior Library Assistant Mrs L Craig
D   Thames View Library, 2A Farr Avenue, Barking, Essex IG11 0NZ
      ☎020 8594 3408
      Assistant Librarian Miss A Sawtell
E   Valence Library, Becontree Avenue, Dagenham, Essex RM8 3HS
      ☎020 8592 6537
      Branch Librarian Mrs J Murphy ALA
F   Wantz Library, Rainham Road North, Dagenham, Essex RM10 7DX
      ☎020 8592 2903
      Branch Librarian Mrs A Brown ALA
G   Whalebone Library, High Road, Chadwell Heath, Essex RM6 6AS
      ☎020 8590 4636
      Branch Librarian Mrs J Sibley ALA
H   Woodward Library, Woodward Road, Dagenham, Essex RM9 4SP
      ☎020 8592 5235
      Branch Librarian Mrs C Pereira ALA

BARNET

Headquarters London Borough of Barnet, Cultural Services, The Old Town Hall, Friern
Barnet Lane, London N11 3DL
☎020 8359 3164 (enquiries)
Fax 020 8359 3171
url: http://www.earl.org.uk/partners/barnet/index.html
Head of Cultural Services Ms P Usher BA(Hons) DMS ALA (e-mail:
pam.usher@barnet.gov.uk)
Head of Development and Support Ms T Little BA ALA
Head of Bibliographical Services Ms M Ross BA(Hons) ALA

Research & Development Officer B Hellen ALA MIInfSc (e-mail: bob.hellen@barnet.gov.uk)

Group libraries

A Chipping Barnet Library, 3 Stapylton Road, Barnet, Herts EN5 4QT
  ☎020 8359 4040
  e-mail: chipping.lib@barnet.gov.uk
B Church End Library, 24 Hendon Lane, Finchley, London N3 1TR
  ☎020 8346 5711
C Edgware Library, Hale Lane, Edgware, Middlesex HA8 8NN
  ☎020 8359 2626
D Hendon Library, The Burroughs, London NW4 4BQ
  ☎020 8359 2628
  e-mail: hendon.lib@barnet.gov.uk

BARNSLEY

Headquarters Barnsley Metropolitan Borough Council, Central Library, Shambles Street, Barnsley, South Yorkshire S70 2JF
☎(01226) 773911/12/30 (enquiries), (01226) 773913 (administration)
Fax (01226) 773955
e-mail: librarian@barnsley.ac.uk
url: http://www.barnsley.ac.uk/sites/library/index.htm
Chief Libraries Officer (Acting) S F Bashforth BA ALA

Central/largest library
Central Library, Shambles Street, Barnsley, South Yorkshire S70 2JF
☎(01226) 773940 (enquiries), (01226) 773929 (administration)
Fax (01226) 773955
e-mail: librarian@barnsley.ac.uk
Lending Services Officer (Acting) Ms K Green BA ALA

Group headquarters

A Goldthorpe Branch Library, Barnsley Road, Goldthorpe, Rotherham, South
  Yorkshire S63 9NE
  ☎(01709) 893278
  Fax (01709) 893278
  e-mail: goldthorpe.lib@barnsley.ac.uk
  Dearne Group Librarian J Coldwell BA ALA
B Royston Branch Library, Midland Road, Royston, Barnsley, South Yorkshire S71 4QP
  ☎(01226) 722870
  e-mail: royston.lib@barnsley.ac.uk
  Royston Group Librarian R Wilson BSc(Econ) ALA
C Penistone Branch Library, High Street, Penistone, Sheffield S30 6BR
  ☎(01226) 762313
  e-mail: penistone.lib@barnsley.ac.uk
  Penistone Group Librarian Ms J Craven ALA
D Priory Information & Resource Centre, Pontefract Road, Lundwood, Barnsley,
  South Yorkshire S71 4QP
  ☎(01226) 770616
  Fax (01226) 771425
  e-mail: priory.lib@barnsley.ac.uk
  Priory Information and Resource Officer Ms S Gray BA CertEd ALA

BATH AND NORTH EAST SOMERSET

Headquarters Bath and North East Somerset Council, Libraries, Arts and Archives, Third

Floor, 16a Broad Street, Bath, Somerset BA1 5LJ
☎(01225) 396404
Fax (01225) 396457
Head of Libraries, Arts and Archives Ms J Campbell BA(Hons) ALA

Central/largest library
Bath Central Library, The Podium, Northgate Street, Bath BA1 5AN
☎(01225) 428144 (enquiries), (01225) 481913 (administration)
Fax (01225) 331839
Group Librarian Mrs E Bevan ALA

Group libraries
A   Midsomer Norton Library, High Street, Midsomer Norton, Somerset BA3 2DA
        ☎(01761) 412024
        Fax (01761) 417838
        Group Librarian Mrs H Moxham BA ALA
B   Keynsham Library, The Centre, Keynsham, Bristol BS31 1ED
        ☎(01225) 394191
        Fax (01225) 394195
        Group Librarian Ms L Byrd ALA

BEDFORDSHIRE
Headquarters Bedfordshire County Council, Department of Education, Arts and Libraries, County Hall, Cauldwell Street, Bedford MK42 9AP
☎(01234) 228752
Fax (01234) 228993
Head of Libraries and Communications B S George ALA (e-mail: georgeb@beal.bedfordshire.gov.uk)
Library Services Manager Ms J Poad BA DMS ALA (01234 350931)
Library Resources Manager A Baker ALA (01234 228301)

Central/largest library
Bedford Central Library, Harpur Street, Bedford MK40 1PG
☎(01234) 350931 (enquiries/administration)
Fax (01234) 342163
Central Library Manager Mrs A Hodson BA(Hons) ALA

BEXLEY
Headquarters London Borough of Bexley, Leisure Services, Libraries and Cultural Services Division, Hill View, Hill View Drive, Welling, Kent DA16 3RY
☎020 8303 7777 ext 4268
Fax 020 8308 4926
e-mail: info@bexley.gov.uk
url: http://www.bexley.gov.uk
Head of Libraries and Cultural Services F V Johnson LLB DMS ALA MIMgt (020 8303 7777 ext 4496; e-mail: fred.johnson@bexley.gov.uk)
Project Development and Support Librarian P Marshall (020 8303 7777 ext 4512; e-mail: peter.marshall@bexley.gov.uk)

Central/largest libraries
Central Library, Townley Road, Bexleyheath, Kent DA6 7HJ
☎020 8301 1066 (reception), 020 8301 5151 (information line)
Fax 020 8303 7872

BIRMINGHAM

Headquarters Birmingham City Council, Central Library, Chamberlain Square, Birmingham B3 3HQ

☎0121 303 4511 (enquiries) 0121 303 2454 (management)

Fax 0121 303 4458 (enquiries) 0121 233 9702 (management)

Assistant Director (Libraries and Learning) Mrs V M Griffiths BA DipLib ALA MSocSci (e-mail: viv.griffiths@birmingham.gov.uk)

Head of Central Library J Dolan BA DipLib ALA (e-mail: john.dolan@birmingham.gov.uk)

Head of Community Library Services G Mills MSc BA DipLib ALA (e-mail: geoff.mills@birmingham.gov.uk)

Head of Children, Youth and Education Services Mrs P Heap BA ALA (e-mail: patsy.heap@birmingham.gov.uk)

Head of Special Client Services Mrs L Butler BA ALA (e-mail: linda.butler@birmingham.gov.uk)

Head of Information Management and Networking B Gambles (e-mail: brian.gambles@birmingham.gov.uk)

Central/largest library
As above

BLACKBURN WITH DARWEN

Headquarters Blackburn with Darwen Borough Council, Central Library, Town Hall Street, Blackburn, Lancs BB2 1AG

☎(01254) 661221 (enquiries), (01254) 587902 (administration)

Fax (01254) 690539

Head of Cultural Services Mrs N Monks ALA

Head of Library Services Mrs S Law ALA (01254 587906)

Central/largest library
As above

BLACKPOOL

Headquarters Blackpool Borough Council, Community and Tourism Services, Cultural Services Division, Central Library, Queen Street, Blackpool, Lancs FY1 1PX

☎(01253) 478111 (enquiries), (01253) 478107 (administration)

Fax (01253) 478071

Head of Cultural Services Mrs P Hansell MBA BA ALA

Principal Librarian, Support Services R Baker BA ALA DMS

Principal Librarian, Customer Services Mrs K Buddle BA(Hons) ALA

Arts Development Officer Ms L Fade MA

Central/largest library
As above

BOLTON

Headquarters Bolton Metropolitan District Council, Central Library, Le Mans Crescent, Bolton, Lancs BL1 1SE

☎(01204) 522311 ext 2173 (enquiries), ext 2169 (administration)

Fax (01204) 363224

Chief Librarian Mrs K C Ryan BA MBA FLA

Assistant Chief Librarian Mrs Y Gill-Martin BA DMS ALA

Area Librarian, Central K F Bell BA ALA

Central/largest library
As above

Branch libraries HQ
Harwood Library, Gate Fold, Harwood, Bolton, Lancs BL2 3HN
☎(01204) 304565
Fax (01204) 306952
Area Librarian K A Beevers BA ALA

BOURNEMOUTH
Headquarters Bournemouth Borough Council, Bournemouth Libraries, Leisure & Tourism
Directorate, Town Hall, Bourne Avenue, Bournemouth, Dorset BH2 6DY
☎(01202) 454614 (enquiries), (01202) 454616 (administration)
Fax (01202) 454620
Head of Arts, Libraries and Museums Ms S Levett BA(Hons) CertEd ALA (01202
454615)
Senior Libraries Officer: North Mrs C Date GradIPD ALA (01202 547876)
Senior Libraries Officer: South Vacant

Central/largest library
Lansdowne Library, Meyrick Road, Bournemouth, Dorset BH1 1DJ
☎(01202) 292021

BRACKNELL FOREST
Headquarters Bracknell Forest Borough Council, Leisure Services, Edward Elgar House,
Skimped Hill Lane, Bracknell, Berks RG12 1LR
☎(01344) 354103 (enquiries), (01344) 424642 (administration)
Fax (01344) 354100
e-mail: bracknell.forest.gov.uk
Head of Libraries, Arts and Information Ms R Burgess BLib ALA (e-mail:
ruth.burgess@bracknell.forest.gov.uk)

Central/largest library
Bracknell Library, Town Square, Bracknell, Berks RG12 1BH
☎(01344) 352400
Fax (01344) 352420
e-mail: bracknell.forest.gov.uk
Library and Information Manager Ms K Chambers BA ALA

BRADFORD
Headquarters City of Bradford Metropolitan District Council, Central Library, Prince's Way,
Bradford, West Yorkshire BD1 1NN
☎(01274) 753600
Fax (01274) 395108
e-mail: public.libraries@bradford.gov.uk
Head of Arts, Museums and Libraries P W G Lawson BA MA AMA FRSA (01274
753640; e-mail: paul.lawson@bradford.gov.uk)
Principal Librarian Mrs M Minshull BA ALA (01274 753653; e-mail:
margaret.minshull@bradford.gov.uk)
Principal Officer, Libraries and Resources J Triffitt ALA (01274 753671; e-mail:
john.triffitt@bradford.gov.uk)

Area libraries
A   Bradford East Area. c/o Eccleshill Library, Bolton Road, Eccleshill, Bradford, West
       Yorkshire BD2 4SR
       ☎(01274) 751544

Fax (01274) 626667
Area Librarian Mrs M Rogerson BA ALA
B   Bradford West/Shipley Area. c/o, Shipley Library, 2 Wellcroft, Shipley, West
        Yorkshire BD18 3QH
        ☎(01274) 757150
        Fax (01274) 530247
        Area Librarian Mrs J Kitwood BA DipLib ALA
C   Keighley & West Area. c/o Keighley Library, North Street, Keighley, West Yorkshire
        BD21 3SE
        ☎(01535) 618212
        Fax (01535) 618214
        Area Librarian Miss J Unwin BA ALA

BRENT

Headquarters London Borough of Brent, Education, Arts and Libraries, 4th Floor,
Chesterfield House, 9 Park Lane, Wembley, Middlesex HA9 7RW
☎020 8937 3144
Fax 020 8937 3023
url: http://www.brent.gov.uk
Head of Library Service Ms K Tyerman BA(Hons) DipLib ALA (020 8937 3146; e-mail:
karen.tyerman@brent.gov.uk)

Area libraries
A   Barham Park Library, Harrow Road, Wembley, Middlesex HA9 2HB
        ☎020 8937 3550
        Ealing Road Library, Coronet Parade, Ealing Road, Middlesex HA0 4BR
        ☎020 8937 3560
        Kingsbury Library, Stag Lane, Kingsbury, London NW9 9AE
        ☎020 8937 3520
        Preston Library, Carlton Avenue East, Wembley, Middlesex HA9 8PL
        ☎020 8937 3510
        Principal Librarian, North K A Batchelor ALA
        Tokyngton Library, Monks Park, Wembley, Middlesex HA9 6JE
        ☎020 8937 3590
        Town Hall Library, Forty Lane, Wembley, Middlesex HA9 9HV
        ☎020 8937 3500
B   Harlesden Library, Craven Park, London NW10 8SE
        ☎020 8965 7132
        Kensal Rise Library, Bathurst Gardens, London NW10 5JA
        ☎020 8969 0942
        Kilburn Library, Salusbury Road, London NW6 9AE
        ☎020 8937 3530
        Principal Librarian, South M Perry BA(Hons) DMS
        Neasden Library, 277 Neasden Lane, London NW10 1QJ
        ☎020 8937 3580
        Outreach Library Services, 2-12 Grange Road, London NW10
        ☎020 8937 3460
        Principal Librarian, Central M Perry BA(Hons) DMS
C   Willesden Green Library, 95 High Road, Willesden, London NW10 2ST
        ☎020 8937 3400
        Principal Librarian, Willesden Green J Verstraete MLIS DLIS BA(Hons)
        Cricklewood Library, Olive Road, London NW2 6UY
        ☎020 8908 7430

BRIGHTON AND HOVE

Headquarters Brighton and Hove Council, Royal Pavilion, Libraries and Museums, 4-5 Pavilion Buildings, Brighton, East Sussex BN1 1EE
☎(01273) 290800 (enquiries), (01273) 296950 (administration)
Fax (01273) 296951 (lending), (01273) 296965 (reference)
Principal Librarian Ms A Saville MA ALA
Head of ICT/Customer Resources Ms S McMahon BA DipLib ALA (01273 296963)
Customer Services Manager Ms J Hugall BA DipLib ALA (01273 296953)
Professional Services Manager, Lending, Stock and Community N Imi BA DipLib ALA (01273 296953)
Professional Services Manager, Reference, IT and Special Collections Ms V Hayward BA ALA

Central libraries
A   Hove Central Library, 182-186 Church Road, Hove, East Sussex BN3 2EG
       ☎(01273) 290700, (01273) 296942 (reference)
       Fax (01273) 296931 (renewals), (01273) 296947 (reference)
B   Brighton Central Library, Church Street, Brighton, East Sussex BN1 1UE
       ☎(01273) 290800 (enquiries), (01273) 296968/9 (reference)
       Fax (01273) 296951 (renewals), (01273) 296965 (reference)

BRISTOL

Headquarters Bristol City Council, Museums and Libraries Division, Leisure Services Dept, Colston House, Colston Street, Bristol BS1 5AQ
☎0117 922 2814
Fax 0117 922 3991
Divisional Director W Sanderson (e-mail: bill_sanderson@bristol-city.gov.uk)
For general enquiries please contact Bristol Central Library (tel/fax etc. as below)

Central/largest library
Central Library, College Green, Bristol BS1 5TL
☎0117 903 7200
Fax 0117 922 1081
Head of Library Services Ms M Davies ALA
Community Services Manager (North and Central) Ms A Casey
Community Services Manager (South and East) Ms J York BA ALA
Support Services Manager A Montgomery MIInfSc MSc FLA

BROMLEY

Headquarters London Borough of Bromley, Central Library, High Street, Bromley, Kent BR1 1EX
☎020 8460 9955 (enquiries & administration)
Fax 020 8313 9975
e-mail: info@cenlibbrl.freeserve.co.uk
Chief Librarian B Walkinshaw BA ALA (e-mail: barry walkinshaw@bromley.gov.uk)
Library Operations Manager L F Favret BA MIMgt DipMgt ALA
Library Development Manager D Brockhurst BA ALA

Central/largest library
Central Library, High Street, Bromley, Kent BR1 1EX
☎Tel/Fax etc. as HQ
e-mail: leisure@bromley.demon.co.uk
Group Manager J Wilkins BSc ALA

District libraries
A   Beckenham Library, Beckenham Road, Beckenham, Kent BR3 4PE

☎020 8650 7292/3
Area Manager Miss C Alabaster BA ALA
B   Orpington Library, The Priory, Church Hill, Orpington, Kent BR6 0HH
☎(01689) 831551
Area Manager T Woolgar ALA

BUCKINGHAMSHIRE

Headquarters Buckinghamshire County Council, County Library, County Hall, Walton
Street, Aylesbury, Bucks HP20 1UU
☎(01296) 383206
Fax (01296) 382405
Assistant Director of Education (Libraries, Information, Museums and Archives)
J Whitter BA ALA (01296 383108; fax 01296 382259; e-mail: jwhitter@buckscc.gov.uk)
Head of Support Services Mrs J Varney ALA (01296 382258; fax 01296 382259; e-mail:
jvarney@buckscc.gov.uk)
Head of Branch and Mobile Library Service W Webb BA ALA (01296 382182; fax 01296
382405; e-mail: wwebb@buckscc.gov.uk)
Head of Reference and Information Service R Strong BA DipLib ALA (01296 382251; fax
01296 382405; e-mail: rstrong@buckscc.gov.uk)

District offices
A   Aylesbury Vale and Chiltern District. Chesham Library, Elgiva Lane, Chesham,
Bucks HP5 2JD
☎(01494) 774242
Fax (01494) 773074
District Librarian M Bryant BA DipLib ALA (01494 774242; e-mail:
mbryant@buckscc.gov.uk)
B   Chiltern and South Bucks District. Chesham Library, Elgiva Lane, Chesham, Bucks
HP5 2JD
☎(01494) 772322
Fax (01494) 773074
District Librarian W Webb BA ALA (01494) 774242
C   Wycombe and South Bucks District. Hazlemere Library, 312 Amersham Road,
Hazlemere, High Wycombe, Bucks HP15 7PY
☎(01494) 814017
Fax (01494) 816621
District Librarian P Mussett ALA (01494 814017; e-mail: wycdist@buckscc.gov.uk)

Main district libraries
A   Aylesbury Central Library, Walton Street, Aylesbury, Bucks HP20 1UU
☎(01296) 382248
Fax (01296) 382405
Assistant District Librarian Miss G Green BA ALA (e-mail:
gmgreen@buckscc.gov.uk)
B   Buckingham Library, Verney Close, Buckingham, Bucks MK18 1JP
☎(01280) 813229
Fax (01280) 823597
Assistant District Librarian S Grant BA ALA
C   Wendover Library, High Street, Wendover, Bucks HP22 6DU
☎(01296) 623649
Assistant District Librarian Mrs G Clipsham BA ALA
D   High Wycombe Central Library, Queen Victoria Road, High Wycombe, Bucks
HP11 1BD

☎(01494) 464004
Fax (01494) 533086
Assistant District Librarian Mrs T Cuthbert ALA
E   Hazlemere Library, 312 Amersham Road, Hazlemere, High Wycombe, Bucks
HP15 7PY
☎(01494) 815266
Fax (01494) 816621
Assistant District Librarian Mrs J Ottaway BA ALA
F   Marlow Library, Institute Road, Marlow, Bucks SL7 1BL
☎(01628) 486163
Fax (01628) 476313
Assistant District Librarian Mrs H Goreham BLib ALA
G   Chesham Library, Elgiva Lane, Chesham, Bucks HP5 2JD
☎(01494) 772322
Fax (01494) 773074
Assistant District Librarian Mrs E Collier BSc DipLib ALA
H   Beaconsfield Library, Reynolds Road, Beaconsfield, Bucks HP9 2NJ
☎(01494) 672295
Fax (01494) 678772
Assistant District Librarian Mrs G Griffin ALA

BURY

Headquarters Bury Metropolitan District Council, Cultural Services, Athenaeum House,
Market Street, Bury, Greater Manchester BL9 0BN
☎0161 253 7217 (enquiries), 0161 253 5863 (administration)
Fax 0161 253 5915
e-mail: information@bury.gov.uk
url: http://www.bury.gov.uk/culture.htm
Principal Librarian Mrs D Sorrigan BA ALA (0161 253 7217; e-mail:
prestwich.lib@bury.gov.uk)
Assistant Principal Librarian Mrs L Kelly BA MA DipLib ALA (0161 253 7579; e-mail:
radcliffe.lib@bury.gov.uk)
Assistant Principal Librarian T Jowett BA MA ALA (0161 253 5876)

Central/largest library
Central Library, Manchester Road, Bury, Greater Manchester BL9 0DG
☎0161 253 5876
Fax 0161 253 5857
e-mail: information@bury.gov.uk
Principal Librarian Mrs D Sorrigan BA ALA

Branch libraries
A   Prestwich Library, Longfield Centre, Prestwich, Greater Manchester M25 1AY
☎0161 253 7214
Fax 0161 253 5372
Librarians i/c Ms A Brumby ALA, Ms W Makin ALA (0161 253 7218; e-mail:
prestwich.lib@bury.gov.uk)
B   Radcliffe Library, Stand Lane, Radcliffe, Greater Manchester M26 9WR
☎0161 253 7161
Fax 0161 253 7165
e-mail: radcliffe.lib@bury.gov.uk
Library Supervisors N Griffin BTEC NEBS, Ms B Walker NEBS (0161 253 7160)
C   Ramsbottom Library, Carr Street, Ramsbottom, Greater Manchester BL0 9AE

☎(01706) 822484
Fax (01706) 824638
e-mail: ramsbottom.lib@bury.gov.uk
Library Supervisor Miss D Smith
D   Tottington Library, Market Street, Tottington, Greater Manchester BL8 3LN
☎(01204) 882839
e-mail: tottington.lib@bury.gov.uk
Library Supervisor Mrs L Snape
E   Unsworth Library, Sunnybank Road, Unsworth, Greater Manchester BL9 8EB
☎0161 253 7560
Library Supervisor Mrs J Smillie
F   Whitefield Library, Pinfold Lane, Whitefield, Greater Manchester M45 7NY
☎0161 253 7510
Library Supervisor Mrs W Rhodes

CALDERDALE

Headquarters Calderdale Metropolitan Borough, Central Library, Northgate, Halifax, West Yorkshire HX1 1UN
☎(01422) 392605
Fax (01422) 392615
e-mail: libraries@calderdale.gov.uk
Assistant Director of Leisure Services (Libraries) M P Stone BA(Hons) ALA

Central/largest library
Central Library, Northgate, Halifax, West Yorkshire HX1 1UN
☎(01422) 392630
Head of Central and Support Services Vacant

Area headquarters
A   East Area HQ, c/o Central Library, Northgate, Halifax, West Yorkshire HX1 1UN
☎(01422) 392623
Area Librarian, East Calderdale J R Jebson ALA
B   West Area HQ, c/o Hebden Bridge Library, Cheetham Street, Hebden Bridge, West Yorkshire HX7 8EP
☎(01422) 842151/843993
Area Librarian, West Calderdale Miss M G Morgan BA ALA

CAMBRIDGESHIRE

Headquarters Cambridgeshire County Council, Cambridgeshire Libraries and Information Services, Castle Court, Shire Hall, Cambridge CB3 0AP
☎(01223) 717067 (enquiries), (01223) 717023 (administration)
Fax (01223) 717079
e-mail: community.services@libraries.camcnty.gov.uk
Head of Libraries and Information Services M G Hosking MIMgt ALA (01223 717063; e-mail: mike.hosking@libraries.camcnty.gov.uk)
Assistant Head of Service (Public Services) Mrs L Noblett MA ALA (01223 717292; e-mail: lesley.noblett@libraries.camcnty.gov.uk)
Assistant Head of Service (Resources) C Heaton MA ALA (01223 717061; e-mail: chris.heaton@libraries.camcnty.gov.uk)

Central/largest library
Central Library, 7 Lion Yard, Cambridge CB2 3QD
☎(01223) 712000

Fax (01223) 712018
e-mail: cambridge.central.library@camcnty.gov.uk
Area Library Officer M Wyatt BA ALA MIMgt (01223 712001; e-mail:
michael.wyatt@libraries.camcnty.gov.uk)

Area library HQs
A   Huntingdon Library, Princes Street, Huntingdon, Cambs PE18 6PH
     ☎(01480) 375894
     Fax (01480) 375732
     e-mail: community.services@libraries.camcnty.gov.uk
     Area Library Officer Mrs J Hibbard ALA (01480 375895; e-mail:
     jenny.hibbard@libraries.camcnty.gov.uk)
B   Fenland and East Cambridgeshire Area Libraries, 19 Gordon Avenue, March,
     Cambs PE15 8AL
     ☎(01354) 660940
     Fax (01354) 658661
     e-mail: community.services@libraries.camcnty.gov.uk
     Area Library Officer D Allanach MLS ALA (e-mail: david.allanach@libraries.
     camcnty.gov.uk)
C   South Cambridgeshire Area Libraries, Roger Ascham School site, Ascham Road,
     Cambridge CB4 2BD
     ☎(01223) 718362
     Fax (01223) 718380
     e-mail: community.services@libraries.camcnty.gov.uk
     Area Library Officer Mrs L Martin ALA DMS MIMgt (01223 718367; e-mail:
     lynda.martin@libraries.camcnty.gov.uk

CAMDEN
Headquarters London Borough of Camden, Leisure and Community Services Department,
The Crowndale Centre, 218 Eversholt Street, London NW1 1BD
☎020 7911 1593
Fax 020 7911 1587
Assistant Director (Libraries, Arts, and Tourism Information) Ms F Mangan MBA
MILAM
Head of Libraries and Information Services N Hounsell BA ALA
Quality and Development Manager Vacant

Leisure/departmental library
Central Library, Swiss Cottage Library, 88 Avenue Road, London NW3 3HA
☎020 7413 6522 (switchboard), 020 7413 6527 (general enquiries), 020 7413 6525 (library
management)
Fax 020 7413 6532
Library Service Manager Ms E Murphy ALA

Main libraries
A   Holborn Library, 32-38 Theobalds Road, London WC1X 8PA
     ☎020 7413 6345/6, 020 7413 6342 (Local studies)
     Fax 020 7413 6356
B   St Pancras Library, Town Hall Extension, Argyle Street, London WC1H 8EQ
     ☎020 7860 5833
     Fax 020 7860 5963
C   Kentish Town Library, 262-8 Kentish Town Road, London NW5 2AA
     ☎020 7413 6253

Fax 020 7482 5650
D   West Hampstead Library, Dennington Park Road, London NW6 1AU
☎020 7413 6610
Fax 020 7413 6539
E   Queen's Crescent Library, 165 Queen's Crescent, London NW5 4HH
☎020 7485 6243
Fax 020 7485 6252
F   Camden Town Library, Crowndale Centre, 218 Eversholt Street, London NW1 1BD
☎020 7911 1563
Fax 020 7911 1582

Neighbourhood libraries
A   Belsize Library, Antrim Road, London NW3 4XN
☎020 7413 6518
B   Heath Library, Keats' Grove, London NW3 2RR
☎020 7413 6520
C   Regent's Park Library, Compton Close, Robert Street, London NW1 3QT
☎020 7911 1530
D   Kilburn Library, Cotleigh Road, London NW6 2NP
☎020 7314 1965
E   Highgate Library, Chester Road, London N19 5DH
☎020 7860 5752, 020 7281 2546 (home library service)
F   Chalk Farm Library, Sharpleshall Street, London NW1 8YN
☎020 7413 6526

CHESHIRE

Headquarters Cheshire County Council, Community Development Department, Libraries and Archives Service, Goldsmith House, Hamilton Place, Chester CH1 1SE
☎(01244) 602424 (County Hall switchboard)
Fax (01244) 602805
url: http://www.cheshire.gov.uk
County Librarian F I Dunn BA DAA FSA (01244 606034; e-mail: dunni@cheshire.gov.uk)
Resources and Development Manager A W Bell ALA (01244 606023; e-mail: bellaw@cheshire.gov.uk)

Regional/district libraries
A   Chester Library, Northgate Street, Chester CH1 2EF
☎(01244) 312935
Fax (01244) 315534
e-mail: ipchester@cheshire.gov.uk
Divisional Librarian, West Cheshire Miss C Sarson ALA (e-mail: sarsoncc@cheshire.gov.uk)
B   Crewe Library, Prince Albert Street, Crewe, Cheshire CW1 2DH
☎(01270) 211123
Fax (01270) 256952
Videophone: ISDN 01270 250771
e-mail: ipcrewe@cheshire.gov.uk
Divisional Librarian, Mid Cheshire G R Pimlett MA ALA (01270 250232; e-mail: pimlettgr@cheshire.gov.uk)
C   Macclesfield Library, 2 Jordangate, Macclesfield, Cheshire SK10 1EE
☎(01625) 422512
Fax (01625) 612818
Videophone: ISDN 01625 611785

e-mail: ipmacclesfield@cheshire.gov.uk
Divisional Librarian, East Cheshire Ms A Taylor BA DipLib ALA (e-mail:
tayloraa@cheshire.gov.uk)

D   Cheshire Information Service, Ellesmere Port Library, Civic Way, Ellesmere Port,
Cheshire L65 0BG
☎0151 357 4689
Fax 0151 357 4698

CORNWALL
Headquarters Cornwall County Council, Information Services Group, Lerryn Building, Old
County Hall, Truro, Cornwall TR1 3AY
☎(01872) 322269 (enquiries)
Fax (01872) 323820
Information Services Director Mrs M Bartz (based at New County Hall, Truro, Cornwall
TR1 3AY)

Libraries Administration and Stock Deliveries, Unit 17, Threemilestone Industrial Estate,
Truro, Cornwall TR4 9LD
☎(01872) 324315
Head of Library Services J W R Gould BA DipLib MLS ALA

Central/largest library
Truro Library, Union Place, Truro, Cornwall TR1 1EP
☎(01872) 279205
Fax (01872) 223772

COVENTRY
Headquarters Coventry Metropolitan District Council, Central Library, Smithford Way,
Coventry CV1 1FY
☎024 7683 2314 (enquiries); 024 7683 2321 (administration)
Fax 024 7683 2315
e-mail: covinfo@discover.co.uk
url: http://www.coventry.org.uk
Head of Cultural Services R Munro BA DMS ALA
Principal Assistant City Librarian R Sidney MA ALA (024 7683 2317)

Central/largest library
Central Library, Smithford Way, Coventry CV1 1FY
☎024 7683 2314
Fax 024 7683 2315
Assistant City Librarian (Central and Special Services) C Scott BA ALA DipLib (024
7683 2457)

CROYDON
Headquarters London Borough of Croydon, Central Library, Katharine Street, Croydon
CR9 1ET
☎020 8760 5400
Fax 020 8253 1004
url: http://www.croydon.gov.uk
Head of Libraries Mrs A Scott BA ALA (020 8253 1001; e-mail: lbadie@croydon.gov.uk)

CUMBRIA

Headquarters Cumbria County Council, Heritage Services, Arroyo Block, The Castle, Carlisle, Cumbria CA3 8UR
☎(01228) 607295 (enquiries & administration); (01228) 607292 (management)
Fax (01228) 607299
e-mail: herithq@dial.pipex.com
url: http://www.cumbria.gov.uk
Heritage Services Officer J D Hendry MA FLA FSA(Scot) FBIM (01228 607290)
Senior Assistant County Heritage Services Officer (Human Resource Management) J Grisenthwaite BA MBA (01228 607282)
Assistant County Heritage Services Officer (Library Services Manager) A J Welton BA ALA (01228 607307)
Assistant County Heritage Services Officer (Finance and Administration) Mrs J Williams Crellin BA CPFA (01228 607291)
Assistant County Heritage Services Officer (Cultural Services) B Bennison BA AMA (01228 607305)

Group libraries
A   Carlisle Library, 11 Globe Lane, Carlisle, Cumbria CA3 8NX
    ☎(01228) 607310
    Fax (01228) 607333
    e-mail: vx72@dial.pipex.com
    Senior Community Librarian J Foster
B   Penrith Library, St Andrews Churchyard, Penrith, Cumbria CA11 7YA
    ☎(01768) 242100
    Fax (01768) 242101
    e-mail: library@penrith.u-net.com
    Senior Community Librarian Mrs E Bowe ALA
C   Kendal Library, Stricklandgate, Kendal, Cumbria LA9 4PY
    ☎(01539) 773520
    Fax (01539) 773530
    e-mail: kendal.library@dial.pipex.com
    Senior Community Librarian Ms S Rochell BA ALA
D   Barrow-in-Furness Library, Ramsden Square, Barrow-in-Furness, Cumbria LA14 1LL
    ☎(01229) 894370
    Fax (01229) 894371
    e-mail: barrow.library@dial.pipex.com
    Senior Community Librarian Ms C Mellor BA ALA
E   Daniel Hay Library, Lowther Street, Whitehaven, Cumbria CA28 7QZ
    ☎(01946) 852900
    Fax (01946) 852911
    e-mail: whitehaven.library@dial.pipex.com
    Senior Community Librarian Mrs L Wood ALA
F   Workington Library, Vulcans Lane, Workington, Cumbria CA14 2ND
    ☎(01900) 325170
    Fax (01900) 325181
    e-mail: workington.library@dial.pipex.com
    Senior Community Librarian O T Jones

DARLINGTON

Headquarters Darlington Borough Council, Central Library, Crown Street, Darlington, Durham DL1 1ND

☎(01325) 462034 (enquiries), 349601 (administration)
Fax (01325) 381556
e-mail: library@dbc-lib.demon.co.uk
Libraries and Museums Manager P White ALA

Branch library
Cockerton Library, Cockerton Green, Darlington, Durham DL3 9AA
☎(01325) 461320
Librarian Mrs L Litchfield ALA

DERBY
Headquarters Derby City Council, Derby City Libraries, Leisure Services Department, Celtic House, Heritage Gate, Derby, Derbyshire DE1 1QX
☎(01332) 716601
Fax (01332) 715549
e-mail: libraries@derby.city.council.gov.uk
City Librarian R Rippingale MA ALA
Assistant City Librarian (Operations) D Potton MA DipLib ALA (01332 716610)
Assistant City Librarian (Planning and Development) Ms U Pakes FIL MAG MA (01332 716609)

Central/largest library
Central Library, The Wardwick, Derby, Derbyshire DE1 1HS
☎(01332) 255398/9 (enquiries), 255389 (administration)
Fax (01332) 369570
Assistant City Librarian (Central Services) B Haigh MLS ALA

DERBYSHIRE
Headquarters Derbyshire County Council, Libraries and Heritage Department, County Hall, Matlock, Derbyshire DE4 3AG
☎(01629) 580000 ext 6591 (enquiries), ext 6590 (administration)
Fax (01629) 585363
e-mail: derbyshire.libraries@derbyshire.gov.uk
Director of Libraries and Heritage M J Molloy BA DipLib ALA
Deputy Director of Libraries and Heritage Miss J A Brumwell ALA
Assistant Director of Libraries and Heritage R P Gent BA DMS MIMgt ALA
Assistant Director of Libraries and Heritage G H Jennings BA ALA

Central/largest library
Chesterfield Library, New Beetwell Street, Chesterfield, Derbyshire S40 1QN
☎(01246) 209292
Fax (01246) 209304
e-mail: chesterfield.library@derbyshire.gov.uk
District Librarian Mrs A Ainsworth BA ALA

Other main libraries
Amber Valley District
A   Alfreton Library, Severn Square, Alfreton, Derbyshire DE55 7BQ
       ☎(01773) 833199
       Fax (01773) 521020
       e-mail: alfreton.library@derbyshire.gov.uk
B   Ripley Library, Grosvenor Road, Ripley, Derbyshire DE5 3JE
       ☎(01773) 743321

Fax (01773) 741057
e-mail: ripley.library@derbyshire.gov.uk
C   Belper Library, Bridge Street, Belper, Derbyshire DE56 1BA
☎(01773) 824333
Fax (01773) 822172
District Librarian Mrs J Potton BA ALA

Bolsover District
D   Bolsover Library, Church Street, Bolsover, Derbyshire S44 6HB
☎(01246) 823179
Fax (01246) 827237
e-mail: bolsover.library@derbyshire.gov.uk
District Librarian Ms H Doherty BA ALA

Chesterfield District
E   Staveley Library, Hall Lane, Staveley, Derbyshire S43 3TP
☎(01246) 472448
Fax (01246) 470132
e-mail: staveley.library@derbyshire.gov.uk
District Librarian Mrs A Ainsworth BA ALA

Derbyshire Dales District
F   Matlock Library, Steep Turnpike, Matlock, Derbyshire DE4 3DP
☎(01629) 582480
Fax (01629) 760749
e-mail: matlock.library@derbyshire.gov.uk
District Librarian Ms T Hill BA DipLib ALA

Erewash District
G   Ilkeston Library, Market Place, Ilkeston, Derbyshire DE7 5RN
☎0115 930 1104
Fax 0115 944 1226
e-mail: ilkeston.library@derbyshire.gov.uk
H   Long Eaton Library, Tamworth Road, Long Eaton, Derbyshire NG10 1JG
☎0115 973 5426
Fax 0115 946 5133
e-mail: longeaton.library@derbyshire.gov.uk
District Librarian Mrs J Colombo BSc ALA

High Peak District
I   Buxton Library, Kents Bank Road, Buxton, Derbyshire SK17 9HJ
☎(01298) 25331
Fax (01298) 73744
e-mail: buxton.library@derbyshire.gov.uk
J   Glossop Library, Victoria Hall, Glossop, Derbyshire SK13 9DQ
☎(01457) 852616
Fax (01457) 856329
e-mail: glossop.library@derbyshire.gov.uk
District Librarian Ms T Cozens BA ALA

North East Derbyshire District
K   Dronfield Library, Manor House, Dronfield, Derbyshire S18 6PY
☎(01246) 414001
Fax (01246) 291489

e-mail: dronfield.library@derbyshire.gov.uk
District Librarian Mrs S Crabb MLS ALA

South Derbyshire District

L   Swadlincote Library, Civic Way, Swadlincote, Derbyshire DE11 0AD
☎(01283) 217701
Fax (01283) 216352
e-mail: swadlincote.library@derbyshire.gov.uk
District Librarian Mrs P Jemison ALA

DEVON

Headquarters Devon County Council, Devon Library and Information Services, Barley House, Isleworth Road, Exeter, Devon EX4 1RQ
☎(01392) 384315
Fax (01392) 384316
e-mail: devlibs@mf.devon-cc.gov.uk
Head of Library and Information Services Mrs L Osborne BA ALA (e-mail: losborne@mf.devon-cc.gov.uk)

Group libraries

A   South and East Devon. Central Library, Castle Street, Exeter, Devon EX4 3PQ
☎(01392) 384222
Fax (01392) 384228
Group Librarian M L G Maguire ALA (e-mail: mmaguire@mf.devon-cc.gov.uk)

B   North and West Devon. North Devon Library and Record Office, Tuly Street, Barnstaple, Devon EX31 1EL
☎(01271) 388619 (Tel/fax)
Group Librarian I P Tansley ALA (e-mail: itansley@mf.devon-cc.gov.uk)

DONCASTER

Headquarters Doncaster Metropolitan District Council, Central Library, Waterdale, Doncaster, South Yorkshire DN1 3JE
☎(01302) 734305 (general enquiries), (01302) 734298 (Principal Librarians' Office)
Fax (01302) 369749
e-mail: reference.library@doncaster.gov.uk
Libraries and Information Manager Ms G Johnson MA ALA

Central/largest library
As above

Area library
Bibliographical Services HQ, Skellow Road, Carcroft, Doncaster, South Yorkshire DN6 8HF
☎01302) 722327
Fax (01302) 727293
Principal Librarian D J L Mellor BA ALA

DORSET

Headquarters Dorset County Council, County Library HQ, Colliton Park, Dorchester, Dorset DT1 1XJ
☎(01305) 224455 (enquiries), (01305) 224449 (administration)
Fax (01305) 224344
Head of Libraries & Arts Service I J Lewis BA ALA

Divisional libraries

A   North Division. Blandford Library, The Tabernacle, Blandford Forum, Dorset DT11 7DW

☎(01258) 454744
Fax (01258) 459644
Senior Manager, North Division Mrs V Chapman ALA

B   South Division. County Library HQ, Colliton Park, Dorchester, Dorset DT1 1XJ
☎(01305) 224458
Fax (01305) 224344
Senior Manager, South Division N L Shirley ALA

C   East Division. Ferndown Library, Penny's Wallk, Ferndown, Dorset BH22 9TH
☎(01202) 896545
Fax (01202) 892416
Senior Manager, East Division R J Dale ALA

D   West Division. Weymouth Library, Great George Street, Weymouth, Dorset
DT4 8NN
☎(01305) 777504
Fax (01305) 768264
Senior Manager, West Division B Evans ALA

DUDLEY

Headquarters Dudley Metropolitan Borough Council, Dudley Library, St James's Road,
Dudley, West Midlands DY1 1HR
☎(01384) 815568 (administration)
Fax (01384) 815543
e-mail: dudlib.pls@mbc.dudley.gov.uk
url: http://www.dudley.gov.uk
Borough Librarian D F Radmore JP MSc MA ALA (e-mail:
dradmore.pls@mbc.dudley.gov.uk)

Central/largest library
Dudley Library, St James's Road, Dudley, West Midlands DY1 1HR
☎(01384) 815552 (administration/central services)
Fax (01384) 815543
e-mail: centserv.pls@mbc.dudley.gov.uk
Principal Librarian, Central Services and Systems Development C A Wrigley BA ALA

Area libraries
A   Dudley Library, St James's Road, Dudley, West Midlands DY1 1HR
☎(01384) 815560
Fax (01384) 815543
e-mail: dudlib.pls@mbc.dudley.gov.uk
Principal Librarian P M Hemmings BLib ALA

B   Brierley Hill Library, High Street, Brierley Hill, West Midlands DY5 3ET
☎(01384) 812865
Fax (01384) 812866
Principal Librarian S R Masters ALA

C   Halesowen Library, Queensway Mall, The Cornbow, Halesowen, West Midlands
B63 4AJ
☎(01384) 812980
Fax (01384) 812981
e-mail: hallib.pls@mbc.dudley.gov.uk
Principal Librarian Mrs E J Woodcock BA ALA

D   Stourbridge Library, Crown Centre, Crown Lane, Stourbridge, West Midlands
DY8 1YE
☎(01384) 812945

Fax (01384) 812946
Principal Librarian D C Hickman MSc ALA

DURHAM

Headquarters Durham County Council, Arts, Libraries and Museums Department, County Hall, Durham DH1 5TY
☎0191 383 3595 (enquiries), 0191 383 3713 (administration)
Fax 0191 384 1336
e-mail: alm@durham.gov.uk
url: http://www.durham.gov.uk
Director, Arts, Libraries and Museums P Conway BA FRSA ALA MIMgt MILAM
Senior Assistant Director, Collections, Events and Strategy Ms P Spencer BSc AMA
Assistant Director, Local Delivery and Support N S Canaway MBA ALA

Divisional libraries
A   Northern Division. Durham City Library, South Street, Durham City DH1 4QS
    ☎0191 386 4003
    Fax 0191 386 0379
    Divisional Manager D English ALA
B   Eastern Division. Peterlee Library, Burnhope Way, Peterlee, Co Durham SR8 1NT
    ☎(01388) 814694
    Fax (01388) 819454
    Acting Divisional Manager (Acting) Ms S Owens BA ALA
C   Western Division. Crook Library, Market Place, Crook, Co Durham DL15 8QH
    ☎(01388) 762269
    Fax (01388) 766170
    Divisional Manager J S Mallam ALA

EALING

Headquarters London Borough of Ealing, Library Administrative Office, 3rd Floor, Perceval House, 14 Uxbridge Road, London W5 2HL
☎020 8579 2424
Fax 020 8579 5280
e-mail: libinfo@ealing.gov.uk
Head of Service B E Cope ALA DMS MIMgt

Central/largest library
Central Library, 103 Ealing Broadway Centre, London W5 5JY
☎020 8567 3670 (enquiries), 020 8567 3656 (reference)
Fax 020 8840 2351
Library Manager L Bowen ALA

Main libraries
A   Acton Library, High Street, London W3 6NA
    ☎020 8752 0999
    Fax 020 8992 6086
B   Greenford Library, Oldfield Lane South, Greenford, Middlesex UB6 9LG
    ☎020 8578 1466
    Fax 020 8575 7800
C   Southall Library, Osterley Park Road, Southall, Middlesex UB2 4BL
    ☎020 8574 3412
    Fax 020 8571 7629
D   West Ealing Library, Melbourne Avenue, London W13 9BT

☎020 8567 2812
Fax 020 8567 1736

EAST RIDING OF YORKSHIRE

Headquarters East Riding of Yorkshire Council, Library and Information Services, Council Offices, Main Road, Skirlaugh, East Yorks HU11 5HN
☎(01482) 884984 (enquiries), (01482) 885082 (administration)
Fax (01482) 885279
Libraries and Museums Manager A Moir (e-mail: alan.moir@east-riding-of-yorkshire.gov.uk)

Central/largest library
Beverley Library, Champney Road, Beverley, East Yorks HU17 9BQ
☎(01482) 885080 (enquiries), (01482) 885355 (administration)
Fax (01482) 881861
Library Operations Manager Ms M Slattery BA DMS (01482 85080)
Central Services Manager Ms E Herbert (01482 885082)

Area libraries
A   East Group. Bridlington Library, King Street, Bridlington, East Yorks
    ☎(01262) 672917
    Fax (01262) 670208
    Senior Librarian, East Group C Mellor BSc DipLib ALA
B   West Group. Goole Library, Carlisle Street, Goole, East Yorks DN14 5AA
    ☎(01405) 762187
    Fax (01405) 768329
    Senior Librarian, West Group Vacant

EAST SUSSEX

Headquarters East Sussex County Council, Libraries, Information and Arts, Southdown House, 44 St Anne's Crescent, Lewes, East Sussex BN7 1SQ
☎(01273) 481870 (enquiries), (01273) 481538 (administration)
Fax (01273) 481716
Head of Libraries, Information and Arts Ms D Thorpe BA MPhil ALA (01273 481534; e-mail: dina.thorpe@eastsussexcc.gov.uk)
Head of Special Client Services Mrs V Warren BA ALA (01273 481329)
Head of Information Services Mrs E Jewell (01273 481882; e-mail: ejewell@dial.pipex.com)
Customer Services Manager P Leivers (01273 481872)

Central/largest library
Hastings Central Library, Brassey Institute, 13 Claremont, Hastings, East Sussex TN34 1HE
☎(01424) 420501 (enquiries), (01424) 461955 (administration)
Fax (01424) 430261
Group Manager G Porter ALA

Group Area Offices
A   Eastbourne Central Library, Grove Road, Eastbourne, East Sussex BN21 4TL
    ☎(01323) 434206
    Fax (01323) 649174
    Group Manager Mrs H Sykes ALA (01323 430318)
B   Lewes Library, Albion Street, Lewes, East Sussex BN7 2ND

☎(01273) 474232
Fax (01273) 477881
Group Manager B Forster ALA
C   Uckfield Library (Wealden), High Street, Uckfield, East Sussex TN22 1AR
☎(01825) 763254
Fax (01825) 769762
Group Manager Mrs J Makin ALA (01825 769761)
D   Bexhill Library (Rother), Western Road, Bexhill, East Sussex TN40 1DY
☎(01424) 212546
Fax (01424) 733390
Group Manager Mrs M Palmer ALA

ENFIELD

Headquarters London Borough of Enfield, Leisure Services Group, PO Box 58, Civic Centre, Enfield, Middlesex EN1 3XJ
☎020 8366 2244 (enquiries), 020 8379 3752 (administration)
Fax 020 8379 3753
Assistant Director (Libraries & Culture) Ms C Lewis BA MSc ALA
Library Resources and Development Manager Ms H Wills Blib ALA

Central/largest library
Central Library, Cecil Road, Enfield, Middlesex EN2 6TW
☎020 8366 2244
Fax 020 8379 8400
Library Network Manager M Allen MPhil ALA (020 8379 8300)

Area libraries
A   Palmers Green Library, Broomfield Lane, London N13 4EY
☎020 8886 3728
Fax 020 8379 2712
Area Library Manager Mrs S Barford ALA (020 8379 2694)
B   Edmonton Green Library, 36/44 South Mall, London N9 0NX
☎020 8807 3618
Fax 020 8379 2615
Area Library Manager P Brown BA ALA (020 8379 2605)
C   Ordnance Road Library, 645 Hertford Road, Enfield, Middlesex EN3 6ND
☎01992) 710588
Fax (01992) 788763
Area Library Manager Ms P Tuttiett BA ALA (01992 710588)

ESSEX

Headquarters Essex County Council, County Library HQ, Goldlay Gardens, Chelmsford, Essex CM2 0EW
☎(01245) 284981
Fax (01245) 492780 (general), (01245) 436769 (Management Team)
e-mail: essexlib@essexcc.gov.uk
url: http://www.essexcc.gov.uk/libraries
Head of Library, Information, Heritage and Cultural Services Ms G Kempster OBE MLIS BA(Hons) ALA (01245 436080; e-mail: grace.kempster@essexcc.gov.uk) (Based at Learning Services, PO Box 47, Chemsford CM2 6WN)
Field Services Manager Ms J Glayzer ALA (01245 436767; e-mail: jenny.glayzer@essexcc.gov.uk)
Policy and Development Manager D Murray BLib ALA (01245 436766; e-mail: david.murray@essexcc.gov.uk)

Central/largest library
Chelmsford, Maldon and Rochford District HQ, Chelmsford Library, PO Box 882, Market Road, Chelmsford, Essex CM1 1LH
☎(01245) 492758
Fax (01245) 492536 (enquiries), (01245) 257406 (administration)
e-mail: cfdlib@essexcc.gov.uk
District Manager Ms M Shipley ALA (01245 436536; e-mail: marions@essexcc.gov.uk)

District Headquarters
A   Basildon, Brentwood and Castle Point District HQ, Basildon Central Library, St Martin's Square, Basildon, Essex SS14 1EE
☎(01268) 288533
Fax (01268) 286326
District Manager Ms E Adams BA ALA DMS
B   Braintree and Uttlesford District HQ, Braintree Library, Fairfield Road, Braintree, Essex CM7 3YL
☎(01376) 320752
Fax (01376) 553316
District Manager Ms M Jones BA(Hons) DipLib ALA
C   Colchester and Tendring District HQ, Colchester Library, Trinity Square, Colchester, Essex CO1 1JB
☎(01206) 245900
Fax (01206) 245901
District Manager Ms N Baker BA ALA
D   Harlow and Epping Forest District HQ, Harlow Library, The High, Harlow, Essex CM20 1HA
☎(01279) 413772
Fax (01279) 424612
District Manager G Bannister MA ALA

GATESHEAD

Headquarters Gateshead Metropolitan Borough Council, Libraries and Arts Department, Central Library, Prince Consort Road, Gateshead, Tyne and Wear NE8 4LN
☎0191 477 3478
Fax 0191 477 7454
e-mail: gateslib@demon.co.uk
Director of Libraries and Arts W J Macnaught MA DipLib ALA
Deputy Director T Durcan BA ALA
Assistant Director, Lending Ms A Borthwick BA ALA
Assistant Director, Support Services M Watson BA ALA
Assistant Director, Information I D Hunter BA ALA
Assistant Director, Arts M White BA
Central Lending Manager Ms A Key BA ALA

Area libraries
A   East Area. Birtley Library, Birtley, Gateshead, Tyne and Wear DH3 1LE
☎0191 410 5364
Area Manager Ms A Parker ALA
B   West Area. Whickham Library, St Mary's Green, Whickham, Newcastle upon Tyne NE16 4DN
☎0191 488 1262
Area Manager Ms D Cameron ALA

GLOUCESTERSHIRE

Headquarters Gloucestershire County Council, County Library, Arts and Museums Service, Quayside House, Shire Hall, Gloucester GL1 2HY
☎(01452) 425020 (general enquiries), (01452) 425048 (management)
Fax (01452) 425042
e-mail: clams@gloscc.gov.uk
url: http://www.gloscc.gov.uk
County Library, Arts and Museums Officer Ms L Hopkins ALA
Assistant County Librarian, Development and Client Services C Campbell MBA ALA
(e-mail: ccampbell@gloscc.gov.uk)
Assistant County Librarian, Field Services J A Holland BA DipLib ALA (e-mail: jholland@gloscc.gov.uk)
Principal Librarian (Information Services and Systems) Ms E Haldon (e-mail: ehaldon@gloscc.gov.uk)
Principal Librarian (Learning and Literacy) Ms E Dubber (e-mail: edubber@gloscc.gov.uk)
Principal Librarian (Reader Services) Ms G Barker (e-mail: gbarker@gloscc.gov.uk)

Central/largest libraries
Gloucester Library, Brunswick Road, Gloucester GL1 1HT
☎(01452) 426973
Fax (01452) 521468
Library Manager Ms J Potter

Cheltenham Library, Clarence Street, Cheltenham, Gloucestershire GL50 3JT
☎(01242) 532688
Fax (01242) 510373
Library Manager Mrs B French

Group libraries
A   North. Based at Cheltenham Library, Clarence Street, Cheltenham, Gloucestershire GL50 3JT
      ☎(01242) 532678
      Fax (01242) 532673
      Group Librarian G R Hiatt BA ALA (e-mail: ghiatt@gloscc.gov.uk)
B   South. Based at Stroud Library, Lansdown, Stroud, Gloucestershire GL5 1BB
      ☎(01453) 756842
      Fax (01453) 762060
      Group Librarian Mrs M E Tucker BA MLib ALA (e-mail: mtucker@gloscc.gov.uk)
C   West. Based at Gloucester Library, Brunswick Road, Gloucester GL1 1HT
      ☎(01452) 426976
      Fax (01452) 521468
      Group Librarian J Hughes BA ALA (e-mail: jhughes@gloscc.gov.uk)

GREENWICH

Headquarters London Borough of Greenwich, Public Services, 147 Powis Street, London SE18 6JL
☎020 8317 4466 (enquiries), 020 8312 5643 (management)
Fax 020 8317 4868 (enquiries), 020 8317 2822 (management)
Head of Service Vacant. Senior posts under review

District libraries
A   Woolwich Library, Calderwood Street, London SE18 6QZ

☎020 8312 5750
Fax 020 8316 1645
B   Eltham Library, Eltham High Street, London SE9 1TS
☎020 8850 2268
Fax 020 8850 1368
C   Blackheath Library, 17-23 Old Dover Road, London SE3 7BT
☎020 8858 1131
Fax 020 8853 3615

HACKNEY

Headquarters London Borough of Hackney, Learning and Leisure Directorate, Maurice Bishop House, Reading Lane, London E8 1HH
☎020 8356 5000
Fax 020 8356 7504
Strategy and Commissioning Officer for Libraries Ms M Guimarin (020 8356 7264; mguimarin@gw.hackney.gov.uk)

Largest library
Hackney Library, 219 Mare Street, London E8 3QE
☎020 8356 2542 (enquiries), 020 8356 2539 (renewals)
Fax 020 8533 3712
Library Manager Ms J Middleton ALA (020 8356 2560)

Town centre libraries
A   Clapton Library, Northwold Road, London E5 8RA
☎020 8356 2570
Fax 020 8806 7849
Library Manager Vacant
B   C L R James Library, 24-30 Dalston Lane, London E8 3AZ
☎020 8356 2571
Fax 020 7254 4655
Library Manager Ms E Hill BA(Hons) ALA (020 7275 0332)
C   Homerton Library, Homerton High Street, London E9 6AS
☎020 8356 2572
Library Manager E S Allberry DipLib ALA (020 8356 2540)
D   Shoreditch Library, 80 Hoxton Street, London N1 6LP
☎020 8356 4350; Business Information Library 020 8356 4358
Fax 020 7739 7180
Library Manager D Keane (020 8356 4356)
E   Stamford Hill Library, Portland Avenue, London N16 6SB
☎020 8356 2573
Fax 020 8809 5986
Library Manager H Coffey BA(Hons) DMS ALA
F   Stoke Newington Library, Stoke Newington Church Street, London N16 0JS
☎020 8356 5230
Fax 020 8356 5233
Library Manager Ms S Comitti (020 8356 5357)
G   Reference Library, 43 De Beauvoir Road, London N1 5SQ
☎020 8356 2576
Site Librarian M Lenihan

HALTON

Headquarters Halton Borough Council, Halton Lea Library, Halton Lea, Runcorn, Cheshire WA7 2PF

☎(01928) 715351
Fax (01928) 790221
Library Services Manager Mrs P Reilly-Cooper BSc DipLib ALA (0151 424 2061 ext 4096;
based at Runcorn Town Hall, Runcorn WA7 5TD)
Specialist Services Manager Mrs J Potter BA(Hons) ALA
Stock Specialist Officer Miss T Burr BA(Hons) ALA
Reference and Information Officer Mrs J Bradburn ALA
Young Persons Officer Mrs a Watt BA(Hons) ALA
Systems Officer P Cooke BA(Hons) MA

Central/largest library
Halton Lea Library, Halton Lea, Runcorn, Cheshire WA7 2PF
☎Tel/Fax etc. as HQ
Senior Librarian Miss S Kirk BA(Hons) ALA

Area libraries
A   Ditton Library, Queens Avenue, Ditton, Widnes, Cheshire WA8 8HR
       ☎0151 424 2459
       Senior Librarian Mrs K Marshall BA ALA (0151 423 4818)
B   Runcorn Library, Egerton Street, Runcorn, Cheshire WA7 1JL
       ☎01928) 574495
       Senior Librarian Miss S Kirk BA(Hons) ALA (01928 715351)
C   Widnes Library, Victoria Square, Widnes, Cheshire WA8 7QY
       ☎0151 423 4818
       Fax 0151 420 5108
       Senior Librarian Mrs K Marshall BA ALA (0151 423 4818)

HAMMERSMITH AND FULHAM
Headquarters London Borough of Hammersmith and Fulham, Hammersmith Library,
Shepherds Bush Road, London W6 7AT
☎020 8576 5050 (enquiries), 020 8576 5055 (administration)
Fax 020 8576 5022
e-mail: info@haflibs.org.uk
url: http://www.ftech.net/~haflibs
Head of Library and Archive Services N E Bouttell BA ALA (020 8576 5055 ext 3810;
e-mail: n.bouttell@libs.lbhf.gov.uk)
Principal Librarian, Public Services D Herbert BA MLS ALA (020 8576 5055 ext 3811)
Support Services Manager J B Aquilina ALA (020 8576 5055 ext 3818; e-mail:
j.aquilina@libs.lbhf.gov.uk)
Research and Development Officer S F Riethmuller BMus(Hons) LGSM ALA (020 8576
5055 ext 3811)
Borough Archivist and Local History Manager Ms J Kimber BA(Hons) DAA MSc (020
8741 5159; e-mail: j.kimber@libs.lbhf.gov.uk)

Central/largest library
Hammersmith Library, Shepherds Bush Road, London W6 7AT
☎Tel/Fax etc. as HQ
Senior Librarian Ms J Samuels ALA

Area libraries
A   Askew Road Library, 87/91 Askew Road, London W12 9AS
       ☎020 8576 5064
B   Barons Court Library, North End Crescent, London W14 8TG

☎020 8576 5258
C   Fulham Library, 598 Fulham Road, London SW6 5NX
    ☎020 8576 5252
    Senior Librarian H Cosker ALA
D   Sands End Library, The Community Centre, 59-61 Broughton Road, London SW6
    2LA
    ☎020 8576 5257
E   Shepherds Bush Library, 7 Uxbridge Road, London W12 8LJ
    ☎020 8576 5060
    Fax 020 8740 1712
    Senior Librarian Ms G Lynch ALA, Ms L Hardman MSc ALA (job-share)

HAMPSHIRE

Headquarters Hampshire County Council, County Library HQ, 81 North Walls, Winchester,
Hampshire SO23 8BY
☎(01962) 846059 (enquiries), (01962) 846057 (administration)
Fax (01962) 856615
BT Gold 76:LMX 236
County Librarian P H Turner BA ALA (01962 846109; e-mail: libspt@hants.gov.uk)
Deputy County Librarian Miss A M Watkins ALA (01962 846100; e-mail:
libsmw@hants.gov.uk)
Assistant County Librarian, Information Services N R Fox BA FLA MIInfSc (01962
846077; e-mail: libsnf@hants.gov.uk)
Assistant County Librarian, Bibliographic and Adult Lending Services B Kempthorne
MA ALA (01962 846083; e-mail: libsbk@hants.gov.uk)
Assistant County Librarian, Children's, Schools and Community Services J F Dunne
BA ALA (01962 846084; e-mail: libsjd@hants.gov.uk)
Assistant County Librarian, Resource Planning J Haylock BA ALA (01962 846089;
e-mail: libsjh@hants.gov.uk)

Divisional libraries
A   Central Division HQ, Lending Library, Jewry Street, Winchester, Hampshire
    SO23 8RX
    ☎(01962) 862748
    Fax (01962) 841489
    Divisional Librarian P A Dix BA ALA (01962 841499; e-mail:
    clcepd@hants.gov.uk)
B   North Division HQ, Basingstoke Library, 19/20 Westminster House, Potters Walk,
    Basingstoke, Hampshire RG21 7LS
    ☎(01256) 473901
    Fax (01256) 470666
    Divisional Librarian Miss S Greenfield BA MIMgt ALA (01256 363793; e-mail:
    clnosg@hants.gov.uk)
C   South Division HQ, Fareham Library, Osborn Road, Fareham, Hampshire
    PO16 7EN
    ☎(01329) 282715
    Fax (01329) 221551
    Divisional Librarian Mrs M Davies ALA (01329 221424; e-mail:
    clsomd@hants.gov.uk)
D   West Division HQ, The Old School, Cannon Street, Lymington, Hampshire
    SO41 9BR
    ☎(01590) 673050
    Fax (01590) 672561

Divisional Librarian Miss M Franklin BA ALA (01590 675767; e-mail: clwemf@hants.gov.uk)

HARINGEY

Headquarters London Borough of Haringey, Haringey Library Services, Central Library, High Road, Wood Green, London N22 6XD
☎020 8888 1292 (enquiries & administration)
Fax 020 8889 0110
Head of Libraries Ms J Earley BA ALA
Principal Librarian (Support Services) R Smith ALA
Principal Librarian (Tottenham Neighbourhood) J Miles BA MLib ALA

Central/largest library
Wood Green Central Library, High Road, Wood Green, London N22 6XD
☎020 8888 1292
Fax 020 8889 0110
Neighbourhood Librarian Ms G Harvey ALA

Area libraries
A   Marcus Garvey Library, Tottenham Green, London N15 4JA
      ☎020 8365 1155
      Acting Neighbourhood Librarian M Bott LLB
B   Hornsey Library, Haringey Park, London N8 9JA
      ☎020 8348 3351
      Neighbourhood Librarian Ms M Stephanou ALA

HARROW

Headquarters London Borough of Harrow, Civic Centre Library, PO Box 4, Civic Centre, Harrow, Middlesex HA1 2UU
☎020 8424 1055/6 (enquiries), 020 8424 1059/1970 (administration)
Fax 020 8424 1971
Library Services Manager R J R Mills BSc ALA DMS (e-mail: bmills@harrow.gov.uk)

Central/largest library
Central Library, Gayton Road, Harrow, Middlesex HA1 2HL
☎020 8427 6012/8986
Principal Librarian (Lending Services) J E Pennells ALA DMS

Area library
☎Address, tel/fax etc. as HQ

HARTLEPOOL

Headquarters Hartlepool Borough Council, Central Library, 124 York Road, Hartlepool, Cleveland TS26 9DE
☎(01429) 272905
Fax (01429) 275685
e-mail: lclijb@hartlepool.gov.uk
Borough Librarian Ms J Blaisdale BA ALA
Central Services Manager Ms A Goult BA(Hons)
Area Manager, South Ms K Tranter BA(Hons)
Area Manager, North Vacant

Central/largest library
As above

Bibliographical services
Bibliographical Services Section, 2 Cromwell Street, Hartlepool, Cleveland TS24 7LR
☎(01429) 523644
e-mail: lclisa@hartlepool.gov.uk
Bibliographical Services Officer Ms S Atkinson BA ALA DipRSA

HAVERING
Headquarters London Borough of Havering, Central Library, St Edwards Way, Romford, Essex RM1 3AR
☎(01708) 772389 (enquiries), (01708) 772380 (administration)
Fax (01708) 772391
Chief Librarian G H Saddington DMA FLA ACIS MIMgt (e-mail: gsaddington.decs@havering.gov.uk)
Principal Librarian, Public Services (Central) Mrs J Cheese ALA (01708 772375)

Central/largest library
As above

HEREFORDSHIRE
Headquarters Herefordshire Council, Libraries and Information Service, Administration Section, Shirehall, Hereford HR1 2HY
☎(01432) 359830
Libraries and Information Services Manager Mrs J Williams BA MA ALA
Acquisitions Manager Mrs C Huckfield BA ALA

Central/largest libraries
Hereford Library, Broad Street, Hereford, Herefordshire HR4 9AU
☎(01432) 272456
Fax (01432) 359668
Hereford Librarian D Greaves MA DMS ALA

Leominster Library, 8 Buttercross, Leominster, Herefordshire HR6 8BN
☎(01568) 612384
Fax (01568) 616025
Leominster Librarian P Holliday BA DipEd ALA

HERTFORDSHIRE
Headquarters Hertfordshire County Council, Community Information Directorate: Libraries, New Barnfield, Travellers Lane, Hatfield, Herts AL10 8XG
☎(01707) 281581 (enquiries & administration)
Fax (01707) 281589
e-mail: firstname.lastname@hertscc.gov.uk   url: http://hertslib.hertscc.gov.uk
Director of Library Services A Robertson
Library Operations Manager Ms G Wood BA DipLib ALA (01707 281585; e-mail: glenda.wood@hertscc.gov.uk)
Information Services Manager R Breakey ALA (01707 281511; e-mail: bob.breakey@hertscc.gov.uk)

Central/largest library
Central Resources Library, New Barnfield, Travellers Lane, Hatfield, Herts AL10 8XG

☎(01707) 281527
Fax (01707) 281514
e-mail: andrew.bignall@hertscc.gov.uk
Library Development Manager A Bignall BA DipLib ALA

District libraries
A   Hemel Hempstead Library, Central Library, Combe Street, Hemel Hempstead, Herts HP1 1HJ
☎(01442) 213331
Fax (01442) 232228
e-mail: hemelhempstead.library@hertscc.gov.uk
District Librarian Ms C Barraclough BA ALA
B   St Albans Library, The Maltings, St Albans, Herts AL1 3JQ
☎(01727) 860000
Fax (01727) 848613
e-mail: stalbans.library@hertscc.gov.uk
District Librarian R Barrow
C   Cheshunt Library, Turners Hill, Cheshunt, Waltham Cross, Herts EN8 8LB
☎(01992) 623582
Fax (01992) 642832
District Librarian Ms C Hill BA ALA
D   Bishop's Stortford Library, The Causeway, Bishop's Stortford, Herts CM23 2EJ
☎(01279) 654946
Fax (01279) 654744
e-mail: bishopsstortford.library@hertscc.gov.uk
District Librarian Ms J Holmes
E   Borehamwood Library, Elstree Way, Borehamwood, Herts WD6 1JX
☎020 8953 1962
Fax 020 8207 6311
District Librarian D Knight
F   Letchworth Library, Broadway, Letchworth, Herts SG6 3PF
☎(01462) 685646
Fax (01462) 481094
District Librarian Ms I Oakey
G   Rickmansworth Library, High Street, Rickmansworth, Herts WD3 1EH
☎(01923) 773563
Fax (01923) 710384
District Librarian Ms M Staunton
H   Watford Library, Hempstead Road, Watford, Herts WD1 3EU
☎(01923) 226230
Fax (01923) 212263
e-mail: watford.library@hertscc.gov.uk
District Librarian Ms M Campbell
I   Welwyn Garden City Library, Campus West, Welwyn Garden City, Herts AL8 6AJ
☎(01707) 332331
Fax (01707) 338784
e-mail: wgc.library@hertscc.gov.uk
District Librarian J Macrae
J   Stevenage Library, Southgate, Stevenage, Herts SG1 1HD
☎(01438) 219010
Fax (01438) 365144
e-mail: stevenage.library@hertscc.gov.uk
District Librarian Ms S Crossley

HILLINGDON

Headquarters London Borough of Hillingdon, Uxbridge Central Library, 14-15 High Street, Uxbridge, Middlesex UB8 1HD
☎(01895) 250600 (enquiries), (01895) 250700 (administration)
Fax (01895) 811164 (administration)
Service Manager Mrs T Grimshaw

Central/largest library
As above

Area libraries
A   Hayes Library, Golden Crescent, Hayes, Middlesex UB3 1AQ
☎020 8573 2855
Fax 020 8848 0269
Customer Services Manager Mrs L Ash BA ALA (01895 250701, Fax 01895 811164)
B   Manor Farm Library, Bury Street, Ruislip, Middlesex HA4 7SU
☎(01895) 633651
Fax (01895) 677555
Area Manager, North Mrs J Mitchell ALA (01895 250701; Fax 01895 811164)
C   Central Library, 14-15 High Street, Uxbridge, Middlesex UB8 1HD
☎(01895) 811164
Central Library Manager Vacant

HOUNSLOW

Headquarters London Borough of Hounslow, Hounslow Library Network (Community Initiative Partnerships), Centrespace, 24 Treaty Centre, High Street, Hounslow, Middlesex TW3 1ES
☎020 8570 0622 (enquiries), 020 8862 6922 (administration)
Fax 020 8862 7602
url: http://www.cip.org.uk
Assistant Chief Executive CIP G Allen ALA (020 8862 5797)
Assistant Borough Librarian Ms L Simpson BA ALA (e-mail: linda-simpson@cip.org.uk)
Principal Librarian Ms F Stanbury ALA (e-mail: frances-stanbury@cip.org.uk)
Library Network Managers (IT and Information) Ms P Cole BA DipLib ALA; **(Outreach)** Ms B King BA; **(Resources)** R Kitchen; **(Staff)** Ms J Harrison ALA; **(Stock)** Ms L Edwards BA ALA; **Team Leaders (Adult Library Services)** M Clift BA (020 8570 0622); **(Bibliographical Services)** Ms E Cutts ALA (020 8570 9106); **(Community Services)** Ms G Iqbal BA DipLib (020 8570 0622); **(Customer Services)** Ms A Greene BA(Lib) (020 8570 0622); **(Systems Team)** Ms S Vass BA(Hons) MSc (020 8862 7623)

Central/largest library
Hounslow Library, 24 Treaty Centre, High Street, Hounslow, Middlesex TW3 1ES
☎020 8570 0622
Fax 020 8862 7602

Branch libraries
A   Beavers Library, 103 Salisbury Road, Hounslow, Middlesex TW4 7NW
☎020 8572 6995
B   Bedfont Library, Staines Road, Bedfont, Middlesex TW14 8DB
☎020 8890 6173
Library Manager Ms V Hardie
C   Brentford Library, Boston Manor Road, Brentford, Middlesex TW8 8DW
☎020 8560 8801
Library Manager Ms S Maidment
D   Chiswick Library, Duke's Avenue, Chiswick, London W4 2AB

☎020 8994 1008
Library Manager Ms R Morrison
E   Cranford Library, Bath Road, Cranford, Middlesex TW5 9TL
☎020 8759 0641
Library Manager A Bondrilla
F   Feltham Library, 210 The Centre, High Street, Feltham, Middlesex TW13 4BX
☎020 8890 3506
Library Manager Ms D Parsons
G   Hanworth Library, 2-12 Hampton Road West, Hanworth, Middlesex TW13 6AW
☎020 8898 0256
Library Manager Ms C Fyfe
H   Heston Library, New Heston Road, Heston, Middlesex TW5 0LW
☎020 8570 1028
Library Manager Ms C Fyfe
I   Isleworth Library, Twickenham Road, Isleworth, Middlesex TW7 7EU
☎020 8560 2934
Library Manager Ms S Maidment
J   Osterley Library, St Mary's Crescent, Osterley, Middlesex TW7 4NB
☎020 8560 4295
Library Manager Ms I Hine

ISLE OF WIGHT

Headquarters Isle of Wight Council, Wight Heritage, The Guildhall, High Street, Newport, Isle of Wight PO30 1TY
☎(01983) 823822 (enquiries & administration)
Fax (01983) 823841
Head of Wight Heritage T Blackmore ALA
Library Operational Manager M Lister BA ALA (01983 825717)
Community Services Librarian B Hawkins BA ALA (01983 825717)
Support Services Librarian A Walker BA ALA (01983 825717)

Central/largest library
Lord Louis Library, Orchard Street, Newport, Isle of Wight PO30 1LL
☎(01983) 527655 (enquiries & administration)
Fax (01983) 825972

Area libraries
A   Ryde Library, George Street, Ryde, Isle of Wight PO33 2JE
☎(01983) 562170
Fax (01983) 615644
B   Sandown Library, High Street, Sandown, Isle of Wight PO36 8AF
☎(01983) 402748
Fax (01983) 402748
C   Shanklin Library, Victoria Avenue, Shanklin, Isle of Wight PO37 6PG
☎(01983) 863126
Fax (01983) 863126
D   Ventnor Library, High Street, Ventnor, Isle of Wight PO38 1LZ
☎(01983) 852039
Fax (01983) 852039
E   Freshwater Library, School Green Road, Freshwater, Isle of Wight PO35 5NA
☎(01983) 752377
Fax (01983) 752377
F   Cowes Library, Beckford Road, Cowes, Isle of Wight PO31 7SG

☎(01983) 293341
Fax (01983) 293341

ISLINGTON
Headquarters London Borough of Islington, Library and Information Service, Central Library, 2 Fieldway Crescent, London N5 1PF
☎020 7619 6900 (enquiries), 020 7619 6905 (administration)
Fax 020 7619 6906
e-mail: library.informationunit@islington.gov.uk
url: http://www.islington.gov.uk
Assistant Head of Information and Customer Services Ms E Roberts MSc DMS ALA (020 7619 6903; e-mail: liz.roberts@easynet.co.uk)
Principal Librarians Ms V Dawson ALA BA(Lib) (020 7619 6907; e-mail: val.dawson@dial.pipex.com), Ms M Snook BLib (020 7619 7962), B Redmond ALA (020 7619 6909), A Issler BA ALA (020 7619 6910)

Central/largest library
Library and Information Service, Central Library, 2 Fieldway Crescent, London N5 1PF
☎020 7619 6900 (enquiries), 020 7619 6905 (administration)
Fax 020 7619 6902
Librarian i/c Ms M Gibson ALA (020 7619 6915/6)

Branch libraries
A	Archway Library, Hamlyn House, Highgate Hill, London N19 5PH
	☎020 7619 7820
	Fax 020 7281 6669
	Librarian i/c Ms J E Adams BA DipLib ALA AMITD
B	Arthur Simpson Library, Hanley Road, London N4 3DL
	☎020 7619 7800
	Fax 020 7272 7975
	Librarian i/c Ms T Gibson
C	Finsbury Library, 245 St John Street, London EC1V 4NB
	☎020 7619 7960
	Fax 020 7278 8821
	Librarian i/c Vacant
D	John Barnes Library, 275 Camden Road, London N7 0JN
	☎020 7619 7900
	Fax 020 7700 4132
	Librarian i/c Ms V Knott MA DipLib (020 7619 7905)
E	Mildmay Library, 21-23 Mildmay Park, London N1 4NA
	☎020 7619 7880
	Fax 020 7704 2498
	Librarian i/c B Millington ALA
F	North Library, Manor Gardens, London N7 6JX
	☎020 7619 7840
	Fax 020 7272 9562
	Librarian i/c A Brown BA DipLib
G	South Library, 115-117 Essex Road, London N1 2SL
	☎020 7619 7860
	Fax 020 7226 2226
	Librarian i/c C Hollitzer ALA
H	West Library, Bridgeman Road, London N1 1BD
	☎020 7619 7920

Fax 020 7607 9829
Librarian i/c P Lyons BA ALA
I   Lewis Carroll Library, 180 Copenhagen Street, London N1 0ST
☎020 7619 7936
Fax 020 7278 0500

KENSINGTON AND CHELSEA
Headquarters Royal Borough of Kensington and Chelsea, Central Library, Phillimore Walk, London W8 7RX
☎020 7937 2542 (general enquiries), 020 7361 3027 (management)
Fax 020 7361 2976
e-mail: fm116@viscount.org.uk
Head of Libraries and Arts J McEachen BSc ALA
Head of Bibliographic and Technical Services Division J Swindells ALA (020 7361 3029)

Area libraries
A   Central Area: Central Library, Hornton Street, London W8 7RX
☎020 7937 2542
Fax 020 7361 2976
Area Librarian Mrs I Pilkington ALA
B   Chelsea Area: Chelsea Library, Kings Road, London SW3 5EZ
☎020 7352 6056
Fax 020 7351 1294
Area Librarian Ms I Lackajis BA ALA
C   North Kensington Area: North Kensington Library, 108 Ladbroke Grove, London W11 1PZ
☎020 7727 6583
Fax 020 7229 7129
Area Librarian Ms C Anley ALA

KENT
Headquarters Kent County Council, Arts and Libraries, Springfield, Maidstone, Kent ME14 2LH
☎(01622) 696517
Fax (01622) 690897
Head of Arts and Libraries R Ward MLib ALA
Specialist Services Manager Ms K Topping
Area Services Manager (East Kent) Ms P Tempest BA ALA
Area Services Manager (Mid Kent) Ms G Bromley ALA
Area Services Manager (West Kent) Ms S Sparks ALA

Central/largest library
County Central Library, Springfield, Maidstone, Kent ME14 2LH
☎(01622) 696511
Fax (01622) 753338
Information Services Manager Ms J Johnson MA DipLib
Principal Librarian Ms S Wheeler BA DipLib ALA
Public Services Supervisor Ms C Bristow

Main town centre libraries
A   Ashford Library, Church Street, Ashford, Kent TN23 1QX
☎(01233) 620649
Fax (01233) 620295

      Library Supervisor Ms L Jones

B   Canterbury Library, High Street, Canterbury, Kent CT1 2JF
      ☎(01227) 463608
      Fax (01227) 768338
      Library Supervisor Ms L Catt

C   Dartford Library, Central Park, Dartford, Kent DA1 1EU
      ☎(01322) 221133
      Fax (01322) 278271
      Library Supervisor Ms H Blackaby

D   Dover Library, Maison Dieu House, Biggin Street, Dover, Kent CT16 1DW
      ☎(01304) 204241
      Fax (01304) 225914
      Library Supervisor Ms M Beatty

E   Gravesend Library, Windmill Street, Gravesend, Kent DA12 1BE
      ☎(01474) 352758
      Fax (01474) 320284
      Library Supervisor Ms F Dutton

F   Maidstone Library, St Faith's Street, Maidstone, Kent ME14 1LH
      ☎(01622) 752344
      Fax (01622) 754980
      Library Supervisor Ms M Griffiths

G   Sevenoaks Library, Buckhurst Lane, Sevenoaks, Kent TN13 1LQ
      ☎(01732) 453118
      Fax (01732) 742682
      Library Supervisor Ms P Olive

H   Shepway – Folkestone Library, 2 Grace Hill, Folkestone, Kent CT20 1HD
      ☎(01303) 850123
      Fax (01303) 242907
      Library Supervisor Ms C Cox

I   Sittingbourne Library, Central Avenue, Sittingbourne, Kent ME10 4AH
      ☎(01795) 476545
      Fax (01795) 428376
      Library Supervisor Ms S Rees

J   Thanet – Margate Library, Cecil Square, Margate, Kent CT9 1RE
      ☎(01843) 223626
      Fax (01843) 293015
      Library Supervisor Ms S Hannaford

K   Tonbridge Library, Avebury Avenue, Tonbridge, Kent TN9 1TG
      ☎(01732) 352754
      Fax (01732) 358300
      Library Supervisor Ms A Bonny

L   Tunbridge Wells Library, Mount Pleasant Road, Tunbridge Wells, Kent TN1 1NS
      ☎(01892) 522352
      Fax (01892) 514657
      Library Supervisor C Markham

KINGSTON UPON HULL

Headquarters Kingston upon Hull City Council, Central Library, Albion Street, Kingston upon Hull HU1 3TF
☎(01482) 210000 (enquiries), (01482) 616822 (administration)
Fax (01482) 616827
e-mail: info@kuhlib.karoo.co.uk
url: http://www.hullcc.gov.uk

Head of Libraries B M Chapman ALA (01482 616801; e-mail: brian@kuhlib.demon.co.uk)
Principal Librarian R J Stanley BA DipLib (01482 616804)
Senior Librarian Mrs G Major (01482 616805)
Senior Librarian Mrs L Benton BA(Lib) (01482 616806)

Central/largest library
As above

Area libraries

A   Anlaby Park Library, The Greenway, Anlaby High Road, Kingston upon Hull HU4 6TX
☎(01482) 505506
Library Supervisor Mrs P Storr

B   Avenues Library, 76 Chanterlands Avenue, Kingston upon Hull HU5 3TS
☎(01482) 445912
Fax (01482) 443764
Library Supervisor N Goodison

C   Bransholme Library, District Centre, Goodhart Road, Bransholme, Kingston upon Hull HU7 4EF
☎(01482) 826585
Senior Library Supervisor Miss D Stanley

D   Carnegie Library, Anlaby Road, Kingston upon Hull HU3 6JA
☎(01482) 352203
Library Supervisor Miss C Gillett

E   Fred Moore Library, Wold Road, Derringham Bank, Kingston upon Hull HU5 5UN
☎(01482) 354765
Senior Library Supervisor Mrs C Culbert

F   Garden Village Library, Shopping Centre, Garden Village, Kingston upon Hull HU8 8QE
☎(01482) 781723
Library Supervisor Mrs K Grout

G   Gipsyville Library, 728-730 Hessle High Road, Kingston upon Hull HU4 6JA
☎(01482) 616973
Library Supervisor Mrs R Grantham

H   Greenwood Avenue Library, Greenwood Avenue, Kingston upon Hull HU6 9RU
☎(01482) 851180
Senior Library Supervisor Miss J Holden

I   Harry Lewis Library, Annandale Road, Kingston upon Hull HU9 5HD
☎(01482) 784044
Senior Library Supervisor Miss D Robinson

J   Ings Library, Savoy Road, Kingston upon Hull HU8 0TX
☎(01482) 796201
Senior Library Supervisor Mrs B Ralph

K   James Reckitt Library, Holderness Road, Kingston upon Hull HU9 1EA
☎(01482) 320015
Library Supervisor Vacant

L   Longhill Library, Shannon Road, Longhill Estate, Kingston upon Hull HU8 9RW
☎(01482) 815612
Library Supervisor Miss J Webster

M   Northern Library, Beverley Road, Kingston upon Hull HU3 1UP
☎(01482) 328397
Library Supervisor Mrs Z Towler

N   Perronet Thompson Library, Wawne Road, Kingston upon Hull HU7 4WR
☎(01482) 878932

Fax (01482) 878937
Senior Library Supervisors Mrs J Munday, Mrs S Tomlinson
O   Preston Road Library, Preston Road, Kingston upon Hull HU9 5UZ
     ☎(01482) 376266
     Library Supervisor Mrs M Budding
P   Western Library, The Boulevard, Hessle Road, Kingston upon Hull HU3 3ED
     ☎(01482) 320399
     Library Supervisor Mrs L Grant

KINGSTON UPON THAMES

Headquarters Royal Borough of Kingston upon Thames, Kingston Library, Fairfield Road,
Kingston upon Thames, Surrey KT1 2PS
☎020 8547 6413 (administration)
Fax 020 8547 6426
Head of Cultural Services S Herbertson BA MA ALA (020 8547 6419; e-mail:
scott.herbertson@rbk.kingston.gov.uk)
Library Services Manager Ms B Lee BA ALA (020 8547 6423; e-mail:
barbara.lee@rbk.kingston.gov.uk)
Information and Acquisitions Manager S Cooper MSc DipLib (020 8547 6420; e-mail:
simon.cooper@rbk.kingston.gov.uk)
Senior Team Librarian (Adult Services) Mrs E Ryder ALA (020 8399 2331)
Senior Team Librarian (Children's and Schools Library Service) M Treacy (020 8408
9100)

Branch libraries
A   Kingston Library, Fairfield Road, Kingston upon Thames, Surrey KT1 2PS
     ☎020 8547 6400
     Fax 020 8547 6401
     Library Manager Ms S Hurlock
B   Hook and Chessington Library, Hook Road, Chessington, Surrey KT9 1EJ
     ☎020 8397 4931
     Fax 020 8391 4410
     Library Manager Ms R Fryer
C   New Malden Library, Kingston Road, New Malden, Surrey KT3 3LY
     ☎020 8547 6540
     Fax 020 8547 6545
     Library Manager Ms C Roberts (020 8547 6544)
D   Old Malden Library, Church Road, Worcester Park, Surrey KT4 7RD
     ☎020 8337 6344
     Fax 020 8330 3118
     Library Manager Ms M Vine
E   Surbiton Library, Ewell Road, Surbiton, Surrey KT6 6AG
     ☎020 8339 2331
     Fax 020 8339 9805
     Senior Library Manager Ms C Dale
F   Tolworth Community Library and IT Learning Centre, The Broadway, Tolworth,
     Surbiton, Surrey KT6 7DJ
     ☎020 8339 6950
     Fax 020 8339 6955
     e-mail: tolworth.library@rbk.kingston.gov.uk
     Library Manager Mrs V Gower
G   Tudor Drive Library, Tudor Drive, Kingston upon Thames, Surrey KT2 5QH
     ☎020 8546 1198

Fax 020 8547 2295
Library Manager Ms S Montague
H   Home and Mobile Library Service, Surbiton Library Annexe, Ewell Road, Surbiton, Surrey KT6 6AG
☎020 8339 7900
Fax 020 8339 9805
Library Manager Mrs I Abrahams

KIRKLEES

Headquarters Kirklees Metropolitan District Council, Kirklees Cultural Services, Cultural Services HQ, Red Doles Lane, Huddersfield, West Yorkshire HD2 1YF
☎(01484) 226300
Fax (01484) 226342
e-mail: cultural-hq@geo2.poptel.org.uk
url: http://www.kirkleesmc.gov.uk
Head of Cultural Services J Drake MA AMA MILAM(Dip) FRGS MIFA
Assistant Head of Cultural Services (Libraries and Information) R Warburton BA ALA

Central/largest library
Central Library, Princess Alexandra Walk, Huddersfield, West Yorkshire HD1 2SU
☎(01484) 226300
Fax (01484) 221952
Librarian i/c Ms C Morris BA DLIS ALA DMS

Area libraries
A   Batley/Cleckheaton Area. Batley Library, Market Place, Batley, West Yorkshire WF17 5DA
☎(01924) 326305
Librarian i/c Vacant
B   Dewsbury/Mirfield Area. Dewsbury Library, Railway Street, Dewsbury, West Yorkshire WF12 8EB
☎(01924) 325085
Librarian i/c T Hobson BA ALA
C   West Kirklees Branches, Cultural Services HQ, Red Doles Lane, Huddersfield, West Yorkshire HD2 1YF
☎(01484) 226319
Librarian i/c D Hatcher BSc DipLib ALA DMS
D   West Kirklees Mobiles, Cultural Services HQ, Red Doles Lane, Huddersfield, West Yorkshire HD2 1YF
☎(01484) 226319
Librarian i/c D Hatcher BSc DipLib ALA DMS

KNOWSLEY

Headquarters Knowsley Metropolitan Borough Council, Municipal Buildings, Archway Road, Huyton, Merseyside L36 9YX
☎0151 443 3680
Fax 0151 443 3492
e-mail: hq12@pipex.dial.com
Head of Libraries Mrs B Jones BA ALA

Central/largest library
Huyton Library, Civic Way, Huyton, Merseyside L36 9UN
☎0151 443 3734 (enquiries), 0151 482 1305 (administration)

Fax 0151 443 3739
Area Library Manager Mrs P Taylor BSc ALA

Branch libraries
A   Kirkby Library, Newtown Gardens, Kirkby, Merseyside L32 8RR
     ☎0151 443 4290
     Fax 0151 546 1453
     Area Library Manager Miss G Hunter BA(Hons)
B   Prescot Library, High Street, Prescot, Merseyside L34 3LD
     ☎0151 426 6449
     Fax 0151 430 7548
     Area Library Manager Miss S Stone BA ALA
C   Halewood Library, Leathers Lane, Halewood, Merseyside L26 0TS
     ☎0151 486 4442
     Fax 0151 486 8101
     Area Library Manager Miss S Stone BA ALA
D   Page Moss Library, Stockbridge Lane, Huyton, Merseyside L36 3SA
     ☎0151 489 9814
     Fax 0151 482 1309
     Area Library Manager Mrs P Taylor BSc ALA
E   Stockbridge Village Library, The Withens, Stockbridge Village, Merseyside L28 1SU
     ☎0151 480 3925
     Area Library Manager Mrs P Taylor BSc ALA
F   Whiston Library, Dragon Lane, Whitston, Merseyside L3 3QW
     ☎0151 426 4757
     Fax 0151 493 0191
     Area Library Manager Miss S Stone BA ALA

LAMBETH

Headquarters London Borough of Lambeth, Directorate of Environmental Services, 1st Floor, Mary Seacole House, 91 Clapham High Street, London SW4 7TF
☎020 7926 0750 (enquiries)
Fax 020 7926 0751
Commissioning Manager A Whittle BA(Hons) ALA (020 7926 0753; e-mail: awhittle@lambeth.gov.uk)
Library Services Manager D Jones BA(Hons) DipLib (020 7926 0752)

Group Libraries North
Carnegie Library, 188 Herne Hill Road, London SE24 0AG
☎020 7926 6066
Fax 020 7926 6072
Area Manager North Ms J Shearer BA ALA

A   Brixton Group. Tate Library Brixton, Brixton Oval, London SW2 1JQ
     ☎020 7926 1056
     Fax 020 7926 1070
     Senior Librarian C Desmond
B   Vauxhall Group. Durning Library, 167 Kennington Lane, London SE11 4HF
     ☎020 7926 8682
     Fax 020 7926 8685
     Senior Librarian D Waller

Group Libraries South
Carnegie Library, 188 Herne Hill Road, London SE24 0AG

☎020 7926 6066
Fax 020 7926 6072
Area Managers South Ms M Locke BA ALA, Mrs S Goodwin

C   Clapham Group. Clapham Library, 1 Northside, Clapham Common, London
SW4 0QW
☎020 7926 0717
Fax 020 7926 4947
Senior Librarians Ms J Richardson BLib ALA, Ms C Tomlin
D   Streatham Group. Tate Library Streatham, 63 Streatham High Road, London
SW16 1PL
☎020 7926 6768
Fax 020 7926 5804
Senior Librarian M Merson
E   West Norwood Group. West Norwood Library, Norwood High Street, London
SE27 9JX
☎020 7926 8092
Fax 020 7926 8032
Senior Librarian Ms M Eaton BA(Hons)

Archives and Local History
Minet Library, 52 Knatchbull Road, London SE5 9QY
☎020 7926 6076
Fax 020 7926 6080
Archivists Ms S McKenzie, J Newman MA DAA

Community Services Unit (Mobile Libraries, Home Visit Service, Library Outreach
Service), South Island Place, London SW9 0DX
☎020 7926 8334
Fax 020 7926 8336
Community Services Manager Ms J Bild ALA

Mobile Library Service HQ, South Island Place, London SW9 0DX
☎020 7926 8334
Fax 020 7926 8336
Mobile Services Librarian Ms L Gardner

Information Services Section
Reference Library, Tate Library Brixton, Brixton Oval, London SW2 1JQ
☎020 7926 1067
Fax 020 7926 1070
Information Services Manager Ms C Maynard ALA
Reference Librarian K Scott BA ALA

Library Commissioning Unit
Directorate of Environmental Services, 1st Floor, Mary Seacole House, 91 Clapham High
Street, London SW4 7TF
☎020 7926 0753
Fax 020 7926 0751
Libraries Development Manager J Readman BA MA ALA (020 7926 0751; e-mail:
jreadman@lambeth.gov.uk)
Library Systems Manager Vacant

Support Services Unit (Finance, Administration, Personnel, Bibliographic Services)

Bibliographic Services Section, Carnegie Library, 188 Herne Hill Road, Brixton, London
SE24 0AG
☎020 7926 6062
Fax 020 7926 6072
Support Services Manager Vacant
Bibliographic Services Librarian Vacant

LANCASHIRE
Headquarters Lancashire County Council, Education and Cultural Services Directorate,
County Library Service, County Hall, PO Box 61, Preston, Lancs PR1 8RJ
☎(01772) 254868
Fax (01772) 264880
County Library Manager D G Lightfoot MA DMS ALA (01772 264010; e-mail:
david.lightfoot@ed.lancscc.gov.uk)

Divisional libraries
A   North Lancashire Division. Divisional Library, Market Square, Lancaster, Lancs
LA1 1HY
☎(01524) 580700
Fax (01524) 580706
Divisional Librarian S J Eccles ALA
B   Central Lancashire Division. Harris Library, Market Square, Preston, Lancs PR1 2PP
☎(01772) 404000
Fax (01772) 404011
Divisional Librarian Mrs L M Farnworth BA DMA ALA
C   South Lancashire Division. Divisional Library, Union Street, Chorley, Lancs PR7 1EB
☎(01257) 277222
Fax (01257) 231730
Divisional Librarian D Whitham BSc ALA
D   South East Lancashire Division. Divisional Library, St James' Street, Accrington,
Lancs BB5 1NQ
☎(01254) 872385
Fax (01254) 301066
Divisional Librarian Mrs J Farrell ALA
E   East Lancashire Division. Divisional Library, Grimshaw Street, Burnley, Lancs
BB11 2BD
☎(01282) 437115
Fax (01282) 831682
Divisional Librarian J D Hodgkinson BA ALA

LEEDS
Headquarters Leeds City Council, Department of Leisure Services, The Town Hall, The
Headrow, Leeds LS1 3AD
☎0113 247 8330 (enquiries)
Fax 0113 247 7747
Head of Library and Information Services Ms C Blanshard BA ALA (e-mail:
catherine.blanshard@leeds.gov.uk)

Library headquarters
Library Headquarters, 32 York Road, Leeds LS9 8TD
☎0113 214 3300
Fax 0113 214 3312
Head of Support Services Ms P Carroll BA ALA (e-mail: patricia.carroll@leeds.gov.uk)

Central/largest library
Central Library, Municipal Buildings, Calverley Street, Leeds LS1 3AB
☎0113 247 8274
Fax 0113 247 8268
url: http://www.leeds.gov.uk
Central Library Manager Ms S Cook ALA

LEICESTER
Headquarters Leicester City Council, Arts and Leisure Department, Block A, New Walk
Centre, Welford Place, Leicester LE1 6ZG
☎0116 252 6762 (administration)
Fax 0116 255 9257
e-mail: libraries@leicester.gov.uk
Head of Libraries and Information Services M E Clarke BA ALA (0116 252 7348; e-mail:
clarm002@leicester.gov.uk)
Operations Manager A Wills BA DMS ALA (0116 252 6762; e-mail:
willa002@leicester.gov.uk)
Quality & Development Manager J R Parsons BA MA DipLib ALA (0116 252 7337; e-mail:
parsj001@leicester.gov.uk)
Community Services Manager Ms P Leahy BA(Hons) ALA (0116 299 5464)

Central/largest library
Central Lending Library, 54 Belvoir Street, Leicester LE1 6QL
☎0116 255 6699 (enquiries), 0116 255 6849 (administration)
Fax 0116 255 5435
Area Librarian Mrs J Brindle BA MA ALA

Area libraries
A   Beaumont Leys Library, Beaumont Way, Leicester LE4 1DS
      ☎0116 299 5460
      Fax 0116 234 0078
      Acting Area Librarian Ms N Morgan (0116 299 5472)
B   Southfields Library, Saffron Lane, Leicester LE2 6QS
      ☎0116 299 5480
      Fax 0116 299 5491
      Area Librarian M Maxwell BA DMS ALA (0116 299 5482)

LEICESTERSHIRE
Headquarters Leicestershire County Council, Libraries and Information Service HQ,
County Hall, Glenfield, Leicester LE3 8SS
☎0116 265 7374 (enquiries), 0116 265 7375 (administration)
Fax 0116 265 7370
Chief Librarian P Oldroyd BA DipLib ALA DMS (poldroyd@leics.gov.uk)

District library HQs
A   Hinckley Library, Lancaster Road, Hinckley, Leics LE10 0AT
      ☎(01455) 635106
      Fax (01455) 251385
      District Librarian N Thomas BLib(Hons) ALA
B   Loughborough Library, Granby Street, Loughborough, Leics LE11 3DZ
      ☎(01509) 212985/266436
      Fax (01509) 610594
      District Librarian S Kettle BA DipLib DipMan ALA

C   Wigston Library, Bull Head Street, Wigston, Leicester LE18 1PA
     ☎0116 288 7381/257 1891
     Fax 0116 281 2985
     District Librarian A Cooke BA ALA DMS

LEWISHAM

Headquarters London Borough of Lewisham, Education and Community Services, c/o 3rd
Floor, Laurence House, Catford, London SE6 4RU
☎020 8314 8024 (enquiries)
Fax 020 8314 3039
Acting Head of Libraries Ms J M Newton ALA (e-mail: julia.newton@lewisham.gov.uk)

Central/largest library
Lewisham Library, 199-201 Lewisham High Street, London SE13 6LG
☎020 8297 9677
Fax 020 8297 1169
Operations Manager (North) J Simmons ALA MILAM

Group libraries
A   Catford Library, Laurence House, Catford, London SE6 4RU
     ☎020 8314 6399
     Fax 020 8314 1110
     Operations Manager (South) K Yeates ALA
B   Management Services Group, c/o 3rd Floor, Laurence House, Catford, London
     SE6 4RU
     ☎020 8314 8025
     Acting Management Services Librarian H Paton BA DipLib ALA (e-mail:
     hugh.paton@lewisham.gov.uk)

LINCOLNSHIRE

Headquarters Lincolnshire County Council, Education and Cultural Services Directorate,
County Offices, Newland, Lincoln, Lincs LN1 1YL
☎(01522) 553207
Fax (01522) 552811
Library Services Manager Ms L M Jubb BA (e-mail: lorraine.jubb@lincolnshire.gov.uk)

Central/largest library
Lincoln Central Library, Free School Lane, Lincoln, Lincs LN2 1EZ
☎(01522) 510800 (general enquiries), (01522) 579200 (management)
Fax (01522) 575011
e-mail: lincoln.library@dial.pipex.com
Resources Manager R Hundleby MA ALA

Library Support Services, Brayford House, Lucy Tower Street, Lincoln, Lincs LN1 1XN
☎(01522) 552866
Fax (01522) 552858
Operations Manager R MacInroy BA ALA (e-mail: mcinroyr@lincolnshire.gov.uk)

Special Services (Schools and Library Services to Centres), Education and Cultural
Services Directorate, County Offices, Newland, Lincoln, Lincs LN1 1YL
☎(01522) 552804
Fax (01522) 552858
Special Services Manager G Elgar BA(Hons) DipLib ALA (e-mail:
elgarg@lincolnshire.gov.uk)

Area libraries
A North (Louth). Louth Library, Northgate, Louth, Lincs LN11 0LY
  ☎(01507) 602218
  Fax (01507) 608261
  Community Services Manager Ms G Fraser MA ALA (e-mail:
  fraserg@lincolnshire.gov.uk)
B Mid-Lincolnshire (Sleaford). Sleaford Library, Market Place, Sleaford, Lincs
  NG34 7SD
  ☎(01529) 414770
  Fax (01529) 415329
  Information Services Manager Vacant
C South (Boston). County Library, County Hall, Boston, Lincs PE21 6LX
  ☎(01205) 310010 ext 2871
  Fax (01522) 552882
  Information Services Manager Ms L Carroll ALA (e-mail:
  carrolll@lincolnshire.gov.uk)

LIVERPOOL

Headquarters Liverpool City Council, Liverpool Libraries and Information Services, Central
Library, William Brown Street, Liverpool L3 8EW
☎0151 233 5829/5835/5836 (enquiries), 0151 233 7851/7843 (administration)
Fax 0151 207 1342
e-mail: lvpublib@lvpublib.demon.co.uk
Head of Libraries and Information Services Ms J Little ALA
Manager (Central Libraries) Vacant (0151 233 5847)
Manager (Library Support Services) Ms K Johnson (0151 233 5808)
Manager (Community Libraries) A Green BA MSc DipLib ALA (0151 233 5819)

Central/largest library
As above

Other large libraries
A Allerton Library, Liverpool L18 6HG
  ☎0151 724 2987
  Senior Community Librarian M Kaufman
B Childwall Fiveways Library, Liverpool L15 6QR
  ☎0151 722 3214
  Senior Community Librarian N Campbell
C Norris Green Library, Townsend Avenue, Liverpool L11 5AF
  ☎0151 226 1714
  Senior Community Librarian J Watson

LONDON, City of

Headquarters Corporation of London, Guildhall Library, Aldermanbury, London EC2P 2EJ
☎020 7332 1852
Fax 020 7600 3384
Director M Barnes OBE DMA ALA FIMgt FRSA
(e-mail: melvyn.barnes@ms.corpoflondon.gov.uk)
Assistant Director (Libraries and Archives) Ms L Blundell BA ALA
(e-mail: lesley.blundell@ms.corpoflondon.gov.uk)
Assistant Director (Art Galleries and Support Services) B Cropper MA DipLib ALA
MIMgt (e-mail: barry.cropper@ms.corpoflondon.gov.uk)

Central/largest libraries
Guildhall Library, Aldermanbury, London EC2P 2EJ
☎020 7332 1868
Fax 020 7600 3384
Librarian i/c Ms I F Gilchrist BD DipLib (e-mail: irene.gilchrist@ms.corpoflondon.gov.uk)

Barbican Library, Barbican Centre, Silk Street, London EC2Y 8DS
☎020 7638 0569
Fax 020 7638 2249
Librarian i/c J Lake BA ALA (e-mail: john.lake@ms.corpoflondon.gov.uk)

Regional/district libraries
A   Camomile Street Library, 12-20 Camomile Street, London EC3A 7EX
     ☎020 7247 8895
     Fax 020 7377 2972
     Librarian i/c M Key BA ALA (e-mail: malcolm.key@ms.corpoflondon.gov.uk)
B   City Business Library, 1 Brewers' Hall Garden, London EC2V 5BX
     ☎020 7638 8215
     Fax 020 7332 1847
     Librarian i/c G P Humphreys ALA FRSA (e-mail: garry.humphreys@ms.
     corpoflondon.gov.uk)
C   St Bride Printing Library, Bride Lane, London EC4Y 8EQ
     ☎020 7353 4660
     Fax 020 7583 7073
     Librarian i/c J Mosley MA (e-mail: james.mosley@ms.corpoflondon.gov.uk)
D   Shoe Lane Library, Hill House, 1 Little New Street, London EC4A 3JR
     ☎020 7583 7178
     Fax 020 7353 0884
     Librarian i/c Mrs J C Coomber MLib ALA (e-mail: janet.coomber@ms.
     corpoflondon.gov.uk)

LUTON

Headquarters Luton Borough Council, Libraries, Information and Communications Service,
Central Library, St George's Square, Luton, Bedfordshire LU1 2NG
☎(01582) 547418/9 (enquiries), (01582) 547404 (administration)
Fax (01582) 547461
Libraries, Information and Communications Manager Ms J George BA DMS ALA
(01582 547422; e-mail: georgej@luton.gov.uk)
Principal Librarian, Adult Services/Branches and Mobiles Ms F Marriott BA ALA (01582
547417; e-mail: marriottf@luton.gov.uk)
Principal Librarian, Information Services/Luton Central R Evans BA ALA (01582
547424; e-mail: evansr@luton.gov.uk)
Principal Librarian, Children and Young People/Schools Library Service Ms J Hair
ALA (01582 574541)

Central/largest library
Central Library, St George's Square, Luton, Bedfordshire LU1 2NG
☎Tel/Fax etc. as HQ
Principal Librarian R Evans BA ALA (01582 547424; e-mail: evansr@luton.gov.uk)

Branch libraries
A   Leagrave Library, Marsh Road, Luton, Bedfordshire LU3 2NL
     ☎(01582) 597851

  Library Manager Mrs D Boother
B Lewsey Library, Landrace Road, Luton, Bedfordshire LU4 0SW
  ☎(01582) 696094
  Library Manager Mrs S Saad
C Marsh Farm Library, Purley Centre, Luton, Bedfordshire LU3 3SR
  ☎(01582) 574803
  Library Manager Mrs L Lindars
D Stopsley Library, Hitchin Road, Luton, Bedfordshire LU2 7UG
  ☎(01582) 722791
  Library Manager Mrs M Woollison
E Sundon Park Library, Hill Rise, Luton, Bedfordshire LU3 3EE
  ☎(01582) 574573
  Library Manager Mrs A Soan
F Wigmore Library, Wigmore Lane, Luton, Bedfordshire LU3 8DJ
  ☎(01582) 455228
  Library Manager Mrs J Wigley
G Housebound Unit, Marsh Farm Library, Purley Centre, Luton, Bedfordshire
  LU3 3SR
  ☎(01582) 491428
  Fax (01582) 574803
  Manager Mrs J Devine

MANCHESTER

Headquarters Manchester City Council, Central Library, St Peter's Square, Manchester
M2 5PD
☎0161 234 1900
Fax 0161 234 1963
Director of Libraries and Theatres P Catcheside BA ALA
Central Library Manager A Gallimore BSc ALA
District Libraries Manager Ms C Morrison ALA

District libraries
A Central District HQ, Longsight Library, 519 Stockport Road, Manchester M12 4NE
  ☎0161 224 1411
  Fax 0161 225 2119
  Principal Officer Ms W Broadbent
B North District HQ, Crumpsall Library, Abraham Moss Centre, Manchester M8 6UF
  ☎0161 721 4555
  Fax 0161 721 4927
  Principal Officer Ms H Blagborough BSc DipLib ALA, Ms J Sharp BA DipLib ALA
C South District HQ, Wythenshawe Library, The Forum, Manchester M22 5RT
  ☎0161 935 4000
  Fax 0161 935 4039
  Principal Officer S Willis BA DipLib ALA

MEDWAY

Headquarters Medway Council, Leisure, Arts and Libraries Department, Civic Centre,
Strood, Rochester, Kent ME2 4AU
☎(01634) 843589 (enquiries); (01634) 306000 (administration)
Assistant Director, Arts, Libraries and Heritage Ms J Maskort BA(Hons) ALA DMS
(01634 306000)
Head of Information Services Ms A Edwards BA(Hons) MA ALA (01634 843589)
Head of Libraries Mrs V Mawhinney BA(Hons) ALA (01634 281066)

Community Services Librarian Mrs K Woollacott ALA (01634 842415)
Reference and Local Studies Officer Mrs L Rainbow BA(Hons) ALA (01634 732714)

Central/largest libraries
Chatham Library, Riverside, Chatham, Kent ME4 4SN
☎(01634) 843589
Fax (01634) 827976

Gillingham Library, High Street, Gillingham, Kent ME7 1BG
☎(01634) 281066
Fax (01634) 855814

Town centre libraries
A   Rainham Library, Birling Avenue, Rainham, Gillingham, Kent ME8 7LR
     ☎(01634) 231745
     Fax (01634) 263415
B   Rochester Library, Northgate, Rochester, Kent ME1 1LU
     ☎(01634) 842415
     Fax (01634) 843837
C   Strood Library, 32 Bryant Road, Strood, Rochester, Kent ME2 3EP
     ☎(01634) 718161
     Fax (01634) 718161
D   Medway Archives and Local Studies Centre, Civic Centre, Strood, Rochester, Kent
     ME2 4AU
     ☎(01634) 732714
     Fax (01634) 297060

MERTON

Headquarters London Borough of Merton, Libraries and Heritage Services, Civic Centre,
London Road, Morden, Surrey SM4 5DX
☎020 8545 3770
Fax 020 8545 4637
e-mail: fm047@viscount.org.uk
Head of Libraries and Heritage Services J Pateman BA DipLib MBA FLA
Principal Librarian, Customer and Community Services S Durrani BA PGDip

Main libraries
A   Mitcham Library, London Road, Mitcham, Surrey CR4 7YR
     ☎020 8648 4070/6516
     Fax 020 8646 6360
     Customer Services Librarian Ms D Chaudhri BA MA DipLIS
B   Morden Library, Civic Centre, London Road, Morden, Surrey SM4 5DX
     ☎020 8545 4040
     Fax 020 8545 4037
     Customer Services Librarian Ms H Rutledge BA(Hons) DipLib ALA MA
C   Wimbledon Library, Wimbledon Hill Road, London SW19 7NB
     ☎020 8946 7979/7432; 020 8946 1136 (Reference and Information)
     Fax 020 8944 6804
     Customer Services Librarian Ms A Williams BEd DipLib ALA

MIDDLESBROUGH

Headquarters Middlesbrough Borough Council, Libraries and Information, Central Library,
Victoria Square, Middlesbrough TS1 2AY

☎(01642) 263372 (administration)
Fax (01642) 263354
Libraries and Information Manager N Bennett BSc DMS ALA (01642 263350; e-mail:
neil_bennett@middlesbrough.gov.uk)

Central/largest library
Central Library, Victoria Square, Middlesbrough TS1 2AY
☎(01642) 263397 (enquiries), (01642) 263372 (administration)
Fax (01642) 263354
Principal Librarians Mrs J M Brittain BA (e-mail: jen_brittain@middlesbrough.gov.uk),
J Alder BA ALA (e-mail: jeremy_alder@middlesbrough.gov.uk)

MILTON KEYNES
Headquarters Milton Keynes Council Library Service, Central Library, 555 Silbury
Boulevard, Saxon Gate East, Central Milton Keynes MK9 3HL
☎(01908) 254050
Fax (01908) 254089
Chief Librarian W Pearson ALA (e-mail: bill.pearson@miltonkeynes.gov.uk)

Central/largest library
Central Library, 555 Silbury Boulevard, Saxon Gate East, Central Milton Keynes MK9 3HL
☎Tel/Fax etc. as HQ
Principal Librarian Mrs T Carroll ALA

Branch libraries HQ
Bletchley Library, Westfield Road, Bletchley, Milton Keynes MK2 2RA
☎(01908) 372797
Fax (01908) 645562
Assistant Principal Librarian S Hobbs MA DMS ALA

NEWCASTLE UPON TYNE
Headquarters Newcastle upon Tyne City Council, City Library, Princess Square,
Newcastle upon Tyne NE99 1DX
☎0191 261 0691
Fax 0191 261 1435
Assistant Director, Education and Libraries D R Gunn BA ALA (e-mail:
david.gunn@newcastle.gov.uk)

Central/largest library
City Library, Princess Square, Newcastle upon Tyne NE99 1DX
☎Tel/Fax etc. as HQ
Library and Information Manager (City-wide Services) A Wraight BA ALA DMS (e-mail:
allan.wraight@newcastle.gov.uk)

Area libraries
A   Gosforth Library (Central Group), Regent Farm Road, Gosforth, Newcastle upon
     Tyne NE3 1JN
     ☎0191 285 4244
     Area Library and Information Manager A Fletcher BA ALA
B   Denton Park Library (Outer West Group), West Denton Way, West Denton,
     Newcastle upon Tyne NE5 2LF
     ☎0191 267 7922
     Area Library and Information Manager Ms E Burt ALA

C   Scotswood Library (Inner West Group), Armstrong Road, Newcastle upon Tyne NE15 6AU
☎0191 274 1860
Area Library and Information Manager Ms E Michael ALA

D   Byker Library (East Group), Brinkburn Street, Byker, Newcastle upon Tyne NE6 2AR
☎0191 265 5750
Area Library and Information Manager Ms J Biggins BA ALA

NEWHAM
Headquarters London Borough of Newham, Library Administration, Leisure Services Department, 292 Barking Road, East Ham, London E6 3BA
☎020 8472 1430 ext 21707 (administration)
Fax 020 8557 8845
Divisional Director, Leisure Services T Brill

Central/largest library
Administrative Office, East Ham Library, High Street South, London E6 4EL
☎020 8472 1430 ext 23804 (lending), 020 8472 23805 (reference)
Fax 020 8557 8845
Site Manager D Hemmings
Head of Library Services R McMaster BA MA ALA (e-mail:
roger.mcmaster@newham.gov.uk)
Acting Principal Advisory Services Librarian (Children, Local Studies and Reference)
Ms J Davies BSc DipLib (Stratford District Library, Water Lane, London E15 4NJ. Tel: 020 8519 6346/020 8519 6346)

Regional/district library
Stratford District Library, Water Lane, London E15 4NJ
☎020 8534 4545 ext 24663 (lending), ext 24661 (reference), ext 24662 (archives/local studies)
Site Manager H Allsop ALA

NORFOLK
Headquarters Norfolk County Council, Library and Information Service, County Hall, Martineau Lane, Norwich NR1 2UB
☎(01603) 222049
Fax (01603) 222422
e-mail: libraries@norfolk.gov.uk
url: http://www.norfolk.gov.uk/council/default.htm
Director of Cultural Services T Turner BA DipLib (01603 223000; e-mail:
terry.turner.lib@norfolk.gov.uk)
Principal Assistant Director (Information and Development Services) J K Creber
BA(Hons) ALA (01603 222273; e-mail: john.creber.lib@norfolk.gov.uk)
Assistant Director (Quality and Support Services) Mrs J Holland BA(Hons) ALA (01603 222272; e-mail: jennifer.holland.lib@norfolk.gov.uk)
Assistant Director (Public and Bibliographic Services) Miss S M Boden BA(Hons) ALA
(01603 222271; e-mail: sue.boden.lib@norfolk.gov.uk)
Principal Administrative and Finance Officer R Snowden CMA (01603 222054; e-mail:
richard.snowden.lib@norfolk.gov.uk)
County Arts Officer M Martin (01603 222269; e-mail: mari.martin.lib@norfolk.gov.uk)

Central/largest libraries
A   Norfolk and Norwich Lending Library, 71 Ber Street, Norwich NR1 3AD
☎(01603) 215214 (enquiries)

e-mail: norwich.central.lib@norfolk.gov.uk
Acting Principal Librarian J Rawlings BA ALA (01603 215200)

B   Norfolk and Norwich Information Library, Gildengate House, Anglia Square, Upper Green Lane, Norwich, Norfolk NR3 1AX
☎(01603) 215255 (reference enquiries), 215254 (local studies enquiries), 215251 (administration)
e-mail: norfolk.ref.library@norfolk.gov.uk
Acting Principal Librarian Miss C Agate BA ALA (01603 215256)

Area library HQs
A   Central Norwich Area. Plumstead Road Library, Plumstead Road, Norwich NR1 4JS
☎(01603) 433455
Principal Librarian Mrs J Emerson BA ALA
B   East Norfolk Area. Wroxham Library, Norwich Road, Wroxham, Norfolk NR12 8RX
☎01603) 782560
Principal Librarian N Buxton ALA
C   North West Norfolk Area. Fakenham Library, Oak Street, Fakenham, Norfolk NR21 9DY
☎(01328) 862715
Acting Principal Librarian D Stoney BA(Hons) DipLib ALA
D   South Norfolk Area. Attleborough Library, 31 Connaught Road, Attleborough, Norfolk NR17 2BW
☎(01953) 452319
Principal Librarian Miss S Hassan BA(Hons) MA ALA

NORTH EAST LINCOLNSHIRE
Headquarters North East Lincolnshire Council, Central Library, Town Hall Square, Grimsby, North East Lincs DN31 1HG
☎(01472) 323600 (enquiries), (01472) 323617 (administration)
Fax (01472) 323618
url: http://www.nelincs.gov.uk
Director of Libraries A S Hipkins BA(Hons) MA DipLib ALA (01472 323611)
Strategy Officer D A H Bell ALA (01472 323612)
Senior Librarian Mrs J Sargent BA (01472 323614)
Stock Officer J English BA (01472 323615)
Support Services Officer Mrs I Blow BA ALA (01472 323616)

Central/largest library
As above

Branch libraries
A   Cleethorpes Library, Alexandra Road, Cleethorpes, North East Lincs DN35 8LG
☎(01472) 323650
Fax (01472) 323652
Senior Library Supervisor Miss S Gamble
B   Grant Thorold Library, Durban Road, Grimsby, North East Lincs DN32 8BX
☎(01472) 323631
Library Supervisor Mrs S Stokes
C   Humberston Library, Church Lane, Humberston, North East Lincs DN36 4WZ
☎(01472) 323682
Library Supervisor Mrs J Scoffin
D   Immingham Library, Civic Centre, Pelham Road, Immingham, North East Lincs DN40 1QF
☎(01469) 516050

Library Supervisor Mrs S Middleton
E   Laceby Library, The Stanford Centre, Cooper Lane, Laceby, North East Lincs
DN37 7AX
☎01472) 323684
Library Supervisor Mrs J Garside
F   Nunsthorpe Library, Sutcliffe Avenue, Grimsby, North East Lincs DN33 1HA
☎(01472) 323636
Library Supervisor Mrs W Stark
G   Scartho Library, St Giles Avenue, Grimsby, North East Lincs DN33 2HB
☎(01472) 323638
Library Supervisor Mrs W Liddall
H   Waltham Library, High Street, Waltham, North East Lincs DN37 0LL
☎(01472) 323656
Library Supervisor Mrs V Brunson
I   Willows Library, Binbrook Way, Grimsby, North East Lincs DN37 9AS
☎(01472) 323679
Library Supervisor Mrs M Atkin
J   Yarborough Library, Cromwell Road, Grimsby, North East Lincs DN31 2BX
☎(01472) 323658
Library Supervisor Mrs P Turner

NORTH LINCOLNSHIRE

Headquarters North Lincolnshire Council, Scunthorpe Central Library, Carlton Street,
Scunthorpe, North Lincs DN15 6TX
☎(01724) 860161
Fax (01724) 859737
e-mail: scunthorpe.ref@central-library.demon.co.uk
url: http://www.northlincs.gov.uk/library/
Principal Librarian Mrs M Carr BA ALA (e-mail: margaret.carr@northlincs.gov.uk)

Central/largest library
As above

NORTH SOMERSET

Headquarters North Somerset Council, Library and Information Service, Economic
Development and Community Leisure Department, PO Box 146, Town Hall, Weston-super-
Mare, Somerset BS23 1LH
☎(01934) 634820
Fax (01934) 612006
Libraries and Museum Manager Mrs J Petherbridge ALA DMS MIMgt (e-mail:
jackie.petherbridge@n.somerset.gov.uk)

Area libraries
A   Weston Library, The Boulevard, Weston-super-Mare, Somerset BS23 1PL
      ☎(01934) 636638 (enquiries), (01934) 620373 (administration)
      Fax (01934) 413046
      e-mail: weston.library@n.somerset.gov.uk
      South Area Library Manager N Kelly BA ALA OMS MIMgt
B   Clevedon Library, 37 Old Church Road, Clevedon, Somerset BS21 6NN
      ☎(01275) 873498/874858
      Fax (01275) 343630
      North Area Library Manager A Brisley BA ALA (e-mail:
      andy.brisley@n.somerst.gov.uk)

NORTH TYNESIDE

Headquarters North Tyneside Metropolitan District Council, Central Library, Northumberland Square, North Shields, Tyne and Wear NE30 1QU
☎0191 200 5424
Fax 0191 200 6118
e-mail: central@ntlib.demon.co.uk
Libraries and Information Manager Mrs J Stafford BA ALA
Central Librarian Ms A Craven BA ALA
Support Services Manager F Miller BA ALA
Children and Young People Manager Mrs J Clements MBE BA ALA

Central/largest library
As above

Group libraries
A   Whitley Bay Library, Park Road, Whitley Bay, Tyne and Wear NE26 1EJ
       ☎0191 200 8500
       Fax 0191 200 8536
B   Wallsend Library, Ferndale Avenue, Wallsend, Tyne and Wear NE28 7NB
       ☎0191 200 6968
       Fax 0191 200 6967

NORTH YORKSHIRE

Headquarters North Yorkshire County Council, County Library HQ, 21 Grammar School Lane, Northallerton, North Yorkshire DL6 1DF
☎(01609) 776271 (enquiries & administration)
Fax (01609) 780793
Head of Libraries and Arts R de Graff BA MA(Lib) ALA (e-mail: raydegraff@northyorks.gov.uk)
Public Services Librarian M K Gibson BA ALA (e-mail: mike.gibson@northyorks.gov.uk)
Support Services Manager C Riley DMA ACIS MIPD (e-mail: chris.riley@northyorks.gov.uk)

Group headquarters
A   Northallerton Group Library HQ, 1 Thirsk Road, Northallerton, North Yorkshire DL6 1PT
       ☎(01609) 776192/776202
       Fax (01609) 780793
       Group Librarian Mrs R A Bullimore ALA
B   Scarborough Group Library HQ, Vernon Road, Scarborough, North Yorkshire YO11 2NN
       ☎(01723) 500802/364285
       Fax (01723) 353893
       Group Librarian D Fay BA ALA
C   Harrogate Group Library HQ, Victoria Avenue, Harrogate, North Yorkshire HG1 1EG
       ☎(01423) 502774/504726/500081
       Fax (01423) 523158
       Group Librarian Ms I M Maynard BA ALA
D   Malton Group Library HQ, St Michael Street, Malton, North Yorkshire YO17 0LJ
       ☎(01653) 696069/692714
       Fax (01653) 691200
       Group Librarian Miss B M Poole BA ALA
E   Skipton Group Library HQ, Water Street, Skipton, North Yorkshire BD23 1PD

☎(01756) 793751/792926/794726 (Reference only)
Fax (01756) 796461
Group Librarian M C E Freeman BA ALA
F   Sherburn Group Library HQ, Finkle Hill, Sherburn-in-Elmet, Leeds LS25 6EA
☎(01977) 685308
Fax (01977) 685308
Group Librarian D A Tanner BA ALA

NORTHAMPTONSHIRE

Headquarters Northamptonshire County Council, Libraries and Information Service, PO
Box 259, 27 Guildhall Road, Northampton, Northants NN1 1BA
☎(01604) 620262 (enquiries & administration)
Fax (01604) 626789
e-mail: genie@northamptonshire.gov.uk
url: http://www.northamptonshire.gov.uk
County Libraries and Information Officer E W Wright MA BSc BPhil ALA (e-mail:
ewright@northamptonshire.gov.uk)
Principal Libraries and Information Officer (Service Delivery) N L Matthews BA ALA
DMS (e-mail: nmatthews@northamptonshire.gov.uk)
Principal Libraries and Information Officer (Service Development) Ms E L Jarvis BA
MDipLib DMS (e-mail: ejarvis@northamptonshire.gov.uk)

Central/largest library
Central Library, Abington Street, Northampton, Northants NN1 2BA
☎(01604) 462040
Fax (01604) 462055
Central Library Manager Ms J Cox BLib ALA (e-mail: jcox@northamptonshire.gov.uk)

Area libraries
A   Daventry Library, North Street, Daventry, Northants NN11 5PN
☎(01327) 703130
Fax (01327) 300501
Principal Librarian I J Clarke BA ALA
B   Kettering Library, Sheep Street, Kettering, Northants NN16 0AY
☎(01536) 512315
Fax (01536) 411349
Principal Librarian Mrs A I Probert BLS ALA
C   Wellingborough Library, Pebble Lane, Wellingborough, Northants NN8 1AS
☎(01933) 225365
Fax (01933) 442062
Principal Librarian Mrs J M Sonpal BSc DipLIS ALA
D   Weston Favell Library, Weston Favell Centre, Northampton, Northants NN3 8JZ
☎(01604) 413327
Fax (01604) 413807
Principal Librarian Ms J Cole BSc PGCE MSc

NORTHUMBERLAND

Headquarters Northumberland County Council, County Library HQ, The Willows, Morpeth,
Northumberland NE61 1TA
☎(01670) 534501
Fax (01670) 534521 (administration)
Divisional Director, Libraries, Arts and Heritage D E Bonser BA ALA

Central/largest library
County Library HQ, The Willows, Morpeth, Northumberland NE61 1TA

☎(01670) 534518 (lending); (01670) 534514 (reference)
Fax (01670) 534513
e-mail: amenities@northumberland.gov.uk

NOTTINGHAM
Headquarters City of Nottingham Council, Department of Leisure and Community Services, Libraries, Information and Museums Services Division, 14 Hounds Gate, Nottingham NG1 7BD
☎0115 915 5555
Fax 0115 915 7200
Assistant Director, Libraries, Information and Museums Services B Ashley BA DipLib ALA (0115 915 7205)

Central/largest library
Nottingham City Library, Angel Row, Nottingham NG1 6HP
☎0115 915 2828
Fax 0115 915 2850
e-mail: notlib@notlib.demon.co.uk
Service Manager J Turner BA ALA

NOTTINGHAMSHIRE
Headquarters Nottinghamshire County Council, Community Services/Libraries, Archives and Information, Trent Bridge House, Fox Road, West Bridgford, Nottingham NG2 6BJ
☎0115 977 4401
Fax 0115 977 2428
Assistant Director (Libraries, Archives and Information) D Lathrope BSc DMS ALA (0115 977 4201; e-mail: david.lathrope@nottscc.gov.uk)
Principal Libraries Officer (Public Services, Operations and Quality) A J Cook BA ALA ALCM (0115 977 4437)
Principal Libraries Officer (Resources and Commissioning) A P Marshall BA ALA (0115 985 4201)

Central/largest library
County Library, Four Seasons Centre, Westgate, Mansfield, Notts NG18 1NH
☎(01623) 627591 (enquiries), (01623) 653551 (administration)
Fax (01623) 629276
e-mail: mansfield@ncclibma.demon.co.uk
Principal Librarian Mrs K Owen BA ALA

Group libraries
A　　North Nottinghamshire Group. County Library, Churchgate, Retford, Notts DN22 6PE
　　　☎(01777) 708724
　　　Fax (01777) 710020
　　　Principal Librarian Mrs L Turner BA ALA
B　　East Nottinghamshire Group. County Library, Beaumond Gardens, Baldertongate, Newark-on-Trent, Notts NG24 1UW
　　　☎(01636) 703966
　　　Fax (01636) 610045
　　　e-mail: newark@ncclibnc.demon.co.uk
　　　Principal Librarian R A J Vinnicombe ALA DMA
C　　West Nottinghamshire Group. County Library, Four Seasons Centre, Westgate, Mansfield, Notts NG18 1NH

☎(01623) 627591
Fax (01623) 629276
e-mail: mansfield@ncclibma.demon.co.uk
Principal Librarian Mrs K Owen BA ALA
D   Central Nottinghamshire Group., County Library, Front Street, Arnold, Notts
NG5 7EE
☎0115 920 2247
Fax 0115 967 3378
e-mail: arnold@ncclibar.demon.co.uk
Principal Librarian R S Jones BA ALA
E   South Nottinghamshire Group., County Library, Foster Avenue, Beeston,
Nottingham NG9 1AE
☎0115 925 5168/925 5084
Fax 0115 922 0841
e-mail: beeston@ncclibbe.demon.co.uk
Principal Librarian S I Robertson BA ALA

Other services
F   Support Services, Units 4-6, Glaisdale Parkway, Bilborough, Nottingham NG8 4GP
☎0115 985 4242
Fax 0115 928 6400
e-mail: glaisdale@ncclibgl.demon.co.uk
Principal Bibliographical Officer, Support Services Ms A Corin BA ALA
(0115 985 4208)
Principal Systems Officer, Support Services N London ALA (0115 985 4205)

OLDHAM

Headquarters Oldham Metropolitan District Council, Oldham Library, Union Street,
Oldham, Lancs OL1 1DN
☎0161 911 4645 (general enquiries)
Fax 0161 911 4630
e-mail: els.reference.lib@oldham.gov.uk
url: http://www.oldham.gov.uk
Library and Information Services Manager Ms P Flynn BA(Hons) (0161 911 4640)
Principal Community Librarian R Lambert MA ALA (0161 911 4632)

OXFORDSHIRE

Headquarters Oxfordshire County Council, Cultural Services, Central Library, Westgate,
Oxford OX1 1DJ
☎(01865) 810191
Fax (01865) 810187
Director T Forrest BA DipLib ALA DMS (e-mail: tom.forrest.occdla@dial.pipex.com)

Central/largest library
Central Library, Westgate, Oxford OX1 1DJ
☎(01865) 815549
Fax (01865) 815983
e-mail: centlib.occdla@dial.pipex.com
Central Library Manager Miss J Turner ALA

Library collections and areas
A   Cultural Services, Holton, Oxford OX33 1QQ
☎(01865) 810234

Fax (01865) 810207
Assistant County Librarian R Harris MA DipLib ALA
B   Area (North), Banbury Library, Marlborough Road, Banbury, Oxon OX16 8DF
☎(01295) 268249
Fax (01295) 264331
Assistant County Librarian Mrs Y McDonald BA DMS DipLib ALA (e-mail:
yvonne.mcdonald.occ@dial.pipex.com)
C   Area (Oxford), Cultural Services, Holton, Oxford OX33 1QQ
☎(01865) 810221
Fax (01865) 810205
Assistant County Librarian C Pettit MA ALA (e-mail: charles.pettit.occ@dial.pipex.
com)
D   Area (South), Wantage Library, Stirlings Road, Wantage, Oxon OX12 7BB
☎(01235) 771131
Fax (01235) 770951
Assistant County Librarian Mrs V Angel BA DipLib ALA (e-mail:
veronica.angel@dial.pipex.com)

PETERBOROUGH

Headquarters Peterborough City Council, Community Services: Libraries, 3rd Floor,
Bayard Place, Broadway, Peterborough PE1 7HZ
☎(01733) 348343
Head of Arts, Libraries and Heritage D Goodwin (01733 742550; e-mail:
daniel.goodwin@peterborough.gov.uk)
Libraries Manager R Hemmings BA ALA DMS MIMgt DipM MCIM (e-mail:
richard.hemmings@peterborough.gov.uk)
Principal Librarian Ms M Bernard BA DipLib ALA (e-mail:
medi.bernard@peterborough.gov.uk)

Central/largest library
Central Library, Broadway, Peterborough PE1 1RX
☎(01733) 348343
Fax (01733) 319140

District libraries
A   Werrington Library, Staniland Way, Werrington, Peterborough PE4 6JT
☎(01733) 576666
Supervisor Mrs S Rampal
B   Bretton Library, Bretton Centre, Bretton, Peterborough PE3 8DS
☎(01733) 265519
Supervisor Mrs M Barr
C   Orton Library, Orton Centre, Orton, Peterborough PE2 0RQ
☎(01733) 234448
Supervisor Mrs V Hindocha

PLYMOUTH

Headquarters Plymouth City Council, Library and Information Services, Central Library,
Drake Circus, Plymouth PL4 8AL
☎(01752) 305930 (enquiries and administration)
Fax (01752) 305929
City Librarian A MacNaughtan BA ALA DMS MIMgt (01752 305901)
Support and Development Librarian F Lowry ALA (01752 305911)
Resources and Technical Services Librarian C Goddard BMus DipLib ALA (01752
305900)

Public Services Librarian B Holgate ALA (01752 306090)
Coordinator of Library Services to Young People Ms S Whittle (01752 306098)

Central/largest library
As above

POOLE

Headquarters Borough of Poole, Cultural Services, Central Library, Dolphin Centre, Poole BH15 1QE
☎(01202) 673910
Fax (01202) 676401
Head of Cultural Services Vacant

Central/largest library
Central Library, Dolphin Centre, Poole BH15 1QE
☎(01202) 673919 (lending), (01202) 671496 (reference)
Library Services Manager Ms L J Pullen BLib ALA

Healthpoint (health information centre also serving Dorset)
Librarian Mrs V Grier BA ALA (01202 675377)

PORTSMOUTH

Headquarters Portsmouth City Council, Library Service, Central Library, Guildhall Square, Portsmouth PO1 2DX
☎023 9281 9311
Fax 023 9283 9855
City Librarian J Thorn ALA

Group libraries
A   North Group. Cosham Library, Spur Road, Portsmouth PO6 3EB
         ☎023 9237 6023
B   South Group. North End Library, Gladys Avenue, North End, Portsmouth PO2 9AX
         ☎023 9266 2651

READING

Headquarters Reading Borough Council, Reading Central Library, Abbey Square, Reading, Berks RG1 3BQ
☎0118 901 5950
Fax 0118 901 5954
Head of Libraries Ms S Lett BA DipLib ALA (0118 901 5964)
Library Services Manager R Thomas BA DipLib ALA (0118 901 5940)
Library Operations Manager Mrs M Newns (0118 901 5963)
Stock Manager Ms A England BA(Hons) DipLib ALA (0118 901 5962)
Senior Reference Librarian D Cliffe BA ALA (0118 901 3315)
Senior Lending Librarian Mrs E Delaney ALA (0118 901 3307)
Central Library Manager B Holder (0118 901 5947)

Central/largest library
As above

Branch libraries
A   Battle Library, 420 Oxford Road, Reading, Berks RG3 1EE
         ☎0118 901 5100

Branch Manager A Barker
B   Caversham Library, Church Street, Caversham, Reading, Berks RG4 8AU
     ☎0118 901 5103
     Branch Manager Mrs J Jones
C   Palmer Park Library, St Bartholomew's Road, Reading, Berks RG1 3QB
     ☎0118 901 5106
     Branch Manager Miss C Gosling
D   Southcote Library, Southcote Lane, Reading, Berks RG3 3BA
     ☎0118 901 5109
     Branch Manager Mrs J Morgan
E   Tilehurst Library, School Road, Tilehurst, Reading, Berks RG3 5AS
     ☎0118 901 5112
     Branch Manager Mrs E Long
F   Whitley Library, Northumberland Avenue, Reading, Berks RG2 7PX
     ☎0118 901 5115
     Branch Manager Mrs C Kelly
G   Mobile Library Services, c/o Tilehurst Library, School Road, Tilehurst, Reading,
     Berks RG3 5AS
     ☎0118 901 5118
     Services Manager A Lewis

REDBRIDGE

Headquarters London Borough of Redbridge, Central Library, Clements Road, Ilford,
Essex IG1 1EA
☎020 8478 7145
Fax 020 8553 3299
Chief Librarian M Timms BA ALA (020 8478 9419; e-mail:
martin.timms@redbridge.gov.uk)
Central Library Manager P Ledger ALA (020 8478 7145 ext 2438; e-mail:
peter.ledger@redbridge.gov.uk)
Development Officer Mrs J Wood BSc ALA (020 8478 7145 ext 2425; e-mail:
janet.wood@redbridge.gov.uk)
Children's and Schools Librarian Ms C Pountney BA ALA (020 8478 7145 ext 2422;
e-mail: christine.pountney@redbridge.gov.uk)

Central/largest library
As above

Community library
Aldersbrook Library, 2a Park Road, London E12 5HQ
☎020 8989 9319
Branch Librarian R Luxmore ALA (020 8989 9462)

Branch libraries
A   Fullwell Cross Library, 140 High Street, Barkingside, Ilford, Essex IG6 2EA
     ☎020 8550 4457
     Branch Librarian S Thorpe BA ALA (e-mail: stephen.thorpe@redbridge.gov.uk)
B   Gants Hill Library, 490 Cranbrook Road, Gants Hill, Ilford, Essex IG2 6LA
     ☎020 8554 5211
     Branch Librarian J Hayward BA ALA (e-mail: john.hayward@redbridge.gov.uk)
C   Goodmayes Library, 76 Goodmayes Lane, Goodmayes, Ilford, Essex IG3 9QB
     ☎020 8590 8362
     Branch Librarian W George ALA (e-mail: bill.george@redbridge.gov.uk)

D   Hainault Library, 100 Manford Way, Chigwell, Essex IG7 4DD
     ☎020 8500 1204
     Branch Librarian Mrs E Reid BA ALA (e-mail: evelyn.reid@redbridge.gov.uk)

E   South Woodford Library, 116 High Road, London E18 2QS
     ☎020 8504 1407
     Branch Librarian Mrs G Pote BA ALA (e-mail: geraldine.pote@redbridge.gov.uk)

F   Wanstead Library, Spratt Hall Road, London E11 2RQ
     ☎020 8989 9462
     Branch Librarian R Luxmore ALA (e-mail: bob.luxmore@redbridge.gov.uk)

G   Woodford Green Library, Snakes Lane, Woodford Green, Essex IG8 0DX
     ☎020 8504 4642
     Branch Librarians Mrs C Clarke BA ALA, Mrs M Barratt BA ALA (e-mail:
     carol.clarke@redbridge.gov.uk; madeline.barratt@redbridge.gov.uk)
     (job-share)

REDCAR AND CLEVELAND

Headquarters Redcar and Cleveland Borough Council, Leisure and Libraries Dept, Redcar and Cleveland House, PO Box 86, Kirkleatham Street, Redcar, Cleveland TS10 1XX
☎(01642) 444357 (enquiries), (01642) 444000 (administration)
Fax (01642) 444341
Libraries and Informatics Officer Mrs C Barnes BA DipLib (01642 444357)
Resource Services Officer Mrs C Zellweger BA ALA (01642 444321)

Central/largest library
Central Library, Coatham Road, Redcar, Cleveland TS10 1RP
☎(01642) 472162
Fax (01642) 492253
Group Librarian I L Wilson BA ALA (01642 489165)

Group library
Guisborough Library, Walkers Row, Guisborough, Cleveland TS14 6HP
☎(01287) 632668
Group Librarian Mrs J Allinson

RICHMOND UPON THAMES

Headquarters London Borough of Richmond upon Thames, Libraries and Information Services, Langholm Lodge, 146 Petersham Road, Richmond, Surrey TW10 6UX
☎020 8940 0031
Fax 020 8940 7568
e-mail: leisure@richmond.gov.uk
Chief Librarian and Arts Officer Ms J E Battye BA ALA (020 8891 7907)
Assistant Chief Librarian (Information Services) Ms K Davenport MA ALA (020 8940 3691; e-mail: k.davenport@richmond.gov.uk)
Assistant Chief Librarian (Lending Services and Promotions) Ms S Harden BA ALA (Pager 01459 135452; e-mail: harden@dial.pipex.com)

Central/largest library
Richmond Lending Library, Little Green, Richmond, Surrey TW9 1QL
☎020 8940 0981/6857
Fax 020 8940 7516
e-mail: richlib@richmond.gov.uk
Team Managers Ms S Kirkpatrick BLS ALA, Mrs C Thompson ALA (020 8332 7310) (job-share)

Branch libraries

A   Twickenham Library, Garfield Road, Twickenham, Middlesex TW1 3JT
     ☎020 8892 8091
     e-mail: twicklib@richmond.gov.uk
     Team Manager M Treacy BA(Hons) PGCE DipLib ALA

B   Teddington Library, Waldegrave Road, Teddington, Middlesex TW11 8LG
     ☎020 8977 1284
     e-mail: teddlib@richmond.gov.uk
     Team Manager P Donaghy BSc(Hons) ALA

C   East Sheen Library, Sheen Lane, London SW14 8LP
     ☎020 8876 8801
     e-mail: sheenlib@richmond.gov.uk
     Team Manager L Cranfield ALA

D   Central Reference Library, Old Town Hall, Whitaker Avenue, Richmond, Surrey
     TW9 1TP
     ☎020 8940 5529/9125
     Fax 020 8940 6899
     e-mail: ref@richmond.gov.uk
     Central Reference Librarian Miss J Hall BA DipLib ALA

ROCHDALE

Headquarters Rochdale Metropolitan Borough Council, Wheatsheaf Library, Wheatsheaf
Shopping Centre, Baillie Street, Rochdale, Greater Manchester OL16 1JZ
☎(01706) 864900 (enquiries), (01706) 647474 ext 4911 (administration)
Fax (01706) 864992
Principal Librarian Mrs S M Sfrijan ALA (01706) 864929
Bibliographical and Special Services Librarian Mrs F Fletcher ALA (01706 864964)
Reference and Information Development Librarians Mrs H M Haynes ALA, D L Martin
MIPD ALA (01706 864989; job-share)
Town Librarian (Rochdale, based at Wheatsheaf Library) Mrs J S McCormack BA
(01706 864976)

Main libraries

A   Heywood Library, Church Street, Heywood, Greater Manchester OL10 1LL
     ☎(01706) 360947
     Fax (01706) 368683
     Town Librarian Mrs P Dawes BA ALA

B   Middleton Library, Long Street, Middleton, Greater Manchester M24 6DU
     ☎0161 643 5228
     Fax 0161 654 0745
     Town Librarian Ms K Standley BA

ROTHERHAM

Headquarters Rotherham Metropolitan Borough Council, Central Library, Walker Place,
Rotherham, South Yorkshire S65 1JH
☎(01709) 823611 (enquiries), (01709) 823602 (management)
Fax (01709) 823650 (enquiries), (01709) 823653 (management)
e-mail: central.library@rotherham.gov.uk
Head of Leisure, Library and Information Services D Hardwick DMS ALA
Manager, Community Library Services S Carney ALA (01709 823699)
Manager, Special Groups K Robinson ALA (01709 813034)
Manager, Information Services Mrs L Wirth ALA (01709 823651)

Central/largest library
As above

RUTLAND

Headquarters Rutland County Council, Rutland County Library, Catmose Street, Oakham, Rutland LE15 6HW
☎(01572) 722918 (enquiries), (01572) 755641 (administration)
Fax (01572) 724906 (enquiries), (01572) 724906 (administration)
url: http://www.rutland-on-line.co.uk/rcc/rutlandlibraries
Head of Libraries and Museums R Knight BA ALA (e-mail: rknight@rutland.gov.uk)

Community libraries

A   Uppingham Library, Queen Street, Uppingham, Rutland LE15 9QR
       ☎(01572) 823218
B   Ketton Library, High Street, Ketton, Stamford, Lincs PE9 3TE
       ☎(01780) 720586
C   Ryhall Library, Coppice Road, Ryhall, Stamford, Lincs PE9 4HY
       ☎(01780) 751726

ST HELENS

Headquarters Metropolitan Borough of St Helens, Community Education and Leisure Services Department, The Rivington Centre, Rivington Road, St Helens, Merseyside WA10 4ND
☎(01744) 456989 (enquiries & administration)
Fax (01744) 20836
e-mail: sthelensmbc@cableinet.co.uk
Assistant Director (Community Education and Leisure Services) Mrs D A Bradley BSc(Hons) ALA DMS (01744 456300; fax 01744 455350)

Central/largest library

Central Library, The Gamble Building, Victoria Square, St Helens, Merseyside WA10 1DY
☎(01744) 456950
Fax (01744) 20836
e-mail: clib.sthelens@cableinet.co.uk
Central Library Manager S Pindard (01744 456955)

SALFORD

Headquarters Salford City Council, Vulcan House, Albion Place, Crescent, Salford M5 4NL
☎0161 736 9448
Fax 0161 745 7806
Principal Libraries and Information Officer Ms S Spence BA(Hons) (0161 793 3571, fax 0161 727 7071)

Main libraries

A   Swinton Library, Chorley Road, Swinton, Lancs M27 2AE
       ☎0161 793 3560
       Fax 0161 727 7071
       Divisional Librarian C Farey BA(Hons) DipLIS DBA ALA
B   Eccles Library, Church Street, Eccles, Salford, Lancs M30 0EP
       ☎0161 789 1430
       Fax 0161 787 8430
       Divisional Librarian Ms R Farnworth DBA ALA
C   Walkden Library, Memorial Road, Walkden, Lancs M28 3AQ
       ☎0161 790 4579

Fax 0161 703 8971
Senior Librarian C Carson BA DMS ALA
D   Broadwalk Library, Broadwalk, Salford, Lancs M6 5JA
☎0161 737 5802
Fax 0161 745 9157
Senior Librarian B Graney BA(Hons) DipLib

SANDWELL

Headquarters Sandwell Metropolitan Borough Council, Dept. of Education and Community Services, Shaftesbury House, PO Box 41, 402 High Street, West Bromwich, West Midlands B70 9LT
☎0121 525 7366
Fax 0121 525 4648
Chief Librarian K W Heyes BA MBA ALA

Central/largest library
West Bromwich Library, High Street, West Bromwich, West Midlands B70 8DZ
☎0121 569 4904
Fax 0121 525 9465
Principal Libraries Officer (Community Libraries) A Piorowski ALA (0121 569 4922)

A   Sandwell Information Services, West Bromwich Library, High Street, West Bromwich, West Midlands B70 8DZ
☎0121 569 4911
Fax 0121 525 9465
Principal Libraries Officer (Information Services) D Gill BLib ALA
B   Community History and Archives Service, Smethwick Library, High Street, Smethwick, West Midlands B66 1AB
☎0121 558 2561
Fax 0121 555 6064
Acting Community Librarian (Smethwick and Oldbury) Vacant
C   Special Needs Library Service, 63 Crosswells Road, Oldbury, West Midlands B68 8HH
☎0121 552 4136
Fax 0121 569 9465
Principal Libraries Officer (Special Needs) Ms P Fouracres BA(Hons) MA ALA
D   Library Support Services, Town Hall, High Street, West Bromwich, West Midlands B70 8DX
☎0121 569 4909
Fax 0121 569 4907
e-mail: dm025@viscount.org.uk
Principal Libraries Officer (Library Support Services) B Clark BLib ALA

SEFTON

Headquarters Sefton Metropolitan District Council, Leisure Services, Libraries and Arts, Pavilion Buildings, 99-105 Lord Street, Southport PR8 1RH
☎0151 934 2381
Fax 0151 934 2370
e-mail: seflib@sefton.bdx.co.uk
Assistant Director (Libraries and Arts) R J Wall DMS ALA
Head of Library and Information Services J Hilton ALA
Principal Library Services Officer (North) Mrs J E Stanistreet MA ALA
Principal Library Services Officer (South) Ms M Wall BA DMS ALA

Central/largest libraries
A Southport Library, Lord Street, Southport PR8 1DJ
☎0151 934 2118
Fax 0151 934 2115
Librarian Mrs V Owen BA ALA
B Crosby Library, Crosby Road North, Liverpool L22 0LQ
☎0151 257 6400
Fax 0151 330 5770
Librarian Miss L Roberts BA ALA

SHEFFIELD
Headquarters Sheffield City Council, Sheffield Libraries, Archives and Information Services, Central Library, Surrey Street, Sheffield S1 1XZ
☎0114 273 4711/2 (enquiries), 0114 273 5052 (library management)
Fax 0114 273 5009
e-mail: sheffield.libraries@dial.pipex.com
City Librarian D Spencer BA ALA (0114 273 4751; e-mail: d.spencer@dial.pipex.com)
Group Manager, Central Circulation Services Ms J Adam MA DipLib ALA (0114 273 6645)
Group Manager, Archives and Local Studies Services Ms M Turner MA BAA (0114 203 9397)
Group Manager, Community Information and Enquiry Services H Matthew BA MA ALA (0114 273 4254)
Group Manager, Central Information Services J Murphy BSc(Hons) MA (0114 273 6645)
Group Manager, North Ms A Jobey BA ALA (0114 203 7121)
Group Manager, South P Barr BA (0114 203 7700)
Group Manager, East M Dutch BA(Hons) DipLib (0114 203 7202)
Group Manager, Mobile Services Ms R Telfer BA(Hons) DipLib ALA (0114 273 4277)

Central/largest library
As above

District libraries
A Broomhill Library, Taptonville Road, Sheffield S10 5BR
☎0114 273 4276
B Chapeltown Library, Nether Ley Avenue, Sheffield S35 1AE
☎0114 203 7000/1
C Darnall Library, Britannia Road, Sheffield S9 5JG
☎0114 203 7429
D Firth Park Library, Firth Park Road, Sheffield S5 6WS
☎0114 203 7433
E Hillsborough Library, Middlewood Road, Sheffield S6 4HD
☎0114 203 9529
F Manor Library, Ridgeway Road, Sheffield S12 2SS
☎0114 203 7805
G Waterthorpe Library, 3 Peak Square, Crystal Peaks Complex, Waterthorpe, Sheffield S20 7PH
☎0114 248 1127
H Woodseats Library, Chesterfield Road, Sheffield S8 0SH
☎0114 274 9149
I Mobile Services, 443 Handsworth Road, Sheffield S13 9DD
☎0114 273 4277

J   Highfield Library, London Road, Sheffield S2 4NF
     ☎0114 203 7204

K   Stocksbridge Library, Manchester Road, Stocksbridge, Sheffield S36 1DH
     ☎0114 273 4205

L   Totley Library, 205 Baslow Road, Sheffield S17 4DT
     ☎0114 236 3067

SHROPSHIRE

Headquarters Shropshire County Council, Community and Economic Services
Department, Shropshire Libraries, Column House, 7 London Road, Shrewsbury, Shropshire
SY2 6NW
☎(01743) 255000
Fax (01743) 255050
e-mail: agnes.thomas@shropshire-cc.gov.uk
County Librarian T Williams FLA MILAM (e-mail: tim.williams@shropshire-cc.gov.uk)
Central Services Librarian P Beech ALA (e-mail: pat.beech@shropshire-cc.gov.uk)

Central/largest library
Castle Gates Library, Shrewsbury, Shropshire SY1 2AS
☎(01743) 255300
Fax (01743) 255309
Area Librarian D Yuile BA ALA

Area libraries

A   North Area. Oswestry Library, Arthur Street, Oswestry, Shropshire SY11 1JN
     ☎(01691) 653211
     Fax (01691) 656994
     Area Librarian J Roads BA (e-mail: jim.roads@shropshire-cc.gov.uk)

B   South Area. Bridgnorth Library, Listley Street, Bridgnorth, Shropshire WV16 4AW
     ☎(01746) 763257
     Fax (01746) 766625
     Area Librarian A Williams BA ALA (e-mail: adrian.williams@shropshire-cc.gov.uk)

C   Shrewsbury Area. Castle Gates Library, Shrewsbury, Shropshire SY1 2AS
     ☎(01743) 255300
     Fax (01743) 255309

D   Information Service, 1a Castle Gates, Shrewsbury, Shropshire SY1 2AQ
     ☎(01743) 255380
     Fax (01743) 255383
     Information Services Librarian Ms E Moss ALA (e-mail:
     elaine.moss@shropshire-cc.gov.uk)

SLOUGH

Headquarters Slough Borough Council, Libraries, Arts and Information, Community
Services, Town Hall, Bath Road, Slough SL1 3UQ
☎(01753) 875578
Fax (01753) 875419
Head of Libraries, Arts and Information Mrs Y M Cope MIMgt ALA

Central/largest library
Slough Library, High Street, Slough SL1 1EA
☎(01753) 535166
Fax (01753) 825050
Senior Librarian Mrs D Flood BA(Hons) DMS ALA

Library Systems and Acquisitions Manager Vacant

SOLIHULL

Headquarters Solihull Metropolitan Borough Council, Central Library, Homer Road, Solihull, West Midlands B91 3RG

☎0121 704 6965 (enquiries), 0121 704 6985 (administration)

Fax 0121 704 6991

Senior Assistant Director, Libraries and Arts R Honeysett BA DipLib ALA

Head of Libraries and Arts N Ward BA MA DMS ALA (0121 704 6945)

Support Services Manager Ms H Halliday BA ALA (0121 704 8227)

Central/largest library

As above

Main area libraries

A   Central Library, Homer Road, Solihull, West Midlands B91 3RG
(0121 704 6965
Fax 0121 704 6991
Central Area Manager Ms T Long BA ALA

B   Chelmsley Wood Library, Stephenson Drive, Chelmsley Wood, Solihull, West Midlands B37 5TA
☎0121 788 4380
Fax 0121 788 4391
North Area Manager Ms J Hand BA(Hons) DipLib ALA

C   Knowle Library, Chester House, 1667-9 High Street, Knowle, Solihull, West Midlands B93 0LL
☎(01564) 775840
Fax (01564) 770593
South Area Manager Ms Y Negus BA ALA

SOMERSET

Headquarters Somerset County Council, Library Administration, Mount Street, Bridgwater, Somerset TA6 3ES

☎(01278) 451201

Fax (01278) 452787

e-mail: aemiller@somerset.gov.uk

County Librarian R N Froud BLib DMS MiMgt FLA (e-mail: rnfroud@somerset.gov.uk)

Area libraries

A   Bridgwater. The Library, Binford Place, Bridgwater, Somerset TA6 3LF
☎(01278) 458373
Fax (01278) 451027
Area Librarian I J Beech BA DipLib ALA

B   Chard. The Library, Boden Street, Chard, Somerset TA20 2AX
☎(01460) 63321
Area Librarian Miss D L Hulbert BLib ALA

C   Frome. The Library, Justice Lane, Frome, Somerset BA11 1BE
☎(01373) 462215
Fax (01373) 472003
Area Librarian N J Humphrey BLib MA

D   Minehead. The Library, Bancks Street, Minehead, Somerset TA24 5DJ
☎(01643) 702942
Area Librarian J R Luke BA ALA

E   Street. The Library, 1 Leigh Road, Street, Somerset BA16 0HA
     ☎(01458) 442032
     Area Librarian Mrs S Crowley BA ALA
F   Taunton. The Library, Paul Street, Taunton, Somerset TA1 3XZ
     ☎(01823) 336334
     Fax (01823) 340302
     Area Librarian B Goddard ALA
G   Yeovil. The Library, King George Street, Yeovil, Somerset BA20 1PY
     ☎(01935) 423144
     Fax (01935) 431847
     Area Librarian R J Pudner BA DipLib ALA

SOUTH GLOUCESTERSHIRE
Headquarters South Gloucestershire Council, Leisure and Community Resources Offices (Libraries), Fiveways, New Cheltenham Road, Kingswood, South Gloucestershire BS15 4RR
☎(01454) 865782
Fax (01454) 868535
Head of Library and Information Service M Burton BA ALA (e-mail: martin_burton@southglos.gov.uk)
Team Manager (North) Ms A Hartridge ALA (01454 324425)
Team Manager (South) M Duffy ALA (01454 868450)

Central/largest library
Yate Library, 44 West Walk, Yate, South Gloucestershire BS37 4AX
☎(01454) 855661
Fax (01454) 319178
Group Librarian N Weston BA ALA

Group libraries
A   Downend Library, Buckingham Gardens, Downend, South Gloucestershire BS16 5TW
     ☎(01454) 865666
     Librarians Mrs A Nicklen BA ALA, Ms A Hooper BA(Hons)
B   Kingswood Library, High Street, Kingswood, South Gloucestershire BS15 4AR
     ☎(01454) 865650
     Librarian Ms E Moore BSc ALA, G Clayton BA ALA
C   Thornbury Library, St Mary Street, Thornbury, South Gloucestershire BS35 2AA
     ☎(01454) 865655
     Librarian R Filer BA ALA

SOUTH TYNESIDE
Headquarters South Tyneside Metropolitan Borough Council, South Tyneside Libraries, Central Library, Prince Georg Square, South Shields, Tyne and Wear NE33 2PE
☎0191 427 1818
Fax 0191 455 8085
e-mail: reference.library@s-tyneside-mbc.gov.uk
Libraries Manager D Abbott ALA

Central/largest library
As above

SOUTHAMPTON

Headquarters Southampton City Council, City Library, Archives and Information Service, Civic Centre, Southampton, Hampshire SO14 7LW

☎023 8083 2664 (enquiries), 023 8083 2459 (administration)

Fax 023 8033 6305

e-mail: sotonlib@interlapha.co.uk

Head of Libraries, Archives and Information Services H A Richards BA ALA

SOUTHEND ON SEA

Headquarters Southend on Sea Borough Council, Education and Library Services, PO Box 6, The Civic Centre, Southend on Sea, Essex SS2 6EX

☎(01702) 215972

Fax (01702) 315090

Director of Education and Libraries S Hay

Assistant Director: Libraries and Lifelong Learning H Gordon BA ALA

Central/largest library

Southend Library, Victoria Avenue, Southend on Sea, Essex SS2 6EX

☎(01702) 612621

Fax (01702) 469241

Head of Operations S May BSc MSc ALA

Head of Information and Resources C Hayes BA DipLib ALA

SOUTHWARK

Headquarters London Borough of Southwark, Southwark Education & Leisure, 15 Spa Road, London SE16 3QW

☎020 7525 1993

Fax 020 7525 1505

Arts, Libraries and Museums Manager A Olsen BA ALA (020 7525 1577)

Libraries Development Manager Vacant

District libraries

A   Blue Anchor Library, Market Place, Southwark Park Road, London SE16 3UQ
☎020 7231 0475
Fax 020 7232 1842

B   Brandon Library, Maddock Way, Cooks Road, London SE17 3NH
☎020 7735 3430 (Tel/Fax)

C   Camberwell Library, 17-21 Camberwell Church Street, London SE5 8TR
☎020 7703 3763
Fax 020 7708 4597

D   Dulwich Library, 368 Lordship Lane, London SE22 8NB
☎020 8693 5171
Fax 020 8693 5135

E   East Street/Old Kent Road Library, 168-170 Old Kent Road, London SE1 5TY
☎020 7703 0395
Fax 020 7703 2224

F   Grove Vale Library, 25-27 Grove Vale, London SE22 8EQ
☎020 8693 5734 (Tel/Fax)

G   John Harvard Library, 211 Borough High Street, London SE1 1JA
☎020 7407 0807 (Tel/Fax)

H   Kingswood Library, Seeley Drive, London SE21 8QR
☎020 8670 4803
Fax 020 8671 5125

I   Local Studies Library, 211 Borough High Street, London SE1 1JA
        ☎020 7403 3507
        Fax 020 7403 8633
J   Newington Library, 155-7 Walworth Road, London SE17 1RS
        ☎020 7703 3324
        Fax 020 7252 6115
K   Newington Reference Library, 155-7 Walworth Road, London SE17 1RS
        ☎020 7708 0516
        Fax 020 7252 6115
L   North Peckham (Civic) Library, 600-8 Old Kent Road, London SE15 1JB
        (020 7639 1255 (Tel/Fax)
M   Nunhead Library, Gordon Road, London SE15 3RW
        ☎020 7639 0264
        Fax 020 7277 5721
N   Peckham Library, 167 Peckham Hill Street, London SE15 5JZ
        ☎020 7639 1624
        Fax 020 7635 0518
O   Rotherhithe Library, Albion Street, London SE16 1JA
        ☎020 7237 2010
        Fax 020 7394 0672
P   Special Library Services, Rotherhithe Library, Albion Street, London SE16 1JA
        ☎020 7237 1487
        Fax 020 7237 8417
Q   Education Library Service, Southwark Education Resource Centre, Cator Street,
        London SE15 6AA
        ☎020 7525 2830
        Fax 020 7525 2837

STAFFORDSHIRE

Headquarters Staffordshire County Council, Library and Information Services HQ, Cultural
and Corporate Services Department, 16 Martin Street, Stafford ST16 2LG
☎(01785) 278311
Fax (01785) 278319
County Librarian R W Hyde ALA (01785 278301; e-mail: ray.hyde@staffordshire.gov.uk)
Senior Assistant County Librarian Mrs M Keeling MA BA(Hons) ALA (01785 278308;
e-mail: margaret.keeling@staffordshire.gov.uk)
Assistant County Librarian (Young People's Services) Mrs M Williams MA(Hons) DipLib
ALA (01785 278587; e-mail: morna.williams@staffordshire.gov.uk)
Assistant County Librarian (Service Delivery) Mrs O Spencer ALA (01785 278422;
e-mail: olivia.spencer@staffordshire.gov.uk)

Group libraries
A   South West Group. Cannock Library, Manor Avenue, Cannock, Staffs WS11 1AA
        ☎(01543) 510365
        Fax (01543) 510373
        e-mail: cannock.library@staffordshire.gov.uk
        Group Librarian Mrs S Briggs BA(Hons) ALA (01543 510366; e-mail:
        sue.briggs@staffordshire.gov.uk)
B   North East Group. Burton Library, Riverside High Street, Burton-on-Trent, Staffs
        DE14 1AH
        ☎(01283) 239556
        Fax (01283) 239571
        e-mail: burton.library@staffordshire.gov.uk

Group Librarian Mrs P Phelps ALA (01283 239559; e-mail:
pat.phelps@staffordshire.gov.uk)

C   South East Group. Lichfield Library, The Friary, Lichfield, Staffs WS13 6QG
☎(01543) 510700
Fax (01543) 510716
e-mail: lichfield.library@staffordshire.gov.uk
Group Librarian Mrs E Rees-Jones BA(Hons) ALA (01543 510702; e-mail:
elizabeth.reesjones@staffordshire.gov.uk)

D   North West Group. Newcastle Library, Ironmarket, Newcastle, Staffs ST5 1AT
☎(01782) 297300
Fax (01782) 297323
e-mail: newcastle.library@staffordshire.gov.uk
Group Librarian Mrs H Jackson BLib ALA (01782 297305; e-mail:
hilary.jackson@staffordshire.gov.uk)

E   Mid Staffs Group. Library and Information Services, 16 Martin Street, Stafford
ST16 2LG
☎(01785) 278585
Fax (01785) 278309
e-mail: stafford.library@staffordshire.gov.uk
Group Librarian Mrs J Goodson ALA (01785 278591; e-mail:
judy.goodson@staffordshire.gov.uk)

STOCKPORT

Headquarters Stockport Metropolitan Borough Council, Community Services Division,
Stopford House, Piccadilly, Stockport, Cheshire SK1 3XE
☎0161 474 4447 (enquiries & administration)
Fax 0161 429 0335
Head of Library and Information Services B Stevenson BA DMS ALA (e-mail:
brian.stevenson@stockport.gov.uk)

Central/largest library

Central Library, Wellington Road South, Stockport, Cheshire SK1 3RS
☎0161 474 4540 (lending), 4524 (information library), 4530 (local heritage library)
Fax 0161 474 7750
e-mail: stockport.cenlibrary@dial.pipex.com
Librarian D Isaac BA DipLib DMS ALA

Bibliographical Services Unit, Phoenix House, Bird Hall Lane, Stockport, Cheshire SK3 0RA
☎0161 474 5605
Fax 0161 491 6516

STOCKTON-ON-TEES

Headquarters Stockton-on-Tees Borough Council, Leisure Services Department, Stockton
Borough Libraries Division, Gloucester House, 72 Church Road, Stockton-on-Tees
TS18 1YB
☎(01642) 393920
Fax (01642) 393924
url: http://www.stockton-bc.gov.uk
Assistant Director Leisure Services (Head of Cultural Services) Mrs A Barker ALA
(01642 393962; e-mail: andrea.barker@stockton-bc.gov.uk)
Libraries Operations Manager Mrs P Wilson ALA (01642 393980; e-mail:
pam.wilson@stockton-bc.gov.uk)
Bibliographical Services Officer Miss H Dean BA(Hons) (01642 393966; e-mail:

helen.dean@stockton-bc.gov.uk)
Priority Services Officer Mrs L King BA(Hons) (01642 397597; e-mail: lesley.king@stockton-bc.gov.uk)

Central/largest library
Stockton Central Library, Church Road, Stockton-on-Tees TS18 1TU
☎(01642) 393999
Fax (01642) 393929
Lending Services Officer Miss V Hobson MA(Hons) DipLib
Open Technology Centre Manager Mrs C Durnton (01642 393997)
Reference Services Officer Mrs J Chesney (01642 393994)

Branch libraries
A   Billingham Branch Library, Bedale Avenue, Billingham, Stockton-on-Tees TS23 1AJ
     ☎(01642) 397595
     Branch Librarian Vacant
B   Egglescliffe Branch Library, Butterfield Drive, Orchard Estate, Egglescliffe, Stockton-on-Tees TS16 0EL
     ☎(01642) 391840
     Branch Librarian Miss M Chapman MA(Lib)
C   Fairfield Branch Library, Fairfield Road, Stockton-on-Tees TS19 7AJ
     ☎(01642) 391750
     Branch Librarian R Lacey ALA
D   Norton Branch Library, 87 High Street, Norton, Stockton-on-Tees TS20 1AE
     ☎(01642) 397592
     Branch Librarian Mrs C Maddison BSc DipLib
E   Roseberry Billingham Branch Library, The Causeway, Billingham, Stockton-on-Tees TS23 2LB
     ☎(01642) 397600
     Branch Librarian Miss B Sandles ALA
F   Roseworth Branch Library, Redhill Road, Stockton-on-Tees TS19 9BX
     ☎(01642) 397604
     Branch Librarian Mrs C Pratt BA ALA
G   Thornaby Westbury Street Branch Library, Westbury Street, Thornaby, Stockton-on-Tees TS17 6PG
     ☎(01642) 393987
     Branch Librarian Vacant
H   Thornaby Central Branch Library, The Pavillion, New Town Centre, Thornaby, Stockton-on-Tees TS17 9EW
     ☎(01642) 391610
     Branch Librarian Mrs S Freeman ALA
I   Yarm Branch Library, 41 High Street, Yarm, Stockton-on-Tees TS15 9BH
     ☎(01642) 391843
     Branch Librarian Mrs W Sandham BA ALA

STOKE-ON-TRENT

Headquarters Stoke-on-Trent City Council, Libraries, Information and Archives, PO Box 816, Civic Centre, Glebe Street, Stoke-on-Trent ST4 1HF
☎(01782) 238455 (enquiries), (01782) 236923 (administration)
Fax (01782) 232544
e-mail: stoke.libraries@stoke01.stoke-cc.gov.uk
Assistant Director, Libraries, Information and Archives Ms M Green BA MLS ALA
(e-mail: margaret.green@stoke01.stoke-cc.gov.uk)

Principal Librarian, Support and Development D Griffiths BA ALA (01782 238401)

Group libraries

A   Hanley Group. Hanley Library, Bethesda Street, Hanley, Stoke-on-Trent ST1 3RS
       ☎(01782) 238455
       Fax (01782) 238499
       Principal Librarian Ms J Simpson BA ALA

B   Longton Group. Longton Library, Sutherland Institute, Lightwood Road, Longton,
       Stoke-on-Trent ST13 4HY
       ☎(01782) 238424
       Fax (01782) 238429
       Principal Librarian I Young MA ALA

SUFFOLK

Headquarters Suffolk County Council, Libraries and Heritage, St Andrew House, County Hall, Ipswich, Suffolk IP4 1LJ
☎(01473) 584564 (enquiries & administration)
Fax (01473) 584549
County Director of Libraries and Heritage Ms A J E Arrowsmith MA MBA FIMT (e-mail: amanda.arrowsmith@libher.suffolkcc.gov.uk)
Assistant Director (Services) C J Evans BA ALA (01473 584557; e-mail: cliff.evans@libher.suffolkcc.gov.uk)
Assistant Director (Resources) Ms G J Pachent BA DLIS ALA MILAM (01473 584558; e-mail: guenever.pachent@libher.suffolkcc.gov.uk)

Central/largest library
County Library, Northgate Street, Ipswich, Suffolk IP1 3DE
☎(01473) 583702/3 (enquiries & administration)
Fax (01473) 583700
Area Service Manager Ms D N Bickerton ALA (e-mail: diana.bickerton@libher.suffolkcc.gov.uk)

Area libraries

A   Central Library, Sergeant's Walk, Off St Andrew's Street North, Bury St Edmunds,
       Suffolk IP33 1TZ
       ☎(01284) 352542
       Fax (01284) 352566
       Area Service Manager V J McDonald BA ALA (e-mail:
       vincent.mcdonald@libher.suffolkcc.gov.uk)

B   Central Library, Clapham Road South, Lowestoft, Suffolk NR32 1DR
       ☎(01502) 405342
       Fax (01502) 405350
       Area Service Manager Ms R A Steer MBA BA DAA (e-mail:
       rosemary.steer@libher.suffolkcc.gov.uk)

SUNDERLAND

Headquarters City of Sunderland Metropolitan District Council, City Library and Arts Centre, Fawcett Street, Sunderland, Tyne and Wear SR1 1RE
☎0191 514 1235 (enquiries & administration)
Fax 0191 514 8444
e-mail: user@edcom.sunderland.gov.uk
Assistant Director, Community Services J P Devine ALA
Head of Libraries, Arts and Information Ms J F Hall BA(Hons) ALA

Assistant Chief Librarian Ms V Craggs ALA
Principal Officer, City Library and Arts Centre Ms H G Hogg BA(Hons) MA DipLib
Principal Officer, Development Ms L Willetts BA(Hons) DipLib ALA
Principal Officer, ICT and Lifelong Learning Ms C Wood BA(Hons) ALA

Area library
Washington Town Centre Library, Independence Square, Washington, Tyne and Wear
NE38 7RZ
☎0191 219 3440
Principal Officer, Community Libraries, Young People and Special Services Ms A
Scott ALA

SURREY
Headquarters Surrey County Council, Community Services, Room 176, County Hall,
Kingston upon Thames, Surrey KT1 2DN
☎020 8541 9071
Fax 020 8541 9003
Head of Community Services J Agnew MA MBA

Area management teams
A   East Area Office. St Davids, 70 Wray Park Road, Reigate, Surrey RH2 0EJ
     ☎(01737) 226136
     Fax (01737) 226135
     Library Service Manager Mrs H Ely MA ALA (020 8541 7060)
     Largest library: Redhill Library, 18-20 London Road, Redhill, Surrey RH1 1NN
     ☎(01737) 763332
     Library Manager Mrs M Saberi
B   South West Area Office. West House, Merrow Lane, Merrow, Guildford, Surrey
     GU4 7BQ
     ☎(01483) 517402
     Fax (01483) 517401
     Library Service Manager I Milton BA DipLib ALA (01483 517407)
     Largest library: Guildford Library, 77 North Street, Guildford, Surrey GU1 4AL
     ☎(01483) 568496
     Library Manager Mrs S Bray
C   Mid-Surrey Area Office. Cobham Library, The Mansion, Church Street,
     Leatherhead, Surrey KT22 8DP
     ☎(01372) 363920
     Fax (01372) 360169
     Library Service Manager Miss S Parker BA ALA (01372 363920)
     Largest library: Ewell Library, Bourne Hall, Spring Street, Ewell, Surrey KT17 1UF
     ☎020 8394 0951
     Library Manager Mrs P Fella
D   North West Area Office. Runnymede Centre, Chertsey Road, Addlestone, Surrey
     KT15 2EP
     ☎(01932) 582700
     Fax (01932) 582727
     Library Service Manager Mrs R Wilson (01932 582700; e-mail:
     r.wilson@surreycc.gov.uk)
     Largest library: Woking Library, Gloucester Walk, Woking, Surrey GU21 1EP
     ☎(01483) 770591
     Library Manager Ms C Simmons

SUTTON

Headquarters London Borough of Sutton, Sutton Central Library, St Nicholas Way, Sutton, Surrey SM1 1EA

☎020 8770 4700 (enquiries), 020 8770 4602 (administration)

Fax 020 8770 4777

e-mail: sutton.lib@dial.pipex.com

Head of Libraries and Heritage T Knight MLib FLA

Principal Librarian Mrs C McDonough BSc ALA DipLib/Mrs Angela Fletcher BA(Hons) PGCE (job share)

Library Manager, Sutton Ms J Selby

Quality Services Manager D Bundy BA ALA

Central/largest library

As above

Main libraries

A   Carshalton Library, The Square, Carshalton, Surrey SM5 3BN
       ☎020 8647 1151

B   Cheam Library, Church Road, Cheam, Surrey SM3 8QH
       ☎020 8644 9377

C   Wallington Library, Shotfield, Wallington, Surrey SM6 0HY
       ☎020 8770 4900

SWINDON

Headquarters Swindon Borough Council, Community and Leisure Services, Premier House, Station Road, Swindon, Wilts SN1 1TZ

☎(01793) 466462

Fax (01793) 466484

Assistant Chief Officer, Cultural Services Ms J Holberry BA AMA

Borough Community and Leisure Officer J Fisher

Central/largest library

Swindon Central Library, Regent Circus, Swindon, Wilts SN1 1QG

☎(01793) 463238 (enquiries), (01793) 463231 (administration)

Fax (01793) 541319

e-mail: swindonref@swindon.gov.uk

Principal Librarian D M Allen ALA (01793 463230; e-mail: davidallen@swindon.gov.uk)

Group libraries

A   Central Group. Central Library, Regent Circus, Swindon, Wilts SN1 1QG
       ☎(01793) 463238 (enquiries), (01793) 463231 (administration)
       Fax (01793) 541319
       Group Librarian Mrs A Eavis ALA (01793 463232)

B   South Group. Park Library, Cavendish Square, Park South, Swindon, Wilts SN3 2LP
       ☎(01793) 464501
       Group Librarian Mrs M Dawes ALA

C   North Group. Upper Stratton Library, Beechcroft Road, Swindon, Wilts SN2 6QQ
       ☎(01793) 464495
       Group Librarian Miss J Hayes ALA (01793 464494)

D   West Group. West Swindon Library, Link Centre, Whitehill Way, Westlea, Swindon, Wilts SN5 7DL
       ☎(01793) 465555

Fax (01793) 465557
Group Librarian Mrs J Kirk-Browne BA ALA (01793 465552)
E   Acquisitions Group. Library Support Unit, Liden Library, Barrington Close, Liden,
Swindon, Wilts SN3 6HF
☎(01793) 464512
Fax (01793) 464513
Group Librarian Ms D Thomas BA ALA

TAMESIDE

Headquarters Tameside Metropolitan District Council, Tameside Education and Leisure
Services Department, Libraries and Heritage Service, Council Offices, Wellington Road,
Ashton-under-Lyne, Tameside OL6 6DL
☎0161 342 3679
Fax 0161 342 3744
Head of Libraries, Heritage and Lifelong Learning B Delve ALA (0161 342 8355)
Principal Officer (Area Services/North) A G Collins DMS ALA
Principal Officer (Area Services/South) Mrs C Simensky ALA
Principal Officer (Bibliographical Services) G Maddock BA ALA

Central/largest library
Tameside Central Library, Old Street, Ashton-under-Lyne, Tameside OL6 7SG
☎0161 342 2029 (lending/enquiries), 0161 342 2029 (admninistration), 0161 342 2035
(bibliographical services), 0161 342 2031 (reference)
Fax 0161 330 4762
e-mail: tameref@dial.pipex.com
Senior Community Librarian Ms J Hall BA ALA
Reference and Information Librarian P F Jones BA ALA
Principal Officer (Bibliographical Services) G Maddock BA ALA

Other large library
Hyde Library, Union Street, Hyde, Cheshire SK14 1ND
☎0161 368 2447
Fax 0161 368 0205
Senior Community Librarian P Chase ALA

TELFORD AND WREKIN

Headquarters Telford and Wrekin Council, Leisure, Culture and Community Services,
Darby House, PO Box 211, Telford, Shropshire TF3 4LA
☎(01952) 202747
Libraries and Heritage Manager Mrs P Davis ALA
Acquisitions Manager Mrs M Criddle ALA (01952 291596)
Senior Librarian, Information Services Miss H Brooks BLib ALA

Central/largest library
Telford Library, St Quentin Gate, Telford, Shropshire TF3 4JG
☎(01952) 292151 (enquiries), (01952) 292135 (administration)
Fax (01952) 292078
Assistant Libraries and Heritage Manager Mrs S Smith BA ALA

THURROCK

Headquarters Thurrock Council, Leisure, Libraries and Cultural Services Department,
Grays Library, Orsett Road, Grays, Essex RM17 5DX
☎(01375) 383611 (enquiries), (01375) 382555 ext 221 (administration)

Fax (01375) 370806
Libraries and Information Manager A Kennedy BA(Hons) ALA DMS (01375 383611 ext 29; e-mail: akennedy@thurrock.gov.uk)
Resources Manager R Worcester MA DipLib ALA (01375 383611 ext 37)
Information Manager A Cairns BA(Hons) DipLib ALA (01375 383611 ext 37)

Central/largest library
Grays Library, Orsett Road, Grays, Essex RM17 5DX
☎(01375) 383611 (enquiries), (01375) 382555 ext 221 (administration)
Fax (01375) 370806
Group Manager Ms C Matthews (01375 383611 ext 28)

TORBAY
Headquarters Torbay Council, Torquay Central Library, Lymington Road, Torquay, Devon TQ1 3DT
☎(01803) 208300 (enquiries), (01803) 208310 (administration)
Fax (01803) 208311
Head of Library Services P J Bottrill BA ALA (01803 208310; e-mail: peter.bottrill@torbay.gov.uk)
Professional Services Librarian G M Langridge MA MLS ALA (01803 208286; e-mail: geoff.langridge@torbay.gov.uk)
Resources and Technical Services Librarian Vacant
Operational Services Librarian N G Niles BA DipLib ALA (01803 208288)

Central/largest library
As above

Branch libraries
A   Paignton Library, Courtland Road, Paignton, Devon TQ3 2AB
       ☎(01803) 208321
       Branch Librarian Miss C M Weeks ALA (01803 208324)
B   Brixham Library, Market Street, Brixham, Devon TQ5 8EU
       ☎(01803) 853870
       Branch Librarian Mrs G M Downes (01803 853870)
C   Churston Library, Broadsands Road, Paignton, Devon TQ4 6LL
       ☎(01803) 843757
       Branch Librarian Mrs V E Tooley

TOWER HAMLETS
Headquarters London Borough of Tower Hamlets, Bancroft Library, 277 Bancroft Road, London E1 4DQ
☎020 8980 4366
Fax 020 8981 9965
Minicom 020 8983 4114
Head of Libraries Ms A Cunningham
Library Manager (Development) Ms K Pitman, Ms S Bridgwater BA MPhil ALA
Library Manager (Customer Services) N Veysey BA ALA (020 7247 5272)
Library Manager (Operations) J Hagerty (020 7364 2527)

Central/largest library
Bancroft Library, 277 Bancroft Road, London E1 4DQ
☎020 8980 4366
Fax 020 8983 4510

Minicom 020 8983 4114
Community Librarian S Clarke BA ALA

Divisional libraries
A   West Division. Bethnal Green Reference Library, Cambridge Heath Road, London
        E2 0HL
        ☎020 8980 3902
        Fax 020 8981 6129
        Minicom 020 8980 3902
        Principal Information Librarian J Jasinski ALA (e-mail:
        100633.624@compuserve.com)
        Community Librarian Ms S Brown BA
B   West Division. Bancroft Library, 277 Bancroft Road, London E1 4DQ
        ☎020 8980 4366
        Fax 020 8983 4510
        Minicom 020 8983 4114
        Local History Librarian C Lloyd BLib ALA
        Borough Archivist M Barr-Hamilton BA DAS
        Principal Librarian, Outreach Services G Pollard
C   Mid Division. Bow Library, William Place, London E3 5ET
        ☎020 8980 2282
        Fax 020 8980 2080
        Minicom 020 8980 2282
        Community Librarians Mrs L Harris ALA, Ms S Paxton
D   Mid Division. Dorset Library, Ravenscroft Street, London E2 7QX
        ☎020 7739 9489
        Fax 020 7729 2548
        Minicom 020 7739 9489
        Community Librarian Ms S Brown BA (020 8980 3902)
E   Mid Division. Stepney Library, Lindley Street, London E1 3AX
        ☎020 7790 5616
        Fax 020 7264 9873
        Minicom 020 7790 5616
        Community Librarian S Clarke BA ALA (020 8980 4366)
F   Mid Division. Watney Market Library, 30-32 Watney Market, London E1 2PR
        ☎020 7790 4039
        Fax 020 7265 9401
        Minicom 020 7790 4039
        Community Librarian S Avery
G   Mid Division. Whitechapel Library, 77 Whitechapel High Street, London E1 7QX
        ☎020 7247 5272
        Fax 020 7377 0396
        Minicom 020 7247 0265
        Community Librarian Ms C Algar BA DipLib ALA
H   East Division. Lansbury Library, 23-27 Market Way, London E14 6AH
        ☎020 7987 3573
        Fax 020 7538 5520
        Minicom 020 7537 4064
        Community Librarian Ms B Stretch
I   East Division. Cubitt Town Library, Strattondale Street, London E14 3HG
        ☎020 7987 3152
        Fax 020 7538 2795
        Minicom 020 7987 3152
        Community Librarian Ms S Murray BA ALA DMS

J   East Division. Fairfoot Library, 102 Campbell Road, London E3 4EA
☎020 7987 3338
Fax 020 7515 4601
Minicom 020 7987 3338
Community Librarians Mrs L Harris ALA, Ms S Paxton (020 8980 2282)

K   East Division. Limehouse Library, 638 Commercial Road, London E14 7HS
☎020 7364 2527
Fax 020 7364 2502
Minicom 020 7364 2552
Community Librarian Ms S Murray BA ALA DMS

L   East Division. Library Resources Department, Limehouse Library, 638 Commercial Road, London E14 7HS
☎020 7364 2527
Fax 020 7364 2502
Minicom 020 7364 2552
Library Resources Coordinator D Chitty (020 7364 2537)

TRAFFORD

Headquarters Trafford Metropolitan Borough Council, Education, Arts and Leisure Department, Trafford Town Hall, Talbot Road, Stretford, Manchester M32 0YZ
☎0161 912 4044 (enquiries & administration)
Fax 0161 912 1227
Assistant Director (Recreation and Culture) R G Luccock BA ALA

Regional/district libraries

A   Altrincham Library, 20 Stamford New Road, Altrincham, Cheshire WA14 1EJ
☎0161 912 5922

B   Sale Library, Tatton Road, Sale, Cheshire M33 1YS
☎0161 912 3005

C   Stretford Library, Kingsway, Stretford, Greater Manchester M32 8AP
☎0161 912 5151

D   Urmston Library, Crofts Bank Road, Urmston, Cheshire M41 0TZ
☎0161 912 2727

E   Bibliographical Services, Davyhulme Site, Hayeswater Road, Davyhulme, Manchester M41 7BL
☎0161 912 2882
Fax 0161 912 2895

UPPER NORWOOD JOINT LIBRARY

Headquarters Upper Norwood Joint Library, Westow Hill, London SE19 1TJ
☎020 8670 2551
Fax 020 8670 5468
Chief Librarian Christopher Dobb BA ALA

WAKEFIELD

Headquarters Wakefield Metropolitan District Council, Library Headquarters, Balne Lane, Wakefield, West Yorkshire WF2 0DQ
☎(01924) 302210 (enquiries & administration)
Fax (01924) 302245
Libraries & Information Services Manager C J MacDonald BA MBA DipLib ALA
Principal Librarian (Community Services) Ms C Threapleton ALA DMS
Principal Librarian (Information Services) Ms L Herbert BA ALA DMS
Principal Librarian (Resource Services) N Scarlett

Major libraries

A   Castleford Library, Carlton Street, Castleford, West Yorkshire WF10 1BB
     ☎(01977) 722085
     Senior Librarian Ms W Mitchell
B   Ossett Library, Station Road, Ossett, West Yorkshire WF5 8AB
     ☎(01924) 303040
     Senior Librarian Ms C Wadsworth
C   Pontefract Library, Shoemarket, Pontefract, West Yorkshire WF8 1BD
     ☎(01977) 727692
     Senior Librarian Ms W Mitchell
D   Drury Lane Library, Drury Lane, Wakefield, West Yorkshire WF1 2TD
     ☎(01924) 305376
     Senior Librarian Mrs A Farrington BA(Hons) ALA
E   Balne Lane Reference and Information Library, Balne Lane, Wakefield, West
     Yorkshire WF2 0DQ
     ☎(01924) 302230
     Senior Librarian Mrs A Farrington BA(Hons) ALA
F   Featherstone Library and Community Centre, Victoria Street, Featherstone, West
     Yorkshire WF7 5BB
     ☎(01977) 722745
     Senior Librarian Mrs C Hayes BA(Hons) ALA
G   Stanley Library and Community Centre, Lake Lock Road, West Yorkshire WF3 4HU
     ☎(01924) 303130
     Senior Librarian P Winterbottom BA(Hons) ALA DMS

WALSALL

Headquarters Walsall Metropolitan District Council, Cultural Services Division, PO Box 42,
Civic Centre, Darwall Street, Walsall, West Midlands WS1 1TZ
☎(01922) 653130
Fax (01922) 722687
url: http://www.earl.org.uk/earl/members/walsall/
Public Library Services Manager I Everall BA ALA (e-mail: everalli@walsall.gov.uk)

Central/largest library
Central Library, Lichfield Street, Walsall, West Midlands WS1 1TR
☎(01922) 653121 (lending), (01922) 653110 (reference)
Fax (01922) 722687 (lending), (01922) 654013 (reference)
Library Manager Ms B Wallace
Information Services Manager Ms R Kennedy

Area libraries
A   Aldridge Library, Rookery Lane, Aldridge, Walsall, West Midlands WS9 8LZ
     ☎(01922) 743601
B   Beechdale Library, Stephenson Square, Beechdale Estate, Walsall, West Midlands
     WS2 7DX
     ☎(01922) 721431
C   Bentley Library, Queen Elizabeth Avenue, Bentley, Walsall, West Midlands
     WS2 0HP
     ☎(01922) 721392
D   Bloxwich Library, Elmore Row, Bloxwich, Walsall, West Midlands WS3 2HR
     ☎(01922) 710059
E   Brownhills Library, Brickiln Street, Brownhills, Walsall, West Midlands WS8 6AU
     ☎(01543) 452017

F   Coalpool Library, Coalpool Lane, Walsall, West Midlands WS3 1RF
     ☎(01922) 721325
G   Darlaston Library, 1 King Street, Darlaston, Walsall, West Midlands WS10 8DD
     ☎0121 526 4530
H   Forest Gate Library, New Invention, Willenhall, Walsall, West Midlands WV12 5LF
     ☎(01922) 710208
I   Furzebank Library, Furzebank Way, Willenhall, Walsall, West Midlands WV12 4BD
     ☎(01902) 630530
J   Pelsall Library, High Street, Pelsall, Walsall, West Midlands WS3 4LX
     ☎(01922) 682212
K   Pheasey Library, Collingwood Drive, Pheasey, Birmingham B43 7NY
     ☎0121 366 6503
L   Pleck Library, Darlaston Road, Pleck, Walsall, West Midlands WS2 9RE
     ☎(01922) 721307
M   Rushall Library, Pelsall Lane, Walsall, West Midlands WS4 1NL
     ☎(01922) 721310
N   Shelfield Library, Birch Lane, Shelfield, Walsall, West Midlands WS4 1AS
     ☎(01922) 682760
O   Sneyd Community Library, Sneyd School, Sneyd Lane, Bloxwich, Walsall, West
     Midlands WS3 2PA
     ☎(01922) 710728
P   South Walsall Library, West Bromwich Road, Walsall, West Midlands WS5 4NW
     ☎(01922) 721347
Q   Streetly Library, Blackwood Road, Streetly, Birmingham B74 3PL
     ☎0121 353 4230
R   Walsall Wood Library, Lichfield Road, Walsall Wood, Walsall, West Midlands
     WS9 9NT
     ☎(01543) 452517
S   Willenhall Library, Walsall Street, Willenhall, Walsall, West Midlands WV13 2EX
     ☎(01902) 366513

WALTHAM FOREST
Headquarters London Borough of Waltham Forest, Administrative Office, Central Library,
High Street, London E17 7JN
☎020 8520 5822 (enquiries & administration)
Fax 020 8509 9539
Library and Information Services Manager C Richardson ALA

Central/largest library
Central Library, High Street, London E17 7JN
☎020 8520 3031/4733; 020 8520 3017 (information services)
Fax 020 8509 0649; 020 8509 9654 (information services)
Customer Services Manager C Prince BA
Information Services Manager S Liddle BA(Hons) DipLib

WANDSWORTH
Headquarters Wandsworth Borough Council, Leisure and Amenity Services Department,
Town Hall, Wandsworth High Street, London SW18 2PU
☎020 8871 6364 (enquiries & administration)
Fax 020 8871 7630
e-mail: libraries@wandsworth.gov.uk
Head of Libraries, Museum and Arts Ms J Allen BA(Hons) DMS DipLib ALA
Assistant Head of Libraries Ms M Jones ALA

Largest libraries
A   Balham Library, Ramsden Road, London SW12 8QY
      ☎020 8871 7195
      Fax 020 8675 4015
      Senior Branch Librarian Ms P Kirwan ALA DipPsych
B   Battersea Library, Lavender Hill, London SW11 1JB
      ☎020 8871 7466
      Fax 020 7978 4376
      Senior Branch Librarian Ms U Morgan BA ALA
C   Putney Library, Disraeli Road, London SW15 2DR
      ☎020 8871 7090
      Fax 020 8789 6175
      Senior Branch Librarian C Lally ALA
D   Tooting Library, Mitcham Road, London SW17 9PD
      ☎020 8871 7175
      Fax 020 8672 3099
      Senior Branch Librarian J Wales ALA

WARRINGTON
Headquarters Warrington Borough Council, Warrington Library, Museum Street,
Warrington, Cheshire WA1 1JB
☎(01925) 442889 (enquiries), (01925) 442733 (administration)
Fax (01925) 411395
e-mail: library@warrington.gov.uk
Library and Information Services Manager Ms J Hill ALA
Resources Manager A Hartley MA ALA (01925 442891)
Field Operations Manager Ms F Barry BA ALA
Field Operations Manager Ms A Mackey BA ALA

WARWICKSHIRE
Headquarters Warwickshire County Council, Department of Libraries and Heritage,
Barrack Street, Warwick, Warwickshire CV34 4TH
☎(01926) 412550 (enquiries), (01926) 412166 (administration)
Fax (01926) 412471/412165
e-mail: warcolib@dial.pipex.com
url: http://www.warwickshire.gov.uk
Director M Henry MA MSc DMS ALA MiMgt MILAM FRSA

Central/largest library
Warwick Library, Barrack Street, Warwick, Warwickshire CV34 4TH
☎(01926) 412488
Fax (01926) 412784
Divisional Manager (Central) Mrs L Kay BA ALA

Divisions
A   Central Warwickshire. Leamington Library, Avenue Road, Leamington Spa,
      Warwickshire CV31 3PP
      ☎(01926) 425873/330800
      Fax (01926) 330285
      Divisional Manager Mrs L Kay BA ALA
B   East Warwickshire. Rugby Library, Little Elborow Street, Rugby, Warwickshire
      CV21 3BZ
      ☎(01788) 542687/571813/535348

Fax (01788) 573289
Divisional Manager Mrs J Wilkinson MA PGDipLib ALA

C   Nuneaton and Bedworth. Nuneaton Library, Church Street, Nuneaton,
        Warwickshire CV11 4DR
        ☎(01203) 384027/347006
        Fax (01203) 350125
        Divisional Manager C W Foster ALA

D   North Warwickshire. Atherstone Library, Long Street, Atherstone, Warwickshire
        CV9 1AX
        ☎(01827) 712395/712034
        Fax (01827) 720285
        Divisional Manager A Litvinoff MA FRSA

E   South Warwickshire. Stratford Library, Henley Street, Stratford-upon-Avon,
        Warwickshire CV37 6PZ
        ☎(01789) 292209/296904
        Fax (01789) 268554
        Divisional Manager J Crossling BSc AMA

WEST BERKSHIRE

Headquarters West Berkshire District Council, West Berkshire Library and Information
Service, Culture and Tourism, Sundial House, 63 Cheap Street, Newbury, Berkshire
RG14 5BT
☎(01635) 519335
Fax (01635) 519624
url: http://www.westberks.gov.uk
Library and Information Manager K Richardson BA(Hons) DipLib ALA (01635 519813;
e-mail: krichardson@westberks.gov.uk)
Customer Services Librarian Mrs E Arthur BA ALA DMS (01635 519820; e-mail:
earthur@westberks.gov.uk)
Stock Manager Vacant
Operations Manager Mrs F Cheney (01635 519819; e-mail: fcheney@westberks.gov.uk)

Central/largest library
Newbury Central Library, Carnegie Road, Newbury, Berkshire RG14 5DW
☎(01635) 40972
Customer Services Librarian Mrs E Arthur BA ALA DMS

WEST SUSSEX

Headquarters West Sussex County Council, Library Service Administration Centre, Tower
Street, Chichester, West Sussex PO19 1QJ
☎(01243) 756700
Fax (01243) 756714
BT Gold 74: SKK125
url: http://www.westsussex.gov.uk
County Librarian R A Kirk BA ALA (e-mail: rkirk@westsussex.gov.uk)
(For management enquiries contact Headquarters; for services contact one of the Principal
Libraries)

Principal libraries
A   Worthing Library, Richmond Road, Worthing, West Sussex BN11 1HD
        ☎(01903) 206961
        Fax (01903) 821902
        Group Librarian: Worthing Mrs A S Boyd MBA ALA MIPM

B   Crawley Library, Northgate Avenue, Crawley, West Sussex RH10 1XG
        ☎(01293) 895130
        Fax (01293) 895141
        Group Librarian: Crawley Mrs R M A Lucas ALA

WESTMINSTER

Headquarters Westminster City Council, Department of Education and Leisure, 13th Floor, Westminster City Hall, 64 Victoria Street, London SW1E 6QP
☎020 7641 2496
Fax 020 7641 3404/6
Assistant Director (Leisure and Libraries) D Ruse ALA MILAM (e-mail: druse@westminster.gov.uk)
Library Strategy Manager Ms C Taylor BA DipLib ALA (020 7641 3347; e-mail: ctaylor@westminster.gov.uk)
Business Unit Manager A Stevens BA ALA (020 7641 6573; e-mail: astevens@dial.pipex.com)
Resources and Operations Manager R Williams (020 7641 6575; e-mail: rogerwilliams@easynet.co.uk)
Adult Lending Services Manager Ms I Cairns ALA (020 7641 4285/6567; e-mail: ionacairns@easynet.co.uk)

Largest libraries
A   Westminster Reference Library, 35 St Martin's Street, London WC2H 7HP
        ☎020 7641 4636
        Fax 020 7641 4606
        Information Services Manager Ms A Duffy BA ALA (020 7641 6518; e-mail: amandaduffy@dial.pipex.com)
B   Marylebone Library, Marylebone Road, London NW1 5PS
        ☎020 7641 1037 (lending), 020 7641 1039 (Marylebone Information Service)
C   Charing Cross Library, 4 Charing Cross Road, London WC2H 0HG
        ☎020 7641 4628 (lending), 020 7641 4626 (music enquiries), 020 7641 4623 (Chinese service enquiries)
D   Victoria Library, 160 Buckingham Palace Road, London SW1W 9UD
        ☎020 7641 4287 (lending), 020 7641 4292 (Westminster Music Library)
E   Paddington Library, Porchester Road, London W2 5DU
        ☎020 7641 4475

Other services
A   Technical Services, 3rd Floor, Marylebone Library, Marylebone Road, London NW1 5PS
        ☎020 7641 1208
        Fax 020 7641 1019
        Manager Ms R Young (020 7641 1016; e-mail: r.young@dial.pipex.com)
B   Home Library Service, Moberly Centre, Kilburn Lane, London W10 4AH
        ☎020 7641 4806
        Manager Mrs P A Bear
C   City of Westminster Archives Centre, 10 St Ann's Street, London SW1P 2XR
        ☎020 7641 5180
        Fax 020 7641 5179
        City Archivist J Farrell MA DipArchAdmin

WIGAN

Headquarters Wigan Metropolitan Borough Council, Leisure Services Department, The Indoor Sports Complex, Loire Drive, Robin Park, Wigan, Lancs WN5 0UL

☎(01942) 828513 (enquiries & administration)
Fax (01942) 828540
e-mail: infounit@wiganmbc.gov.uk
Assistant Director: Service Development Mrs M A Sharples MA DMS

Central libraries
A   Wigan Library, College Avenue, Wigan, Lancs WN1 1DQ
    ☎(01942) 827621 (lending), (01942) 827619 (information)
    Fax (01942) 827640
    Manager S E Ruffley BA(Hons) ALA DMS
B   Turnpike Centre, Civic Square, Leigh, Lancs WN7 1EB
    ☎(01942) 404556 (lending), (01942) 404557 (information)
    Fax (01942) 404567
    Manager S E Ruffley BA(Hons) ALA DMS

District libraries
C   Ashton Library, Wigan Road, Ashton-in-Makerfield, Wigan, Lancs WN4 9BH
    ☎(01942) 727119/273978
    Manager R Patterson
D   Atherton Library, York Street, Atherton, Manchester M29 9JH
    ☎(01942) 878369/404817
    Manager S M Underwood BA
E   Standish Library, Cross Street, Standish, Wigan, Lancs WN6 0HQ
    ☎(01257) 421755/422743/400496/400498
    Manager M A Mason BA ALA

WILTSHIRE
Headquarters Wiltshire County Council, Libraries and Heritage HQ, Bythesea Road, Trowbridge, Wilts BA14 8BS
☎(01225) 713700 (enquiries), (01225) 713727 (information)
Fax (01225) 713993
e-mail: trowreflib@compuserve.com
Head of Libraries and Heritage Ms P Dyer ALA DMS MIMgt
Principal Librarian B M Little MPhil FLA (01225 713702)
Heritage Manager T Craig MA BA

District libraries
A   Salisbury District: Salisbury Library, Market Place, Salisbury, Wilts SP1 1BL
    ☎(01722) 324145
    Fax (01722) 413214
    District Librarian N Goddard ALA MIMgt (01722 330606)
B   Kennet District: Devizes Library, Sheep Street, Devizes, Wilts SN10 1DL
    ☎(01380) 726878/9
    Fax (01380) 722161
    District Librarian M A Chandler ALA (01380 724099)
C   West Wilts District: Trowbridge Library, Mortimer Street, Cradle Bridge, Trowbridge, Wilts BA14 8LD
    ☎(01225) 761171
    Fax (01225) 769447
    District Librarian Mrs M Liddle BA ALA (01225 713706)
D   North Wilts District: Chippenham Library, Timber Street, Chippenham, Wilts SN15 3EJ
    ☎(01249) 650536

Fax (01249) 443793
District Librarian Ms J Davis BLib ALA (01249 445005)

WINDSOR AND MAIDENHEAD

Headquarters Royal Borough of Windsor and Maidenhead, Cultural and Information
Services, Maidenhead Library, St Ives Road, Maidenhead, Berks SL6 1QU
☎(01628) 796989
Fax (01628) 796971
Head of Cultural and Information Services Mrs W Grant BA ALA (01628 796314; fax:
01628 796738; e-mail: wilma.grant@rbwm.gov.uk; based at 1st Floor, York Stream House,
St Ives Road, Maidenhead, Berks SL6 1QS)
Research Officer Ms S Hudson BA DipLib ALA (01628 796742)
Information Services Officer Ms M Harper BSc DipLib ALA (01628 796741)
Secretary Mrs J Dixon (01628 796482)

Central/largest library

Maidenhead Library, St Ives Road, Maidenhead, Berks SL6 1QU
☎(01628) 796968 (reference), 796969 (issue desk), 796985 (administration)
Fax (01628) 796971
Library Services Manager M Taylor BA ALA (01628 796989)
Assistant Library Services Manager B Marpole (01628 696976)
Senior Librarian, Reference and Information Ms P Curtis (01628 796974)
Senior Librarian, Adult Lending N Davies (01628 796974)
Senior Librarian, Young People Ms P Dobby (01628 796974)
Stock Services Officer, Stock Services Unit R High (01628 796987)
Administration Officer Mrs M Simpson (01628 796985)

Other libraries

A   Windsor Library, Bachelors Acre, Windsor, Berks SL4 1ER
     ☎(01753) 743940
B   Ascot Library, Winkfield Road, Ascot, Berks SL5 7EX
     ☎(01344) 820653
C   Cookham Library, High Road, Cookham Rise, Maidenhead, Berks SL6 9JF
     ☎(01626) 526147
D   Datchet Library, Village Hall, Horton Road, Datchet, Berks SL3 9AU
     ☎(01753) 545310
E   Dedworth Library, Dedworth County School, Smith's Lane, Windsor, Berks SL4 5PE
     ☎(01753) 868733
F   Eton Library, 136 High Street, Eton, Berks SL4 6AR
     ☎(01753) 860506
G   Eton Wick Library, Village Hall, Eton Wick, Berks SL4 6LT
     ☎(01753) 857933
H   Old Windsor Library, Memorial Hall, Straight Road, Windsor, Berks SL4 2JL
     ☎(01753) 852098
I   Sunninghill Library, Reading Room, School Road, Sunninghill, Berks SL5 7AD
     ☎(01344) 621493

Container library operating at four sites: Cox Green (01628 673942), Holyport (01628
673931), Sunningdale (01344 626720), Wraysbury (01784 482431)

WIRRAL

Headquarters Metropolitan Borough of Wirral, Department of Leisure Services & Tourism,
Westminster House, Hamilton Street, Birkenhead, Wirral L41 5FN

☎0151 647 2366
Fax 0151 666 1343
e-mail: dlst@wirral.gov.uk
Senior Assistant Director, Library, Information and Cultural Services J I Coles DMS ALA

Central/largest library
Birkenhead Central Library, Borough Road, Birkenhead, Wirral L41 2XB
☎0151 652 6106 (enquiries), 0151 653 4700 (administration)
Fax 0151 653 7320
e-mail: birkenhead.library@merseymail.com
Principal Librarian J C Baxter BA DipLib ALA

Regional/district libraries
A   Bebington Central Library, Civic Way, Bebington, Wirral L63 7PN
     ☎0151 643 7219
     Fax 0151 643 7231
     e-mail: beb@library.wirral.gov.uk
     Lending Librarian J Hougham BA DipLib ALA
B   Wallasey Central Library, Earlston Road, Wallasey, Wirral L45 5DY
     ☎0151 639 2334
     Fax 0151 691 2040
     e-mail: wallasey.central.lib@merseymail.com
     Lending Librarian R Macdonald ALA
C   West Kirby Library, The Concourse, West Kirby, Wirral L48 4HX
     ☎0151 625 6381
     Fax 0151 625 2558
     e-mail: westkirby.library@merseymail.com
     Lending Librarian Mrs J Mann BA ALA

WOKINGHAM

Headquarters Wokingham District Council, Libraries and Information Services, Education and Cultural Services Dept, PO Box 156, Wokingham, Berks RG40 1WN
☎0118 974 6000
Libraries and Information Manager C J Hamilton ALA (0118 974 6261; e-mail: chris.hamilton@wokingham.gov.uk)

Central/largest library
Wokingham Library, Denmark Street, Wokingham, Berks RG40 2BB
☎0118 978 1368
Fax 0118 989 1214
Branch Supervisor R Alexander (0118 979 3474)

WOLVERHAMPTON

Headquarters Wolverhampton Metropolitan Borough Council, Libraries and Information Services, Central Library, Snow Hill, Wolverhampton WV1 3AX
☎(01902) 552025 (enquiries & administration)
Fax (01902) 552024
e-mail: wolverhampton.libraries@dial.pipex.com
Head of Libraries and Information Mrs K Lees BA ALA (01902 552010)
Principal Libraries Officer (Central) G Kent BA DipLib (01902 552011)
Principal Libraries Officer A Scragg DipHE LLB(Hons) ALA (01902 552012)

Central/largest library
As above

Branch libraries
Group One
Branch Group Librarian Mrs K Fletcher ALA (0192 556293)
A   Ashmore Park Library, Griffiths Drive, Wednesfield, Wolverhampton WV11 2JW
     ☎(01902) 556296
B   Low Hill Library, Showell Circus, Low Hill, Wolverhampton WV10 9JJ
     ☎(01902) 556293
C   Mary Pointon Library, Ettingshall Road, Wood Cross, Wolverhampton WV14 9UG
     ☎(01902) 556263
D   Pendeford Library, Whitburn Close, Pendeford, Wolverhampton WV9 5NJ
     ☎(01902) 556250
E   Penn Library, Coalway Avenue, Penn, Wolverhampton WV3 7LT
     ☎(01902) 556281
F   Whitmore Reans Library, Bargate Drive, Evans Street, Whitmore Reans,
     Wolverhampton WV6 0QW
     ☎(01902) 556269

Group Two
Branch Group Librarian K Hudson BA (01902 556257)
G   Bilston Library, Mount Pleasant, Bilston, Wolverhampton WV14 7LU
     ☎(01902) 556253
H   Daisy Bank Library, Ash Street, Bradley, Bilston, Wolverhampton WV14 8UP
     ☎(01902) 556305
I   Eastfield Library, Hurstbourne Crescent, Eastfield, Wolverhampton WV1 2EE
     ☎(01902) 556257
J   Finchfield Library, White Oak Drive, Finchfield, Wolverhampton WV3 9AF
     ☎(01902) 556260
K   Heath Town Community Library, Tudor Road, Heath Town, Wolverhampton
     WV10 0LT
     ☎(01902) 556266
L   Oxley Library, Probert Road, Oxley, Wolverhampton WV10 6UF
     ☎(01902) 556287
M   Tettenhall Library, Upper Street, Tettenhall, Wolverhampton WV6 8QF
     ☎(01902) 556308

Group Three
Branch Group Librarian Mrs D Jones BA (01902 556284)
N   Bradmore Community Library, Bantock House, Bradmore Road, Wolverhampton
     WV3 9BH
     ☎(01902) 556299
O   Long Knowle Library, Wood End Road, Wednesfield, Wolverhampton WV11 1YG
     ☎(01902) 556290
P   Scotlands Community Library, Masefield Road, Wolverhampton WV10 8SA
     ☎(01902) 552198
Q   Spring Vale Library, Bevan Avenue, Wolverhampton, Wolverhampton WV4 6SG
     ☎(01902) 556284
R   Warstones Library, Pinfold Grove, Penn, Wolverhampton WV4 9PT
     ☎(01902) 556275
S   Wednesfield Library, Church Street, Wednesfield, Wolverhampton WV11 1SR
     ☎(01902) 556278

WORCESTERSHIRE

Headquarters Worcestershire County Council, Cultural Services Division (Libraries and Information Service), County Hall, Spetchley Road, Worcester WR5 2NP
☎(01905) 766240 (enquiries); (01905) 766231 (administration)
Fax (01905) 766244
Library Services Manager Mrs C Evans ALA (01905 766232; e-mail: cevans@worcestershire.gov.uk)
Principal Librarian, North and Services to Young People Mrs C Reed BA ALA (01905 766233; e-mail: creed@worcestershire.gov.uk)
Principal Librarian, South and Special Services N Preedy BSc ALA (01905 766239; e-mail: npreedy@worcestershire.gov.uk)
Principal Librarian, Information Services D Drewitt BA ALA (01905 766240; e-mail: ddrewitt@worcestershire.gov.uk)
Senior Librarian, Planning Ms S Hickman BA (01905 766242; e-mail: shickman@worcestershire.gov.uk)

Main libraries

A   Bromsgrove Library, Stratford Road, Bromsgrove, Worcestershire B60 1AP
      ☎(01527) 575855 (575856 outside office hours)
      Fax (01905) 575855
      e-mail: bromsgrovelib@worcestershire.gov.uk
      Bromsgrove Librarian G T C Marshall BA ALA

B   Evesham Library, Oat Street, Evesham, Worcestershire WR11 4JP
      ☎(01386) 442291/41348
      Fax (01386) 765855
      e-mail: eveshamlib@worcestershire.gov.uk
      Evesham Librarian Mrs L Downes ALA

C   Kidderminster Library, Market Street, Kidderminster, Worcestershire DY10 1PE
      ☎(01562) 824500
      Fax (01562) 512907
      e-mail: kidderminsterlib@worcestershire.gov.uk
      Kidderminster Librarian R Hoggarth MA ALA

D   Malvern Library, Graham Road, Malvern, Worcestershire WR14 2HU
      ☎(01684) 561223/573582
      Fax (01684) 892999
      e-mail: malvernlib@worcestershire.gov.uk
      Malvern Librarian K E Barber BA ALA

E   Redditch Library, 15 Market Place, Redditch, Worcestershire B98 8AR
      ☎(01527) 63291
      Fax (01527) 68571
      e-mail: redditchlib@worcestershire.gov.uk
      Redditch Librarian C Johnson ALA

F   Worcester Library, Foregate Street, Worcester WR1 1DT
      ☎(01905) 765314
      Fax (01905) 726664
      e-mail: worcesterlib@worcestershire.gov.uk
      Worcester Librarian Ms R Foster BA ALA

G   Countywide Information Service, Information and Business Systems Division, County Hall, Spetchley Road, Worcester WR5 2NP
      ☎(01497) 847987
      url: http://www.worcestershire.gov.uk
      Webmaster and CWIS Manager D Morris BMus PGCE (e-mail: dmorris@worcestershire.gov.uk)

YORK

Headquarters City of York Council, York Library, Museum Street, York, North Yorkshire
YO1 2DS
☎(01904) 655631
Fax (01904) 611025
Principal Officer Mrs A J Henesey BA ALA

NORTHERN IRELAND

BELFAST EDUCATION AND LIBRARY BOARD

Headquarters Belfast Education and Library Board, Belfast Public Libraries, Central Library, Royal Avenue, Belfast, Northern Ireland BT1 1EA

☎028 9024 3233

Fax 028 9033 2819

e-mail: libraries@belfast-elb.gov.uk

Chief Librarian T Watson ALA (e-mail: t.watson@belfast-elb.gov.uk)

NORTH EASTERN EDUCATION AND LIBRARY BOARD

Headquarters North Eastern Education and Library Board, Area Library HQ, Demesne Avenue, Ballymena, Co Antrim, Northern Ireland BT43 7BG

☎028 2566 4100

Fax 028 2563 2038

Chief Librarian Mrs P Valentine BA(Hons) FLA (028 2566 4101)

Assistant Chief Librarian (Information and Support) B Cooper BSc(Econ) GradCertEd AdvDipBFM(CIPFA) ALA (028 2566 4102)

Assistant Chief Librarian (Public Services) Mrs L Houston BLS DMS ALA (028 2566 4104)

Assistant Chief Librarian (Youth and Training) M McFaul MBA(Hons) DipM ALA (028 2566 4103)

Group libraries

A   Group Library, Ballycraigy School, Antrim, Co Antrim, Northern Ireland BT41 1PU

☎028 9448 7172

Group Librarian A Armstrong BA(Hons) DipLib DMS ALA

B   Group Library, Demesne Avenue, Ballymena, Co Antrim, Northern Ireland BT43 7BG

☎028 2566 4126

Group Librarian Mrs M Bryson BA ALA

C   Group Library, Joymount Court, Carrickfergus, Northern Ireland BT38 7DQ

☎028 9336 2261

Group Librarian Mrs J Austin BA ALA

D   Group Library, Coleraine Branch, Queen Street, Coleraine, Northern Ireland BT52 1BE

☎028 7034 2561

Group Librarian Mrs E E Cooper BA(Hons) MA ALA

E   Group Library, 18B The Diamond Centre, Market Street, Magherafelt, Northern Ireland BT45 6ED

☎028 7963 4887

Group Librarian B Porter BSc ALA

SOUTH EASTERN EDUCATION AND LIBRARY BOARD

Headquarters South Eastern Education and Library Board, Library Headquarters, Windmill Hill, Ballynahinch, Co Down, Northern Ireland BT24 8DH

☎028 9756 6400

Fax 028 9756 5072

Chief Librarian Mrs B Porter BA(Hons) DipLibStud ALA (028 9756 6402)
Assistant Chief Librarian Mrs L Plummer BA(Hons) DipLibStud ALA (028 9756 6406)

Area libraries

A   Dairy Farm Library, Dairy Farm Centre, Unit 17, Stewartstown Road, Dunmurry, Belfast, Co Antrim, Northern Ireland BT17 0AW
     ☎028 9043 1266
     Fax 028 9043 1278
     Group Library Manager Mrs M Bell BLS ALA

B   Downpatrick Library, Market Street, Downpatrick, Co Down, Northern Ireland BT30 6LZ
     ☎028 4461 2895
     Fax 028 4461 9039
     Group Library Manager Mrs P Cooper BLS PGDipA&LS ALA

C   Holywood Library, Sullivan Building, 86-88 High Street, Holywood, Co Down, Northern Ireland BT18 9AE
     ☎028 9042 4232
     Fax 028 9042 4194
     Group Library Manager Vacant

D   Tullycarnet Library, Kinross Avenue, Belfast, Co Antrim, Northern Ireland BT5 7GF
     ☎028 9048 5079
     Fax 028 9048 2342
     Group Library Managers Mrs H Mills BLib ALA, Mrs A McVey BA DipLibStud ALA

SOUTHERN EDUCATION AND LIBRARY BOARD

Headquarters Southern Education and Library Board, Library Headquarters, 1 Markethill Road, Armagh, Co Armagh, Northern Ireland BT60 1NR
☎028 3752 5353
Fax 028 3752 6879
url: http://www.campus.bt.com/CampusWorld/orgs/org3551/index.html
Chief Librarian A Morrow ALA
Assistant Chief Librarians R Dougan ALA, P Reid DipLib

Divisional library headquarters

A   Dungannon Divisional Library Headquarters, Market Square, Dungannon, Co Tyrone, Northern Ireland BT70 1JB
     ☎028 8772 2885
     Divisional Librarian B McGeown BA(Hons) MBA

B   Craigavon Divisional Library Headquarters, 113 Church Street, Portadown, Co Armagh, Northern Ireland BT62 3DB
     ☎028 3833 5247/5296
     Divisional Librarian G Burns BA

C   Newry Divisional Library Headquarters, 79 Hill Street, Newry, Co Down, Northern Ireland BT34 1DG
     ☎028 3066 1652
     Divisional Librarian Miss J Blair ALA

Local History Service, Library Headquarters, 1 Markethill Road, Armagh, Co Armagh, Northern Ireland BT60 1NR
☎028 3752 5353
Fax 028 3752 6879
Local History Librarian Ms M McVeigh BA MSSc(Irish Studies) DipLib

Local Government Information Service, 113 Church Street, Portadown, Co Armagh, Northern Ireland BT62 3DB
☎028 3833 5247/5296
Librarian Mrs S Young BA ALA

WESTERN EDUCATION AND LIBRARY BOARD

Headquarters Western Education and Library Board, Library Headquarters, 1 Spillars Place, Omagh, Co Tyrone, Northern Ireland BT78 1HL
☎028 8224 4821
Fax 028 8224 6716
e-mail: librarian@omalib.demon.co.uk
Chief Librarian R T A Farrow BA ALA ALAI FRSA
Assistant Chief Librarians Mrs R A Adams BA ALA, L P Crossey BA ALA

Central/largest library
Central Library, Foyle Street, Londonderry, Northern Ireland BT48 1AL
☎028 7126 6888
Fax 028 7126 9084
Librarian Mrs P Ward BA ALA

Divisional library headquarters
A   North West Divisional HQ, Central Library, Foyle Street, Londonderry, Northern Ireland BT48 1AL
☎028 7126 6888
Fax 028 7127 2312
Divisional Librarian Ms A Peoples BA ALA DMS
B   South West Divisional HQ, Hall's Lane, Enniskillen, Co Fermanagh, Northern Ireland BT74 7DR
☎028 6632 2886
Fax 028 6632 4685
Divisional Librarian D Preston BA ALA
C   Omagh Library, 1 Spillars Place, Omagh, Co Tyrone, Northern Ireland BT78 1HL
☎028 8224 4821
Fax 028 8224 6772
Librarian Ms G McSorley BA ALA
D   Enniskillen Library, Halls Lane, Enniskillen, Co Fermanagh, Northern Ireland BT74 7DR
☎028 6632 2886
Fax 028 6632 4685
Librarian S Bleakley BA(Hons) DLS
E   Strabane Library, Butcher Street, Strabane, Co Tyrone, Northern Ireland BT82 8BJ
☎028 7138 3686
Fax 028 7138 2745
Librarian Mrs A Harron BA ALA
F   Limavady Library, 5 Connell Street, Limavady, Londonderry, Northern Ireland BT47 0EA
☎028 7776 2540
Fax 028 7772 2006
Librarian Mrs L Brown BA ALA

SCOTLAND

ABERDEEN

Headquarters Aberdeen City Council, Arts and Recreation Dept, Library and Information Services, Central Library, Rosemount Viaduct, Aberdeen AB25 1GW
☎(01224) 652500 (enquiries & administration)
Fax (01224) 641985
e-mail: centlib@arts-rec.aberdeen.net.uk
Principal Officer, Library and Information Services N M Bruce MA DipLib ALA (01224 652536)
Public Services Librarian (Lending) J D Grant BA ALA (01224 652515)
Public Services Librarian (Information) J A Pratt ALA (01224 652534)
Network Development Librarian Vacant

Central/largest library
As above

ABERDEENSHIRE

Headquarters Aberdeenshire Council, Library and Information Service, Meldrum Meg Way, Oldmeldrum, Aberdeenshire AB51 0GN
☎(01651) 872707 (enquiries & administration)
Fax (01651) 872142
Principal Librarian G Moore BA ALA (e-mail: gmoore.lr@aberdeenshire.gov.uk)
Media Resources Manager Mrs M J Strachan ALA DMS (01651 872707; e-mail: mstrachan.ed@aberdeenshire.gov.uk)
Central Support Services Manager Mrs A A M Harrison ALA (01651 872707; e-mail: aharrison.ed@aberdeenshire.gov.uk)

Other libraries
A   Ellon Library, Station Road, Ellon, Aberdeenshire AB41 9NE
      ☎(01358) 720865
      Fax (01358) 722864
      Client Services Librarian Mrs H W Dewar MA ALA (e-mail: hdewar.ed@aberdeenshire.gov.uk)
B   Banchory Library, Bridge Street, Banchory, Aberdeenshire AB31 3SU
      ☎(01330) 823784
      Fax (01330) 824516
      Client Services Librarian R A de Silva BA MBA ALA MEd (e-mail: rdesilva.ed@aberdeenshire.gov.uk)

ANGUS

Headquarters Angus Council, County Buildings, Market Street, Forfar, Angus DD8 3WF
☎(01307) 461460
Fax (01307) 462590
Director of Cultural Services G N Drummond ALA
Head of Community Resources N K Atkinson DipEd AMA

Central/largest library
Central Services Unit, 50 West High Street, Forfar, Angus DD8 1BA
☎(01307) 466966
Fax (01307) 468451

e-mail: central.services@angus.gov.uk
Central Services Librarian J Fraser BA DipLib ALA

Area libraries

A   Arbroath Library, Hill Terrace, Arbroath, Angus DD11 1AH
☎(01241) 872248
Fax (01241) 434396
e-mail: arbroath.library@angus.gov.uk
Principal Librarian Ms T Roby ALA

B   Brechin Library, 10 St Ninian's Square, Brechin, Angus DD9 7AA
☎(01356) 622687
Fax (01356) 624271
e-mail: brechin.library@angus.gov.uk
Principal Librarian Ms A Pirie BA

C   Carnoustie Library, 21 High Street, Carnoustie, Angus DD7 6AN
☎(01241) 859620
e-mail: carnoustie.library@angus.gov.uk
Principal Librarian A Sutherland BA ALA

D   Forfar Library, 50-56 West High Street, Forfar, Angus DD8 1BA
☎(01307) 466071
Fax (01307) 468451
e-mail: forfar.library@angus.gov.uk
Principal Librarian I K Neil MA ALA

E   Kirriemuir Library, Town Hall, 28/30 Reform Street, Kirriemuir, Angus DD8 4BS
☎(01575) 572357
Principal Librarian J MacRitchie BA ALA

F   Monifieth Library, High Street, Monifieth, Angus DD5 4AE
☎(01382) 533819
e-mail: monifieth.library@angus.gov.uk
Principal Librarian Ms D Milne ALA

G   Montrose Library, 214 High Street, Montrose, Angus DD10 8PH
☎(01674) 673256
Fax (01674) 671810
e-mail: montrose.library@angus.gov.uk
Principal Librarian Ms M Taylor BA

ARGYLL AND BUTE

Headquarters Argyll and Bute Council, Library and Information Service HQ, Highland
Avenue, Sandbank, Dunoon, Argyll PA23 8PB
☎(01369) 703214/703735
Fax (01369) 705797
Principal Library and Information Services Officer A I Ewan ALA (e-mail:
andyewan@abc-libraries.demon.co.uk)

Area libraries

A   Campbeltown Library, Hall Street, Campbeltown, Argyll PA28 6BS
☎(01586) 552366 ext 2237
Fax (01586) 552938
Area Librarian Ms S Fortune ALA

B   Dunoon Library, 248 Argyll Street, Dunoon, Argyll PA23 7LT
☎(01369) 703735 ext 7522
Fax (01369) 701323
Area Librarian Ms P Flynn BA ALA

C Helensburgh Library, West King Street, Helensburgh, Dunbartonshire G84 8EB
  ☎(01436) 674626
  Fax (01436) 679567
  Area Librarian/IT Systems Development Manager P McCann BA ALA

D Oban Library, Corran Halls, Oban, Argyll PA34 5AB
  ☎(01631) 567921
  Fax (01631) 570761
  Area Librarian K Baker BA DipLib ALA

E Rothesay Library, Moat Centre, Stuart Street, Rothesay, Bute PA20 0EP
  ☎(01700) 503266
  Fax (01700) 500511
  Branch Librarian E Monaghan ALA

CLACKMANNANSHIRE

Headquarters Clackmannanshire Council, Clackmannanshire Libraries, Alloa Library, 26-28 Drysdale Street, Alloa, Clackmannanshire FK10 1JL
☎(01259) 722262
Fax (01259) 219469
e-mail: clack.lib@mail.easynet.co.uk
Library Services Manager D A Hynd ALA
Team Leader, Community Library Service J A Blake BSc DipLib ALA DipEdTech

Branches within community access points

A Alva Community Access Point, 153 West Stirling Street, Alva, Clackmannanshire
  ☎(01259) 760652
  Fax (01259) 760354
  Senior Community Access Officer Ms N Foster

B Clackmannan Community Access Point, Main Street, Clackmannan, Clackmannan-shire
  ☎(01259) 721579
  Fax (01259) 212493
  Senior Community Access Officer Ms J Laird

C Dollar Community Access Point, Dollar Civic Centre, Park Place, Dollar, Clackmannanshire
  ☎(01259) 743253
  Fax (01259) 743328
  Senior Community Access Officer Ms K Waddell

D Menstrie Community Access Point, The Dumyat Leisure Centre, Main Street East, Menstrie, Clackmannanshire
  ☎(01259) 769439
  Fax (01259) 762941
  Senior Community Access Officer W Huggan

E Sauchie Community Access Point, 42-48 Main Street, Sauchie, Clackmannanshire
  ☎(01259) 721679
  Fax (01259) 218750
  Senior Community Access Officer Ms M Hunter

F Tillicoultry Branch Library, 99 High Street, Tillicoultry, Clackmannanshire
  ☎(01259) 751685
  Branch Librarian Ms L Paterson

G Tullibody Library, Leisure Centre, Abercromby Place, Tullibody, Clackmannanshire
  ☎(01259) 218725
  Branch Librarian Ms A Ruddy

COMHAIRLE NAN EILEAN SIAR (formerly Western Isles)

Headquarters Comhairle nan Eilean Siar, Public Library, Cromwell Street, Stornoway, Isle of Lewis HS1 2DA
☎(01851) 703064
Fax (01851) 705657
e-mail: stornoway_library@w-isles.gov.uk
Chief Librarian R M Eaves BA DipEd ALA
Senior Librarian, Adult Services D J Fowler ALA
Senior Librarian, Youth Services Mrs J Robson AALIA ALA

Area libraries
A   Community Library, Sgoil Lionacleit, Liniclate, Isle of Benbecula HS7 5PJ
     ☎(01870) 602211
     Fax (01870) 602817
     e-mail: sgoil_lionacleit_library@cne-siar.gov.uk
     Community Librarian Mrs J F Bramwell BA ALA
B   Community Library, Castlebay Community School, Castlebay, Isle of Barra HS9 5XD
     ☎(01871) 810471
     Fax (01871) 810650
     e-mail: castlebay_library@cne-siar.gov.uk
     Senior Library Assistant Mrs L Mackinnon
C   Community Library, Sgoil Shiaboist, Shawbost, Isle of Lewis HS2 9PQ
     ☎(01851) 710213
     e-mail: shawbost_library@cne-siar.gov.uk
     Library Assistant Mrs C A Campbell
D   Community Library, Sir E Scott School, Tarbert, Isle of Harris HS3 3BG
     ☎(01859) 502000
     e-mail: sir_e_scott_library@cne-siar.gov.uk
     Library Assistant Mrs F Morrison MA
E   Community Library, Daliburgh School, Daliburgh, Isle of South Uist HS8 5SS
     ☎(01878) 700673
     e-mail: daliburgh_library@cne-siar.gov.uk
     Library Assistant Vacant
F   Community Library, Paible School, Paible, Isle of North Uist HS6 5DX
     ☎(01876) 510275
     e-mail: paible_library@cne-siar.gov.uk
     Librarian i/c Mrs F Campbell MA

DUMFRIES AND GALLOWAY

Headquarters Dumfries and Galloway Council, Libraries, Information and Archives, Central Support Unit, Catherine Street, Dumfries DG1 1JB
☎(01387) 253820 (enquiries), (01387) 252070 (administration)
Fax (01387) 260294
e-mail: libs&i@dumgal.gov.uk
Libraries, Information and Archives Manager A R Johnston BA ALA FSA(Scot)
(Mobile Libraries based at CSU and Newton Stewart libraries. Open Learning Service now available: contact CSU or any branch/mobile library for details)

District libraries
A   Annan Library, Charles Street, Annan, DG12 5AG
     ☎(01461) 202809
     Fax (01461) 202809

B   Archive Centre, 33 Burns Street, Dumfries DG1 2PS
     ☎(01387) 269254
     Fax (01387) 264126
C   Castle Douglas Library, Market Hill, King Street, Castle Douglas DG7 3AT
     ☎(01556) 502643
     Fax (01556) 502643
D   Dalbeattie Library, High Street, Dalbeattie DG5 4AD
     ☎(01556) 610898
     Fax (01556) 610898
E   Dalry Library, Main Street, Dalry, Castle Douglas DG7 3UP
     ☎(01644) 430234
     Fax (01644) 430234
F   Eastriggs Library, Eastriggs Community School, Eastriggs, Annan DG12 6PZ
     ☎(01461) 40844
     Fax (01461) 40844
G   Ewart Library, Catherine Street, Dumfries DG1 1JB
     ☎(01387) 253820/252070
     Fax (01387) 260294
H   Gatehouse Library, High Street, Gatehouse of Fleet DG7 4EJ
     ☎(01557) 814646
     Fax (01557) 814646
I   Georgetown Library, Gillbrae Road, Georgetown, Dumfries DG1 4EJ
     ☎(01387) 256059
     Fax (01387) 256059
J   Gretna Library, The Richard Greenhow Centre, Gretna DG16 5AQ
     ☎(01461) 338000
     Fax (01461) 338000
K   Kirkconnel Library, Greystone Avenue, Kelloholm DG4 6RA
     ☎(01659) 67191
     Fax (01659) 67191
L   Kirkcudbright Library, Sheriff Court House, High Street, Kirkcudbright DG6 4JW
     ☎(01557) 331240
     Fax (01557) 331240
M   Langholm Library, Charles Street, Old Langholm DG13 0AA
     ☎(013873) 80040
     Fax (013873) 80040
N   Lochmaben Library, High Street, Lochmaben, Lockerbie DG11 1NQ
     ☎(01387) 811865
     Fax (01387) 811865
O   Lochside Library, Lochside Road, Dumfries DG2 0IW
     ☎(01387) 268751
     Fax (01387) 268751
P   Lochthorn Library, Lochthorn, Dumfries DG1 1UF
     ☎(01387) 265780
     Fax (01387) 266424
Q   Lockerbie Library, 31-33 High Street, Lockerbie DG11 2JL
     ☎(01576) 203380
     Fax (01576) 203380
R   Moffat Library, Town Hall, High Street, Moffat DG10 9HF
     ☎(01683) 220952
     Fax (01683) 220952
S   Newton Stewart Library, Church Road, Newton Stewart DG8 6ER
     ☎(01671) 403450
     Fax (01671) 403450

T   Port William Library, Main Street, Port William, Newton Stewart DG8 9QJ
☎(01988) 700406
Fax (01988) 700406
U   Sanquhar Library, 106 High Street, Sanquhar DG4 6DZ
☎(01659) 502626
Fax (01659) 502626
V   Stranraer Library, North Strand Street, Stranraer DG9 8ES
☎(01776) 707400/707440
Fax (01776) 703565
W   Thornhill Library, Townhead Street, Thornhill DG3 5NW
☎(01848) 330654
Fax (01848) 330654
X   Whithorn Library, St John Street, Whithorn DG8 8PF
☎(01988) 500406
Fax (01988) 500406
Y   Wigtown Library, Duncan Park, Wigtown DG8 9HY
☎(01988) 403329
Fax (01988) 403329

DUNDEE

Headquarters Dundee City Council, Neighbourhood Resources and Development
Department, Floor 1, Podium Block, Tayside House, Crichton Street, Dundee DD1 3RR
☎(01382) 433283 (administration), (01382) 433187 (enquiries)
Fax (01382) 433871
Chief Neighbourhood Resources Officer F Patrick BA DipYCW
Neighbourhood Resources Manager Mrs M Methven ALA (e-mail:
moira.methven@dundeecity.gov.uk)

Development and QA Team, Arthurstone, Dundee
Unit Leader R Hardie (01382 433461)
Senior Adult Resource Worker Ms F Macpherson (01382 438893)
Senior Youth Resource Worker Ms L Moy (01382 438889)
Senior Resource Worker Ms F Robertson (01382 438893)

Central/largest library
Central Library, The Wellgate, Dundee DD1 1DB
☎(01382) 434318 (enquiries), (01382) 434324 (administration)
Fax (01382) 434642
Section Leader I Copland ALA (01382 434323)
Unit Leader Ms C Ferguson MA ALA (01382 434376)
Team Leader Ms P Tulloch MA ALA (01382 434336)

Neighbourhood libraries
A   Ardler Neighbourhood Library, Turnberry Avenue, Ardler, Dundee DD2 3TP
☎(01382) 432863
Fax (01382) 432862
Neighbourhood Resource Worker Miss B Cook BA ALA
B   Arthurstone Neighbourhood Library, Arthurstone Terrace, Dundee DD4 6RT
☎(01382) 438881
Fax (01382) 438885
Senior Neighbourhood Resource Assistant Mrs S Westgate
C   Blackness Neighbourhood Library, 225 Perth Road, Dundee DD2 1EJ
☎(01382) 435843

Fax (01382) 435942
Neighbourhood Resource Worker Mrs E Young
D   The Hub Neighbourhood Centre and Library, Pitkerro Road, Dundee DD4 8ES
☎(01382) 438626
Fax (01382) 438627
Senior Neighbourhood Resource Assistant Mrs L Kell
E   Broughty Ferry Neighbourhood Library, Queen Street, Broughty Ferry, Dundee
DD5 2HN
☎(01382) 436919
Fax (01382) 436913
Neighbourhood Resource Worker I Cranmer ALA
F   Charleston Neighbourhood Library, 60 Craigowan Road, Dundee DD2 4NL
☎(01382) 436723
Fax (01382) 436643
Senior Neighbourhood Resource Assistant Mrs E Darling
G   Coldside Neighbourhood Library, 150 Strathmartine Road, Dundee DD3 7SE
☎(01382) 432849
Fax (01382) 432850
Neighbourhood Resource Worker Ms C Andrew
H   Douglas Community and Library Centre, Balmoral Place, Douglas, Dundee
DD4 8SH
☎(01382) 436864
Fax (01382) 436922
Senior Neighbourhood Resource Assistants Mrs M Vivian, Mrs R McDowell
I   Fintry Neighbourhood Library, Findcastle Street, Dundee DD4 9EW
☎(01382) 432560
Fax (01382) 432559
Neighbourhood Resource Worker Mrs S Wood
J   Kirkton Neighbourhood Library, Derwent Avenue, Dundee DD3 0BW
☎(01382) 432851
Fax (01382) 432852
Senior Neighbourhood Resource Assistant Mrs A Smith
K   Lochee Neighbourhood Library, High Street, Lochee, Dundee DD2 3AU
☎(01382) 432675
Fax (01382) 432677
Senior Neighbourhood Resource Assistant Mrs J Rodger
L   Menzieshill Neighbourhood Library, Orleans Place, Menzieshill, Dundee DD2 4BN
☎(01382) 435965
Fax (01382) 435992
Senior Neighbourhood Resource Assistant Miss L Andrews
M   Whitfield Library and Learning Centre, Whitfield Drive, Dundee DD4 0DX
☎(01382) 432569
Fax (01382) 432509
Neighbourhood Resource Worker I Campbell MA

EAST AYRSHIRE

Headquarters East Ayrshire Council, Library and Information Services, Dick Institute, 14
Elmbank Avenue, Kilmarnock, Ayrshire KA1 3BU
☎(01563) 526401
Fax (01563) 529661
e-mail: libraries@east-ayrshire.gov.uk
url: http://www.east-ayrshire.gov.uk
Library and Information Services Manager G Cairns BA DipLib ALA DMS (e-mail:

gerard.cairns@east-ayrshire.gov.uk)
Senior Librarian Mrs E Gray MA ALA (e-mail: elaine.gray@east-ayrshire.gov.uk)
Senior Librarian J Laurenson BA ALA (e-mail: john.laurenson@east-ayrshire.gov.uk)
Community and Development Librarian Ms D Vallance BA ALA (e-mail:
dawn.vallance@east-ayrshire.gov.uk)

EAST DUNBARTONSHIRE

Headquarters East Dunbartonshire Council, Education and Leisure Services, William
Patrick Library, 2 West High Street, Kirkintilloch, East Dunbartonshire G66 1AD
☎0141 766 5666
Fax 0141 766 0408
Libraries Manager Ms E Brown MA ALA
Operations Librarian D Kenvyn BA ALA (e-mail: david_kenvyn@edlibrary.demon.co.uk)
Support Services Librarian Ms A Hamilton BA ALA
Outreach Services J Fergusson BA ALA
Reference and Information Librarian D Martin FLA (0141 776 8080; e-mail:
don_martin@edlibrary.demon.co.uk)
Young People's Services Librarian Mrs F McArthur ALA

Central/largest library
William Patrick Library, 2 West High Street, Kirkintilloch, East Dunbartonshire G66 1AD
☎0141 776 7484 (enquiries), 0141 776 5666 (administration)
Fax 0141 776 0408
Branch Librarian Mrs D Fergusson, Mrs E Morris BA (job share)

Branch libraries

A   Brookwood Library, 166 Drymen Road, Bearsden, East Dunbartonshire G61 3RJ
    ☎0141 942 6811
    Fax 0141 943 1119
    Branch Librarian J Rae BA ALA
B   Bishopbriggs Library, 170 Kirkintilloch Road, Bishopbriggs, East Dunbartonshire
    G64 2LX
    ☎0141 772 4513
    Fax 0141 762 5363
    Branch Librarian Mrs E Clifford ALA, Mrs F Warner BA ALA (job share)
C   Craighead Library, Craighead Road, Milton of Campsie, East Dunbartonshire
    G65 8DL
    ☎(01360) 311925
    Assistant in Charge Mrs M Newton, Mrs S Vernon (job share)
D   Lennoxtown Library, Main Street, Lennoxtown, East Dunbartonshire G65 7DG
    ☎(01360) 311436
    Fax (01360) 311436
    Senior Library Supervisor Ms E Gordon
E   Lenzie Library, 13 Alexandra Avenue, Lenzie, East Dunbartonshire G66 5BG
    ☎0141 776 3021
    Library Supervisor Ms L Finlayson
F   Milngavie Library, Community Centre, Allander Way, Milngavie, East
    Dunbartonshire G62 8PN
    ☎0141 956 2776
    Fax 0141 570 0052
    Branch Librarian J Murray ALA
G   Westerton Library, 82 Maxwell Avenue, Bearsden, East Dunbartonshire G61 1NZ
    ☎0141 943 0780
    Library Supervisor Mrs L Mann, Ms E Bushfield (job share)

EAST LOTHIAN

Headquarters East Lothian Council, Library and Museum Headquarters, Dunbar Road, Haddington, East Lothian EH41 3PJ
☎(01620) 828205 (enquiries), (01620) 828200 (administration)
Fax (01620) 828201
e-mail: hq@elothlib.demon.co.uk
url: http://www.earl.org.uk/partners/eastlothian/index.html
Libraries Officer D Moody ALA

Largest library
Musselburgh Library, 10 Bridge Street, Musselburgh, East Lothian EH21 6AG
☎0131 665 2183
Branch Librarian Ms J Paterson BA DipLib

Branch libraries
A   Dunbar Library, Castellau, Belhaven Road, Dunbar, East Lothian EH42 1DA
        ☎(01368) 863521
        Assistant i/c Ms R Barton
B   Haddington Library, Newton Port, Haddington, East Lothian EH41 3NA
        ☎(01620) 822531
        Fax (01620) 822531
        Branch Librarian Ms T Gavan ALA, Ms M Daly ALA (job share)
C   North Berwick Library, The Old School, School Road, North Berwick, East Lothian
        EH39 4JU
        ☎(01620) 893470
        Branch Librarian Ms S Butts MA DipLib
D   Prestonpans Library, West Loan, Prestonpans, East Lothian EH32 9NX
        ☎(01875) 810788
        Branch Librarian Ms E Thomson BA ALA
E   Tranent Library, 3 Civic Square, Tranent, East Lothian EH33 1LH
        ☎(01875) 610254
        Branch Librarian Ms D Elliott MA DipLib

Specialist library
A   Local History Centre, Newton Port, Haddington, East Lothian EH41 3NA
        ☎(01620) 823307
        Librarian i/c Mrs V Wallace ALA

EAST RENFREWSHIRE

Headquarters East Renfrewshire Council, Cultural Services, Glen Street, Barrhead, East Renfrewshire G78 1QA
☎0141 577 3500 (enquiries)
Fax 0141 577 3501
url: http://www.eastrenfrewshire.gov.uk
Head of Cultural Services K McKinlay MA(Hons) PGDipLib ALA (0141 577 3103; e-mail: mckinlayk@eastrenfrewshire.gov.uk)
Operations Manager E Fox ALA (0141 577 3512; e-mail: foxe@eastrenfrewshire.gov.uk)
Information Development Manager Mrs E McGettigan BA ALA (0141 577 3503; e-mail: mcgettiganl@eastrenfrewshire.gov.uk)
Systems Manager S Simpson BA PGDipIT (0141 577 3509; e-mail: simpsons@eastrenfrewshire.gov.uk)
Youth and Community Services Manager M Wright ALA (0141 577 3502; e-mail: wrightm@eastrenfrewshire.gov.uk)

Community libraries

A   Barrhead Community Library, Glen Street, Barrhead, East Renfrewshire G78 1QA
     ☎0141 577 3518
     e-mail: barrheadl@eastrenfrewshire.gov.uk

B   Busby Community Library, Duff Memorial Hall, Main Street, Busby, East
     Renfrewshire G76 8DX
     ☎0141 577 4971
     e-mail: busbyl@eastrenfrewshire.gov.uk

C   Clarkston Community Library, Clarkston Road, Clarkston, East Renfrewshire
     G76 8NE
     ☎0141 577 4972
     Fax 0141 577 4973
     e-mail: clarkstonl@eastrenfrewshire.gov.uk

D   Eaglesham Community Library, Montgomerie Hall, Eaglesham, East Renfrewshire
     G76 0LH
     ☎(01355) 302649
     Fax (01355) 302649
     e-mail: eagleshaml@eastrenfrewshire.gov.uk

E   Giffnock Community Library, Station Road, Giffnock, East Renfrewshire G46 6JF
     ☎0141 577 4976
     Fax 0141 577 4978
     e-mail: giffnockl@eastrenfrewshire.gov.uk

F   Mearns Community Library, McKinley Place, Newton Mearns, East Renfrewshire
     G77 6EZ
     ☎0141 577 4979
     Fax 0141 577 4980
     e-mail: meansl@eastrenfrewshire.gov.uk

G   Neilston Community Library, Main Street, Neilston, East Renfrewshire G78 3NN
     ☎0141 577 4981
     Fax 0141 577 4982
     e-mail: neilstonl@eastrenfrewshire.gov.uk

H   Thornliebank Community Library, 1 Spiersbridge Road, Thornliebank, East
     Renfrewshire G46 7SJ
     ☎0141 577 4983
     Fax 0141 577 4816
     e-mail: thornliebankl@eastrenfrewshire.gov.uk

EDINBURGH

Headquarters City of Edinburgh Council, Central Library, George IV Bridge, Edinburgh
EH1 1EG
☎0131 225 5584
Fax 0131 225 8783
Head of Libraries and Information Services Mrs M Sharp ALA
Central Library and Information Services Manager W Wallace MA ALA
Strategic Library Services Manager Ms M Corr BA DipLib ALA
Bibliographic and Support Services Manager M Hinds BA DipLib ALA
Community Library Services Manager Ms G McCaig DipLib ALA

Central/largest library
As above

Divisional libraries
A   West Division. Blackhall Library, 56 Hillhouse Road, Edinburgh EH4 5EG

☎0131 529 5595
Fax 0131 529 5593
Principal Library Officer E Kilmurry BA ALA
B   North Division. Leith Library, 28 Ferry Road, Edinburgh EH6 4AE
        ☎0131 529 5517
        Fax 0131 554 2720
        Principal Library Officer J Thompson BA DipLib ALA
C   South Division. Wester Hailes Library, 1 Westside Plaza, Wester Hailes, Edinburgh
        ☎0131 453 2181
        Fax 0131 453 2187
        Principal Library Officer Ms L Spells BSc DipLib ALA
D   East Division. Newington Library, 17 Fountainhall Road, Edinburgh EH9 2LN
        ☎0131 529 5536
        Fax 0131 529 5491
        Principal Library Officer M Spells

FALKIRK

Headquarters Falkirk Council, Library, Victoria Buildings, Queen Street, Falkirk FK2 7AF
☎(01324) 506800
Fax (01324) 506801
Libraries Manager Mrs S Allison MA ALA

Central/largest library
Falkirk Library, Hope Street, Falkirk FK1 5AU
☎(01324) 503605
Fax (01324) 503606
Librarian i/c Ms A Herron MA DipLib ALA

Other libraries
A   Grangemouth Library, Bo'ness Road, Grangemouth, Falkirk FK3 8AG
        ☎(01324) 504690
        Fax (01324) 504691
        Joint Librarians i/c Mrs M Robertson ALA, Mrs R Williams BSc(Hons) DipLib
B   Larbert Library, Main Street, Stenhousemuir, Larbert, Falkirk FK5 3JX
        ☎(01324) 503590
        Fax (013424) 503592
        Joint Librarians i/c Mrs S Young ALA, Miss K Wright BSc ALA
C   Denny Library, 49 Church Walk, Denny, Falkirk FK6 6DF
        ☎(01324) 504242
        Fax (01324) 504240
        Joint Librarians i/c Mrs L Alexander BA ALA, Mrs S Hill BA ALA
D   Bo'ness Library, Scotland's Close, Bo'ness, Falkirk EH51 0AH
        ☎(01506) 778520
        Fax (01506) 778521
        Joint Librarians i/c R Murray ALA, Miss C Simm BA ALA
E   Bonnybridge Library, Bridge Street, Bonnybridge, Falkirk FK4 1AD
        ☎(01324) 503295
        Fax (01324) 503295
        Librarian i/c Mrs K Jaffray BA ALA

FIFE

Headquarters Fife Council, Arts, Libraries and Museums, Town House, Kirkcaldy, Fife
KY1 1XW
☎(01592) 417388

Fax (01592) 417847
Service Manager, Arts, Libraries, Museums I Whitelaw

Area libraries
A   Central Area Library HQ, East Fergus Place, Kirkcaldy, Fife KY1 1XT
     ☎(01592) 412930
     Fax (01592) 412941
     Libraries Cultural Services Coordinator D Spalding ALA
     Libraries Systems and Support Coordinator D Burns
B   East Area Library HQ, Area Library, County Buildings, St Catherine Street, Cupar,
     Fife KY15 4TA
     ☎(01334) 412736
     Fax (01334) 412941
     Libraries Information Services Coordinator Ms A McLachlan MA ALA
C   West Area Library HQ, Central Library, Abbot Street, Dunfermline, Fife KY12 7NL
     ☎(01383) 312604
     Fax (01383) 312608
     Libraries Pollicy and Learning Services Coordinator Ms D Miller MBA MA ALA

Area/group libraries
A   Central Library, War Memorial Gardens, Kirkcaldy, Fife KY1 1YG
     ☎(01592) 412878
     Fax (01592) 412750
     Area Librarian (Central South) Ms J Pratt ALA
B   Glenwood Library, Glenwood Shopping Centre, Glenrothes, Fife KY6 1PA
     ☎(01592) 416840
     Fax (01592) 416843
     Senior Library Assistant Ms M Cook
C   Methil Library, Wellesley Road, Methil, Fife KY8 3QR
     ☎(01333) 592470
     Fax (01333) 592415
     Temporary Librarian i/c Ms J Stewart BA ALA
D   Leven Library, Durie Street, Leven, Fife KY8 4HE
     ☎(01333) 592650
     Fax (01333) 592655
     Temporary Area Librarian (Central North) Mrs J Taylor BA(Hons) ALA
E   Rosyth Library, Parkgate Community Centre, Rosyth, Fife KY11 2JW
     ☎(01383) 416177
     Fax (01383) 416777
     Senior Library Assistant Ms D Hutton
F   Dalgety Bay Library, Regents Way, Dalgety Bay, Fife KY11 5UY
     ☎(01383) 318981
     Fax (01383) 318988
     Senior Library Assistant Ms B Gilmour
G   St Andrews Library, Church Square, St Andrews, Fife KY16 9NN
     ☎(01334) 412687
     Fax (01334) 413029
     Community Librarian Ms L Cordiner ALA
H   Cupar Library, 33-35 Crossgate, Cupar, Fife KY15 5AS
     ☎(01334) 412285
     Fax (01334) 412467
     Community Librarian Miss A Beattie BA ALA

GLASGOW

Headquarters City of Glasgow Council, Cultural and Leisure Services, The Mitchell Library, North Street, Glasgow G3 7DN
☎0141 287 2999 (enquiries), 0141 287 2809 (administration)
Fax 0141 287 2871
Head of Libraries and Archives M Wade BA Mlib ALA (0141 287 5114; e-mail: martyn.wade@cls.glasgow.gov.uk)
Director of Cultural and Leisure Services Ms B McConnell MA(Hons) DIA Med (0141 287 5058)
Deputy Director of Cultural Services Ms C Hamilton (0141 287 5464)
Archivist A M Jackson MA DAA (0141 287 2907, fax: 0141 226 8452; e-mail: archives@gcl.glasgow.gov.uk)

Lending libraries

A   Lending Services Department, The Mitchell Library, North Street, Glasgow G3 7DN
☎0141 287 2870 (enquiries)
Fax 0141 287 2871

B   Anderston Library, Berkeley Street, Glasgow G3 7DN
☎0141 287 2872

C   Baillieston Library, 141 Main Street, Glasgow G69 6AA
☎0141 771 2433 (tel./fax)

D   Barmulloch Library, 99 Rockfield Road, Glasgow G21 3DY
☎0141 558 6185

E   Bridgeton Library, 23 Landressy Street, Glasgow G40 1BP
☎0141 554 0217

F   Cardonald Library, 1113 Mosspark Drive, Glasgow G52 3BU
☎0141 882 1381
Fax 0141 810 5490

G   Castlemilk Library, 100 Castlemilk Drive, Glasgow G45 9TN
☎0141 634 2066 (tel./fax)

H   Couper Institute Library, 84 Clarkston Road, Glasgow G44 3DA
☎0141 637 1544

I   Dennistoun Library, 2a Craigpark, Glasgow G31 2NA
☎0141 554 0055
Fax 0141 551 9971

J   Drumchapel Library, 65 Hecla Avenue, Glasgow G15 8LX
☎0141 944 5698

K   Easterhouse Library, 5 Shandwick Street, Glasgow G34 9DP
☎0141 771 5986
Fax 0141 771 5643

L   Elder Park Library, 228a Langlands Road, Glasgow G51 3TZ
☎0141 445 1047

M   Govanhill Library, 170 Langside Road, Glasgow G42 7JU
☎0141 423 0335

N   Hillhead Library, 348 Byres Road, Glasgow G12 8AP
☎0141 339 7223
Fax 0141 337 2783

O   Ibrox Library, 1 Midlock Street, Glasgow G51 1SL
☎0141 427 5831
Fax 0141 427 1139

P   Knightswood Library, 27 Dunterlie Avenue, Glasgow G13 3BB
☎0141 959 2041 (tel./fax)

Q   Langside Library, 2 Sinclair Drive, Glasgow G42 9QE

☎0141 632 0810
Fax 0141 632 8982
R   Maryhill Library, 1508 Maryhill Road, Glasgow G20 9AD
    ☎0141 946 2348 (tel./fax)
S   Milton Library, 163 Ronaldsay Street, Glasgow G22 7AP
    ☎0141 772 1410
T   Parkhead Library, 64 Tollcross Road, Glasgow G31 4XA
    ☎0141 554 0198
U   Partick Library, 305 Dumbarton Road, Glasgow G11 6AB
    ☎0141 339 1303
V   Pollok Library, 100-106 Peat Road, Glasgow G53 6DH
    ☎0141 881 3540
W   Pollokshaws Library, 50-60 Shawbridge Street, Glasgow G43 1RW
    ☎0141 632 3544
X   Pollokshields Library, 30 Leslie Street, Glasgow G41 2LF
    ☎0141 423 1460
Y   Possilpark Library, 127 Allander Street, Glasgow G22 5JJ
    ☎0141 336 8110
Z   Riddrie Library, 1020 Cumbernauld Road, Glasgow G33 2QS
    ☎0141 770 4043
Aa   Royston Library, 67 Royston Road, Glasgow G21 2QW
    ☎0141 552 1657
Bb   Shettleston Library, 154 Wellshot Road, Glasgow G32 7AX
    ☎0141 778 1221
    Fax 0141 778 9004
Cc   Springburn Library, 179 Ayr Street, Glasgow G21 4BW
    ☎0141 558 5559
Dd   Stirling's Library, 62 Miller Street, Glasgow G1 1DT
    ☎0141 221 1876
    Fax 0141 226 2498
Ee   Temple Library, 350 Netherton Road, Glasgow G13 1AX
    ☎0141 954 5265
Ff   Whiteinch Library, 14 Victoria Park Drive South, Glasgow G14 9RL
    ☎0141 959 1376
Gg   Woodside Library, 343 St George's Road, Glasgow G3 6JQ
    ☎0141 332 1808

HIGHLAND

Headquarters The Highland Council, Library Support Unit, 31A Harbour Road, Inverness IV1 1UA
☎(01463) 235713
Fax (01463) 236986
Head of Libraries and Culture S C Brownlee BA DipLib ALA
Library and Information Services Coordinator C Phillips BA DipLib ALA

Area libraries
Inverness
A   Culloden Library, Keppoch Road, Culloden, Inverness IV1 2LL
    ☎(01463) 792531
    Fax (01463) 739162
    Librarian Ms A Donald ALA
B   Inverness Library, Farraline Park, Inverness IV1 1NH
    ☎(01463) 236463

Fax (01463) 237001
Libraries Officer Ms C Goodfellow MA ALA

Lochaber
C   Fort William Library, Airds Crossing, Fort William, Inverness-shire PH33 6BA
☎(01397) 703552
Fax (01397) 703538
Libraries Officer S J Moore BA(Hons) MA MLib MPhil ALA

Ross and Cromarty
D   Dingwall Library, Old Academy Buildings, Tulloch Street, Dingwall, Ross-shire
IV15 9JZ
☎(01349) 863163
Fax (01349) 865239
Librarian Ms F Robertson BA ALA
Libraries Officer Ms A Nicol MA DipEd DipLib ALA

Caithness
E   Thurso Library, Davidson's Lane, Thurso, Caithness KW14 7AF
☎(01847) 893237
Fax (01847) 896114
Libraries Officer Ms J Brown BA ALA
F   Carnegie Public Library, Sinclair Terrace, Wick, Caithness KW1 5AB
☎(01955) 602864
Fax (01955) 603000
Librarian Ms J Shanks BA

Skye and Lochalsh
G   Portree Library, Bayfield Road, Portree, Isle of Skye, Inverness-shire IV51 9EL
☎(01478) 612697
Fax (01478) 613314
Libraries Officer D Linton ALA

Badenoch and Strathspey
H   Nairn Library, 68 High Street, Nairn, Nairn-shire IV12 4AU
☎(01667) 458506
Fax (01667) 458548
Libraries Officer Ms E Somerville BEd DipLib ALA

Sutherland
I   Dornoch Library, Carnegie Building, High Street, Dornoch, Sutherland IV25 3SH
☎(01862) 811585
Fax (01862) 811079
Libraries Officer Ms A Forrest BA ALA

INVERCLYDE
Headquarters Inverclyde Council, Central Library, Clyde Square, Greenock, Renfrewshire
PA15 1NA
☎(01475) 712323
Fax (01475) 712334
Principal Officer, Department of Libraries Mrs C McGilvray BA ALA

MIDLOTHIAN

Headquarters Midlothian Council, Library HQ, 2 Clerk Street, Loanhead, Midlothian EH20 9DR
☎0131 271 3980
Fax 0131 440 4635
e-mail: library.hq@midlothian.gov.uk
url: http://www.earl.org.uk/partners/midlothian/index.html
Library Services Manager A Reid MA ALA

Central/largest library
Dalkeith Library, White Hart Street, Dalkeith, Midlothian EH22 1AE
☎0131 663 2083
Senior Librarian Ms J Fergus ALA

Branch libraries
A   Bonnyrigg Library, Polton Street, Bonnyrigg, Midlothian EH19 3DJ
     ☎0131 663 6762
     Senior Librarian D Stevenson BA ALA
B   Danderhall Library, 1A Campview, Danderhall, Midlothian EH22 1QD
     ☎0131 663 9293
     Assistant i/c Ms J Brown
C   Gorebridge Library, Hunterfield Road, Gorebridge, Midlothian EH23 4TT
     ☎(01875) 820630
     Assistant i/c Ms J Hamilton
D   Loanhead Library, George Avenue, Loanhead, Midlothian EH20 9HD
     ☎0131 440 0824
     Assistant i/c Ms G Renwick
E   Mayfield Library, Stone Avenue, Mayfield, Dalkeith, Midlothian EH22 5PB
     ☎0131 663 2126
     Assistant i/c Ms I Swanston
F   Newtongrange Library, St Davids, Newtongrange, Midlothian EH22 4LQ
     ☎0131 663 1816
     Assistant i/c Ms J Elliot
G   Penicuik Library, Bellmans Road, Penicuik, Midlothian EH26 0AB
     ☎(01968) 672340
     Assistant Librarian Ms F Bell BA ALA
H   Roslin Library, 9 Main Street, Roslin, Midlothian EH25 9LD
     ☎0131 448 2781
     Assistant i/c Ms B Duncan

MORAY

Headquarters The Moray Council, Department of Technical and Leisure Services, Council Office, High Street, Elgin, Moray IV30 1BX
☎(01343) 562600 (enquiries), (01343) 563398 (administration)
Fax (01343) 563410
Libraries and Museums Manager G A Campbell MA BCom ALA (e-mail: campbea@techleis.moray.gov.uk)

Central/largest library
Elgin Library, Cooper Park, Elgin, Moray IV30 1HS
☎(01343) 562600
Fax (01343) 562630
e-mail: lib.support@techleis.moray.gov.uk

Principal Librarian (Central Services) Ms S Campbell ALA (e-mail: sheila.campbell@techleis.moray.gov.uk)

Area libraries

A   Buckie Library, Cluny Place, Buckie, Banffshire AB56 1HB
       ☎(01542) 832121
       Fax (01542) 835237
       e-mail: buckie.library@techleis.moray.gov.uk
       Senior Librarian (Buckie) I Leith ALA

B   Forres Library, Forres House, High Street, Forres, Moray IV36 0BU
       ☎(01309) 672834
       Fax (01309) 675084
       e-mail: forres.library@techleis.moray.gov.uk
       Senior Librarian (Forres) R Plunkett BSc ALA

C   Keith Library, Union Street, Keith, Banffshire AB55 5DP
       ☎(01542) 882223
       Fax (01542) 882177
       e-mail: keith.library@techleis.moray.gov.uk
       Senior Librarian (Keith) P Marland BA ALA

NORTH AYRSHIRE

Headquarters North Ayrshire Council, Library, 39-41 Princes Street, Ardrossan, Ayrshire KA22 8BT
☎(01294) 469137
Fax (01294) 604236
e-mail: reference@naclibhq-prestel.co.uk
Libraries and Information Services Manager Miss J Martin MA DipLib ALA
Reference and Cataloguing Librarian Miss S E E Kerr ALA
Acquisitions Librarian J Macaulay ALA DipLib

Central/largest library

Irvine Library, Cunninghame House, Irvine, Ayrshire KA12 8EE
☎(01294) 324251
Fax (01294) 324252
Area Librarian Miss M A Scott ALA

Area libraries

A   Saltcoats Library, Springvale Place, Saltcoats, Ayrshire KA21 5LS
       ☎(01294) 469546
       Area Librarian P Cowan BEd(Hons) DipLib ALA

B   Kilwinning Library, St Winnings Lane, Kilwinning, Ayrshire KA13 6EP
       ☎(01294) 554699
       Fax (01294) 557682
       Area Librarian Mrs M Vint ALA

C   Largs Library, Allanpark Street, Largs, Ayrshire KA30 9AS
       ☎(01475) 673309
       Area Librarian Mrs I Gilmour BA

D   Beith Library, Main Street, Beith, Ayrshire KA15 2AD
       ☎(01505) 503613
       Fax (01505) 503417
       Area Librarian Mrs E Bell MA DipLib ALA

NORTH LANARKSHIRE

Headquarters North Lanarkshire Council, Dept of Community Services, Buchanan Tower, Buchanan Business Park, Cumbernauld Road, Stepps, Glasgow, North Lanarkshire G33 6HR
☎0141 304 1800
Fax 0141 304 1859
Libraries and Information Manager J Fox DMS ALA

Central/largest library
Motherwell Library, 35 Hamilton Road, Motherwell, North Lanarkshire ML1 3BZ
☎(01698) 251311
Fax (01698) 254543
e-mail: informationsection@compuserve.com
Information Support Manager Ms M Hamilton MA DipLib ALA
Lending Services Manager South Mrs C Wales BA ALA

Area libraries
A Cumbernauld Library, 8 Allander Walk, Cumbernauld, North Lanarkshire G67 6EE
 ☎(01236) 725664
 Fax (01236) 458350
 Lending Services Manager North Mrs W Bennett BA ALA
B Coatbridge Library, 25 Academy Street, Coatbridge, North Lanarkshire ML5 3AW
 ☎(01236) 424150
 Fax (01236) 437997
 Lending Services Manager Central D McGuinness ALA

ORKNEY

Headquarters Orkney Islands Council, Council Offices, School Place, Kirkwall, Orkney KW15 1NW
☎(01856) 873166 (enquiries & administration)
Fax (01856) 875260
Chief Librarian R K Leslie ALA

Central/largest library
The Orkney Library, Laing Street, Kirkwall, Orkney KW15 1NW
☎(01856) 873166 (enquiries & administration)
Fax (01856) 875260
Chief Librarian R K Leslie ALA
Depute Librarian Ms K I Walker BA

PERTH AND KINROSS

Headquarters Perth and Kinross Council, The A K Bell Library, York Place, Perth, Perthshire PH2 8EP
☎(01738) 444949
Fax (01738) 477010
e-mail: library@pkc.gov.uk
Head of Libraries and Archives M C G Moir BA ALA (e-mail: mmoir@pkc.gov.uk)
Principal Librarian I MacRae BA ALA

Area libraries
A Auchterarder Branch Library, Aytoun Hall, Chapel Wynd, Auchterarder, Perthshire PH3 1BL
 ☎(01764) 663850

Fax (01764) 663917
Branch Librarian Mrs K Mayall BA
B   Blairgowrie Branch Library, 46 Leslie Street, Blairgowrie, Perthshire PH10 6AW
☎(01250) 872905
Fax (01250) 872905
Branch Librarian S McGowan MA
C   Crieff Branch Library, 6 Comrie Street, Crieff, Perthshire PH7 4AX
☎(01764) 653418
Fax (01764) 653418
Branch Librarian Ms M Gordon BA
D   Kinross Branch Library, 112-114 High Street, Kinross, Kinross-shire KY13 7DA
☎(01577) 864202
Branch Library Assistant Ms M Garden
E   Scone Branch Library, Sandy Road, Scone, Perth, Perthshire PH2 6LJ
☎(01738) 553029
Fax (01738) 553029
Branch Librarian Miss E Hart BA

RENFREWSHIRE

Headquarters Renfrewshire Council, Library, 8A Seedhill Road, Paisley, Renfrewshire PA1 1AJ
☎0141 840 3003
Fax 0141 848 3004
Principal Librarian Ms V Kerr BA ALA MSc MIM (0141 840 3001)

Central/largest library
Paisley Central Library, High Street, Paisley, Renfrewshire PA1 2BB
☎0141 887 2360 (enquiries), 0141 887 3672 (administration)
Fax 0141 887 6468
e-mail: renlib4@cqm.co.uk
Senior Librarian Ms E Murray MA ALA

Community libraries
A   Renfrew Community Library, Paisley Road, Renfrew, Renfrewshire PA2 8LJ
☎0141 886 3433
Fax 0141 886 1660
Renfrew Community Librarian Ms L Henderson ALA
B   Johnstone Community Library, Houston Court, Johnstone, Renfrewshire PA5 8DL
☎(01505) 329726
Fax (01505) 336657
Johnstone Community Librarian Ms A Horsburgh BLib ALA

SCOTTISH BORDERS

Headquarters Borders Council, Library HQ, St Mary's Mill, Selkirk, Selkirkshire TD7 5EW
☎(01750) 20842
Fax (01750) 22875
e-mail: library1@netcomuk.co.uk
Head of Cultural and Interpretative Services A Hasson MA MBA DipLib ALA MIMgt
Chief Librarian J A Beedle BA ALA
Principal Librarian, Adult Services Ms R A Brown BLib ALA

Area libraries
A   Hawick Library, North Bridge Street, Hawick, Roxburghshire TD9 9QT
☎(01450) 372637

Fax (01450) 370991
Area Librarian Ms P G McNay MA ALA
B   Galashiels Library, Lawyer's Brae, Galashiels, Selkirkshire TD1 3JQ
☎(01896) 752512
Fax (01896) 753575
Area Librarian Ms C R Letton MA FSA(Scot) ALA
C   Peebles Library, Chambers Institution, High Street, Peebles, Peeblesshire
EH45 8AG
☎(01721) 720123
Fax (01721) 724424
e-mail: library2@netcomuk.co.uk
Area Librarian P Taylor BSc FSA ALA
D   Kelso Library, Bowmont Street, Kelso, Roxburghshire TD5 7JN
☎(01573) 223171
Fax (01573) 226618
Branch Librarian Ms M Blake
E   Selkirk Library, Ettrick Terrace, Selkirk, Selkirkshire TD7 4LE
☎(01750) 20267
Fax (01750) 20267
Branch Librarian Ms J Gammie
F   Duns Library, Newtown Street, Duns, Berwickshire TD11 3AU
☎(01361) 882622
Fax (01361) 884104
Branch Librarian Ms N Lawson

SHETLAND ISLANDS

Headquarters Shetland Islands Council, Shetland Library, Lower Hillhead, Lerwick,
Shetland ZE1 0EL
☎(01595) 693868 (enquiries and administration)
Fax (01595) 604430
e-mail: info@shetland-library.gov.uk
Chief Librarian J G Hunter ALA (01950 422364; e-mail: john@shetland-library.gov.uk)
Assistant Chief Librarian Ms E A Brown BA ALA (e-mail:
elspeth@shetland-library.gov.uk)
Assistant Chief Librarian D L W Garden MA ALA (e-mail:
douglas@shetland-library.gov.uk)
Secretary/Administration Assistant Mrs A J Anderson (e-mail:
agnes@shetland-library.gov.uk)
Secretarial/Library Assistant Miss L Ratter (e-mail: louise@shetland-library.gov.uk)

SOUTH AYRSHIRE

Headquarters South Ayrshire Council, Library HQ, 26 Green Street, Ayr KA8 0SS
☎(01292) 288820
Fax (01292) 619019
Libraries and Galleries Manager C Deas BA ALA (e-mail:
charles.deas@south-ayrshire.gov.uk)

Central/largest library
Carnegie Library, 12 Main Street, Ayr KA8 8ED
☎(01292) 286385
Fax (01292) 611593
e-mail: carnegie@rmplc.co.uk

SOUTH LANARKSHIRE

Headquarters South Lanarkshire Council, Library and Information Service, Education Resources, Council Offices, Almada Street, Hamilton, South Lanarkshire ML3 0AA
☎(01698) 454444
Fax (01698) 454465
Library and Information Service Manager Ms D Barr BA ALA MIMgt (01698 454412)
Library Support Services Manager J McGarrity BA ALA (01355 248581)
Reference Services Manager Ms I Walker ALA (01698 452402)

Central/largest library
East Kilbride Central Library, 40 The Olympia, East Kilbride, South Lanarkshire G74 1PG
☎(01355) 220046
Fax (01355) 229365
Assistant Lending Services Manager D Leitch ALA

Divisional libraries
A   Hamilton Central Library, 98 Cadzow Street, Hamilton, South Lanarkshire ML3 6HQ
      ☎(01698) 452406
      Fax (01698) 286374
      Assistant Lending Services Manager Ms F Roberts BA ALA
B   Rutherglen Library, 163 Main Street, Rutherglen, Glasgow G73 2HB
      ☎0141 647 6453
      Fax 0141 647 5164
      Assistant Lending Services Manager D Moncrieff ALA
C   Lanark Central Library, Hope Street, Lanark, Lanarkshire ML11 7NH
      ☎(01555) 661144
      Fax (01555) 665884
      Assistant Lending Services Manager Ms F Renfrew BA ALA

STIRLING

Headquarters Stirling Council, Library HQ, Borrowmeadow Road, Springkerse, Stirling FK7 7TN
☎(01786) 432383 (enquiries), (01786) 432381 (administration)
Fax (01786) 432395
Head of Service, Libraries, Heritage and Culture A Gillies ALA (Based at Libraries, Heritage and Culture Service, Stirling Council, Viewforth, Stirling FK8 2ET) (01786 443398)
Development and Direct Services Librarian Ms M Blyth BA ALA (01786 432388)
Operations Librarian A Muirhead MA MLitt ALA (01786 432386)

Central/largest library
Central Library, Corn Exchange Road, Stirling FK8 2HX
☎(01786) 432106/7 (enquiries), (01786) 432108 (administration)
Fax (01786) 473094
Area Librarian Ms M McIntyre MA ALA

WEST DUNBARTONSHIRE

Headquarters West Dunbartonshire Council, West Dunbartonshire Libraries, Levenford House, Helenslee Road, Dumbarton G82 4AH
☎(01389) 738328 (enquiries), (01389) 738327 (administration)
Fax (01389) 734204
Principal Officer (Libraries) Mrs S Carragher BA(Hons) ALA

Area libraries
A   Clydebank Library, Dumbarton Road, Clydebank, Dumbarton G81 1XH

☎0141 952 1416 (enquiries), 0141 952 8765 (administration)
Fax 0141 951 8275
Senior Officer (Libraries) Miss F MacDonald MA ALA
B   Dumbarton Library, Strathleven Place, Dumbarton G82 1BD
☎(01389) 763129 (enquiries), (01389) 738324 (administration)
Fax (01389) 733018
Senior Officer (Libraries) I Baillie ALA

WEST LOTHIAN

Headquarters West Lothian Council, Library HQ, Connolly House, Hopefield Road,
Blackburn, West Lothian EH47 7HZ
☎(01506) 776336 (enquiries), (01506) 776342 (administration)
Fax (01506) 776345
e-mail: info@libhq.demon.co.uk
Library Services Manager W S Walker BA ALA (01506 776780)
Customer Services Manager G Kerr BA ALA (01506 776325)
Area Manager Mrs I Brough (01506 776327)
Area Manager Ms M Menzies BA MLib ALA (01506 776326)

Central/largest library
Carmondean Library, Carmondean Centre, Livingston, West Lothian EH54 8PT
☎(01506) 777602 (enquiries)
Branch Manager Mrs B Main BA DipLib

Branch libraries
A   Linlithgow Branch Library, The Vennel, Linlithgow, West Lothian EH49 7EX
☎(01506) 775490
Branch Manager Ms K Ali BA
B   East Calder Branch Library, Main Street, East Calder, West Lothian EH53 0EJ
☎(01506) 883633
Branch Manager Ms G Downie BA ALA
C   Armadale Branch Library, West Main Street, Armadale, West Lothian EH48 3JB
☎(01501) 778400
Branch Manager Ms E Hunter ALA
D   Almondbank Branch Library, The Mall, Craigshill, Livingston, West Lothian EH54 5EJ
☎(01506) 777500
Branch Manager R Fisher BA ALA
E   Fauldhouse Branch Library, Lanrigg Road, Fauldhouse, West Lothian EH47 9JA
☎(01501) 770358
Branch Manager Ms M James
F   Bathgate Branch Library, 66 Hopetoun Street, Bathgate, West Lothian EH48 1TD
☎(01506) 776400
Branch Manager Mrs A Mackintosh BA ALA
G   Lanthorn Branch Library, Lanthorn Centre, Kenilworth Rise, Dedridge, Livingston,
West Lothian EH54 6NY
☎(01506) 777700
Branch Manager Ms G Downie BA ALA
H   Broxburn Branch Library, West Main Street, Broxburn, West Lothian EH52 5RH
☎(01506) 775600
Branch Manager Ms L Reid BA ALA
I   Whitburn Branch Library, Union Road, Whitburn, West Lothian EH47 0AR
☎(01506) 778050
Branch Manager Ms H Gibson

J West Calder Branch Library, Main Street, West Calder, West Lothian EH55 8BJ
  ☎(01506) 871371
  Branch Manager Ms L Reid BA ALA

K Blackburn Branch Library, Ash Grove, Blackburn, West Lothian EH47 7LJ
  ☎(01506) 776500
  Branch Manager Ms H Reid

L Blackridge Branch Library, Craig Inn Centre, Blackridge, West Lothian EH48 3RJ
  ☎(01501) 752396
  Branch Manager Ms M McCabe

M Pumpherston Branch Library, Pumpherston Primary School, 18 Uphall Station
  Road, Pumpherston, West Lothian EH53 0LP
  ☎(01506) 435837
  Branch Manager Ms M Lamond

WALES

ANGLESEY, ISLE OF

Headquarters Isle of Anglesey County Council, Department of Leisure and Heritage, County Offices, Llangefni, Ynys Môn LL77 7TW
☎(01248) 752092 (enquiries); (01248) 752024 (administration)
Fax (01248) 750365
Director of Leisure and Heritage Mrs E A Mitcheson BA DipLib ALA (01248 752024; e-mail: eamlh@ynysmon.gov.uk)
Assistant Director (Libraries, Information and Archives) J R Thomas BSc(Econ) DipLib ALA (01248 752093; e-mail: jrtlh@ynysmon.gov.uk)
Community Librarian R B Jones BA DipLib ALA (01407 762917)
Archivist Ms A Venables BA DipAA (01248 752080)

Central/largest library
Llangefni Central Library, Lôn-y-Felin, Llangefni, Ynys Môn LL77 7RT
☎(01248) 752092
Fax (01248) 750197
e-mail: dhelh@ynysmon.gov.uk

Branch libraries
A   Holyhead Library, Newry Fields, Holyhead, Ynys Môn LL65 1LA
     ☎(01407) 762917
     Fax (01407) 769616
     e-mail: mon@cybi.demon.co.uk
B   Amlwch Library, Lôn Parys, Amlwch, Ynys Môn LL68 9EA
     ☎(01407) 830145
     Fax (01407) 830145
C   Menai Bridge Library, Ffordd y Ffair, Menai Bridge, Ynys Môn LL59 5AS
     ☎(01248) 712706
     Fax (01248) 712706
D   Record Office, Shirehall, Glanhwfa Street, Llangefni, Ynys Môn LL77 7TW
     ☎(01248) 752083

BLAENAU GWENT

Headquarters Blaenau Gwent County Borough Council, Community Services, Central Depot, Barleyfield Industrial Estate, Brynmawr, Blaenau Gwent NP3 4YF
☎(01495) 355301 (enquiries), (01495) 355319 (administration)
Fax (01495) 355468
e-mail: bg.libs@dial.pipex.com
County Borough Librarian Mrs M Jones MLib ALA (01495 355311; e-mail: mjones.bg.libs@dial.pipex.com)
Information Officer S Hardman (01495 355318; e-mail: steve.bg.libs@dial.pipex.com)

Central/largest library
Ebbw Vale Library, 21 Bethcar Street, Ebbw Vale, Blaenau Gwent NP3 6HS
☎(01495) 303069
Fax (01495) 350547
e-mail: ebbw.vale.lib@dial.pipex.com
Senior Librarian Mrs S White ALA (01495 301122; e-mail: s.white.bg.libs@dial.pipex.com)

Area libraries

A   Abertillery Library, Station Hill, Abertillery, Blaenau Gwent NP13 1UJ
☎(01495) 212332/217640
Fax (01495) 320995
e-mail: abertillery.lib@dial.pipex.com
Senior Librarian Ms A Maund ALA (e-mail: a.maund.bg.libs@dial.pipex.com)

B   Blaina Library, Reading Institute, High Street, Blaina, Blaenau Gwent NP3 3BN
☎(01495) 290312
Fax (01495) 290312
Librarian J Leacy BA ALA

C   Tredegar Library, The Circle, Tredegar, Blaenau Gwent NP22 3PS
☎(01495) 722687
Fax (01495) 717018
Librarian Miss J C Karn BA ALA

D   Brynmawr Library, The Square, Brynmawr, Blaenau Gwent NP3 4AJ
☎(01495) 310045
Fax (01495) 310045
Librarian Miss J Davies BA

E   Reaching Out Mobile, c/o Tredegar Library, The Circle, Tredegar, Blaenau Gwent
NP22 3PS
☎(01495) 722687
Fax (01495) 717018
Special Services Librarian Miss I J Corey BSc ALA

F   Acquisitions Dept, c/o Abertillery Library, Station Hill, Abertillery, Blaenau Gwent
NP13 1UJ
☎(01495) 217640
Fax (01495) 320995
e-mail: px49@dial.pipex.com
Acquisitions Librarian Ms A Maund ALA

BRIDGEND

Headquarters Bridgend County Borough Council, Library and Information Service, Coed
Parc, Park Street, Bridgend CF31 4BA
☎(01656) 767451
Fax (01656) 645719
e-mail: blis@bridgendlib.gov.uk
County Borough Librarian John C Woods BSc ALA

Central/largest libraries

A   Reference and Information Centre, Coed Parc, Park Street, Bridgend CF31 4BA
☎Tel/Fax etc. as HQ
Reference Librarian C Williams ALA

B   Bridgend Lending Library, Wyndham Street, Bridgend CF31 1EF
☎(01656) 653444
Fax (01656) 667886
Branch Librarian R P Bellinger BLib ALA

C   Maesteg Library, North's Lane, Maesteg CF34 9AA
☎(01656) 733201
Fax (01656) 731098
Branch Librarian J Robinson MA ALA

D   Pencoed Library, Penybont Road, Pencoed CF35 5RA
☎(01656) 860358
Fax (01656) 863042

Branch Librarian Ms A Uren BA ALA

E Porthcawl Library, Church Place, Porthcawl CF36 3AG
☎(01656) 782059
Fax (01656) 722745
Branch Librarian Ms J Willment ALA

CAERPHILLY

Headquarters Caerphilly County Borough Council, Community Education, Leisure and Libraries, Unit 7, Woodfieldside Business Park, Penmaen Road, Pontllanfraith, Blackwood, Caerphilly NP2 2DG
☎(01443) 864963 (enquiries), (01443) 235587 (administration)
Fax (01495) 235567
e-mail: caer.libs@dial.pipex.com
Principal Officer: Libraries Ms M Palmer MLib ALA

Central/largest library
Caerphilly Library, Morgan Jones Park, Caerphilly CF8 1AP
☎(01222) 852543 (enquiries)
Fax (01222) 865585
Group Librarian: South Ms Y Harris ALA

Group libraries
A Blackwood Library, 192 High Street, Blackwood, Caerphilly NP2 1AJ
☎(01495) 223345
Fax (01495) 221369
Group Librarian: North Mrs J Lee ALA
B Risca Library, Park Place, Risca, Caerphilly NP1 6AS
☎(01633) 612462/612945
Fax (01633) 615726
Group Librarian: Central Ms M Davies ALA

CARDIFF

Headquarters Cardiff County Council, Central Library, St David's Link, Frederick Street, Cardiff CF10 4DT
☎029 2038 2116
Fax 029 2087 1599
Chief Librarian P Sawyer ALA (e-mail: p.sawyer@cardiff.gov.uk)
Assistant Chief Librarian R J Phillips ALA (e-mail: r.phillips@cardiff.gov.uk)
Central Library Manager R Boddy BA ALA (e-mail: r.boddy@cardlib.demon.co.uk)

Branch library
Llandaff North Library, Gabalfa Avenue, Cardiff CF14 2HU
Branch Libraries Manager Ms E Morris BA ALA

CARMARTHENSHIRE

Headquarters Carmarthenshire County Council, Carmarthenshire Cultural Centre, Richmond Terrace, Carmarthen, Carmarthenshire SA31 1DS
☎(01267) 224661 (enquiries and administration)
Fax (01267) 238584
Head of Cultural Services D F Griffiths FLA

Area libraries
A Carmarthen Area Library, St Peter's Street, Carmarthen, Carmarthenshire SA31 1LN

☎(01267) 224830
Fax (01267) 221839
Area Librarian D P Thomas BA DipLib ALA
B   Llanelli Area Library, Vaughan Street, Llanelli, Carmarthenshire SA15 3AS
☎(01554) 773538
Fax (01554) 750125
Area Librarian R H Davies BSc DipLib ALA
C   Ammanford Area Library, Talbot Road, Ammanford, Carmarthenshire SA16 3BB
☎(01269) 592207
Fax (01269) 592207
Area Librarian W T Phillips BA DipLib ALA

CEREDIGION

Headquarters Ceredigion County Council, Public Library, Corporation Street, Aberystwyth, Ceredigion SY23 2BU
☎(01970) 617464
Fax (01970) 625059
Assistant Director (Cultural Services) D Geraint Lewis MA ALA
County Libraries Officer W H Howells BA MLib ALA (e-mail: williamh@ceredigion.gov.uk)

Branch library
Branch Library, Canolfan Teifi, Pendre, Cardigan, Ceredigion SA43 1JL
☎(01239) 612578
Fax (01239) 612285
e-mail: teifillb@ceredigion.gov.uk
Branch Librarian D G Evans ALA

CONWY

Headquarters Conwy County Borough Council, Library, Information and Archives Service, Bodlondeb, Conwy LL32 8DU
☎(01492) 576140
Fax (01492) 592061
County Librarian and Archivist Ms R Aldrich MLib ALA (e-mail: rona.aldrich@conwy.gov.uk)
Principal Librarian, Service Delivery Ms Rh G Williams BA DipLib ALA (01492 576139; e-mail: rhian.williams@conwy.gov.uk)
Corporate Information Librarian D Smith BA DipMgt ALA MIMgt (01492 576137; e-mail: david.smith@conwy.gov.uk)
Senior Archivist Mrs S Ellis BA DAA

Regional/community libraries
A   Colwyn Bay Library, Woodland Road West, Colwyn Bay, Conwy LL29 7DH
☎(01492) 532358
Fax (01492) 534474
e-mail: llyfr/lib.baecolwynbay@conwy.gov.uk
Senior Community Librarian Ms R France ALA
B   Abergele Library, Market Street, Abergele, Conwy LL22 7BP
☎(01745) 832638
Fax (01745) 823376
e-mail: llyfr/lib.abergele@conwy.gov.uk
Community Librarian Mrs C Williams BA ALA
C   Conwy Library, Civic Hall, Castle Street, Conwy LL32 6AY
☎(01492) 596242

Fax (01492) 582359
e-mail: llyfr/lib.conwy@conwy.gov.uk
Community Librarian Mrs T Caffell ALA, Mrs C Hesketh BA (job-share)
D   Llandudno Library, Mostyn Street, Llandudno, Conwy LL30 2RP
☎(01492) 574010/574020
Fax (01492) 876826
e-mail: llyfr/lib.llandudno@conwy.gov.uk
Community Librarian Ms L Jones BA ALA
E   Llanrwst Library, Plas yn Dre, Station Road, Llanrwst, Conwy LL26 0DF
☎(01492) 640043
Fax (01492) 642316
e-mail: llyfr/lib.llanrwst@conwy.gov.uk
Community/County Children's Librarian Mrs T Jones BA(Hons) ALA

DENBIGHSHIRE

Headquarters Denbighshire County Council, Library and Information Service, Directorate of Education, Culture and Information, Yr Hen Garchar, Clwyd Street, Ruthin, Denbighshire LL15 1HP
☎(01824) 708203 (enquiries)
Fax (01824) 708202
e-mail: library.services@denbighshire.gov.uk
Principal Librarian R Arwyn Jones BMus ALA DipLib (01824 708203; e-mail: arwyn.jones@denbighshire.gov.uk)
Head of Cultural Services W Gwyn Williams OBE HonFLA MInstAM FRSA (01824 708200; e-mail: gwyn.williams@denbighshire.gov.uk)

Central/largest library
Rhyl Library, Museum and Arts Centre, Church Street, Rhyl, Denbighshire LL18 3AA
☎(01745) 353814
Fax (01745) 331438
e-mail: rhyllib@dircon.co.uk
Principal Community Librarian A Barber BSc DipLib ALA

FLINTSHIRE

Headquarters Flintshire County Council, Library and Information Services, Library Headquarters, County Hall, Mold, Flintshire CH7 6NW
☎(01352) 704400 (enquiries), (01352) 704406 (administration)
Fax (01352) 753662
e-mail: flintslib@dial.pipex.com
Head of Libraries and Archives L Rawsthorne MLib FLA MIMgt
Principal Librarian, Community Services Mrs S Kirby ALA (01352 704402)
Senior Reference Librarian Mrs G Fraser BA ALA (01352 704416)

Group libraries
A   Mold Library, Earl Road, Mold, Flintshire CH7 1AP
☎(01352) 754791
Fax (01352) 754655
Community Librarian Miss N W Jones BLib ALA
B   Flint Library, Church Street, Flint, Flintshire CH6 5AP
☎(01352) 733168
Fax (01352) 731010
Community Librarian Mrs E A Martin BLib ALA

C   Connah's Quay Library, Wepre Drive, Connah's Quay, Deeside, Flintshire CH5 4HA
☎(01244) 830485
Fax (01244) 856672
Community Librarian Mrs C A Guy BA ALA

D   Buckley Library, The Precinct, Buckley, Flintshire CH7 2EF
☎(01244) 549210
Fax (01244) 548850
Community Librarian Mrs C Shone BA DipLib ALA

E   Broughton Library, Broughton Hall Road, Broughton, Nr Chester, Flintshire
CH4 0QQ
☎(01244) 533727
Community Librarian Miss K Morris BA DipLib ALA

F   Holywell Library, North Street, Holywell, Flintshire CH8 7TQ
☎(01352) 713157
Fax (01352) 710744
Community Librarian Mrs P Corbett MLib ALA, Mrs M Wallbank ALA

GWYNEDD

Headquarters Gwynedd Council, Caernarfon Library, Pavilion Hill, Caernarfon, Gwynedd
LL55 1AS
☎(01286) 679465
Fax (01286) 671137
e-mail: llyfrgell@gwynedd.gov.uk
Principal Librarian H James BA DipLib ALA

Central/largest library
Caernarfon Library, Pavilion Hill, Caernarfon, Gwynedd LL55 1AS
☎(01286) 679463
Fax (01286) 671137
Community Librarian Mrs E Thomas ALA

Community libraries
A   Bangor Library, Ffordd Gwynedd, Bangor, Gwynedd LL57 1DT
☎(01248) 353479
Fax (01248) 370149
Community Librarian Miss S W Jones BA DipLib ALA

B   Porthmadog Library, Stryd Wesla, Porthmadog, Gwynedd LL49 9BT
☎(01766) 514091
Fax (01766) 513821
Community Librarian Mrs D Eckley BA DipLib ALA

C   Dolgellau Library, Ffordd y Bala, Dolgellau, Gwynedd LL40 2YF
☎(01341) 422771
Fax (01341) 423560
Community Librarian E Evans

MERTHYR TYDFIL

Headquarters Merthyr Tydfil County Borough Council, Central Library, High Street, Merthyr
Tydfil, South Wales CF47 8AF
☎(01685) 723057
Fax (01685) 370690
e-mail: library@merthyr.gov.bt.internet.com
Libraries and Arts Officer G James BA ALA

Central/largest library
As above

Area libraries
A   Dowlais Library, Church Street, Merthyr Tydfil, South Wales CF48 3HS
     ☎(01685) 723051
     Fax (01685) 723051
     Librarian North Mrs C Roberts
B   Treharris Library, Perrott Street, Treharris, Merthyr Tydfil, South Wales CF46 5ET
     ☎(01443) 410517
     Fax (01443) 410517
     Librarian South Mrs V Mitchell

MONMOUTHSHIRE
Headquarters Monmouthshire County Council, Libraries and Information Service, Leisure Community and Culture Department, County Hall, Cwmbran NP44 2XH
☎(01633) 644550 (enquiries), (01633) 644547 (administration)
Fax (01633) 644545
url: http://www.monmouthshire.gov.uk
Head of Libraries and Culture K A Smith BA ALA (e-mail: kevinsmith@monmouthshire.gov.uk)

Community libraries
A   Abergavenny Library, Baker Street, Abergavenny, Monmouthshire NP7 5BD
     ☎(01873) 735980
     Fax (01873) 735985
     Community Librarian Mrs A M Newsam BA DipLis ALA
B   Caldicot Library, Woodstock Way, Caldicot, Monmouthshire NP6 4DB
     ☎(01291) 426425
     Fax (01291) 426426
     Community Librarian Miss F J Ashley ALA
C   Chepstow Library, Manor Way, Chepstow, Monmouthshire NP6 5HZ
     ☎(01291) 635730
     Fax (01291) 635736
     Community Librarian Ms P H Clarkson BA MA DipLib ALA, Ms S E Bradford DipLib
D   Monmouth Library, Rolls Hall, Whitecross Street, Monmouth, Monmouthshire NP5 3BY
     ☎(01600) 775215
     Fax (01600) 775218
     Community Librarian Miss L A James BA ALA

NEATH PORT TALBOT
Headquarters Neath Port Talbot County Borough Council, Library and Information Services, Reginald Street, Velindre, Port Talbot SA13 1YY
☎(01639) 899829
Fax (01639) 899152
e-mail: lloyd@nptlib.clara.net
County Borough Librarian J L Ellis BA ALA

Central/largest library
Neath Library, Victoria Gardens, Neath SA11 3BA
☎(01639) 644604/635017

Fax (01639) 641912
Team Leader, Neath A W John ALA

Area library
Taibach Library, Commercial Road, Taibach, Port Talbot SA13 1LN
☎(01639) 883831
Team Leader, Port Talbot E G Williams ALA

NEWPORT
Headquarters Newport County Borough Council, Central Library, John Frost Square, Newport NP20 1PA
☎(01633) 265539 (enquiries & administration)
Fax (01633) 222615
e-mail: central.library@newport.gov.uk
url: http://www.earl.org.uk/earl/members/newport
Borough Librarian Ms H Osborn MLib ALA

Central/largest library
As above

PEMBROKESHIRE
Headquarters Pembrokeshire County Council, County Library, Dew Street, Haverfordwest, Pembrokeshire SA61 1SU
☎(01437) 762070 (enquiries), (01437) 775241 (administration)
Fax (01437) 769218
Cultural Services Manager Mrs M C John BA ALA (01437 775240)
Community Services Librarian Mrs S Matthews ALA (01437 775242)
Bibliographic Services Librarian C Richards ALA (01437 775243)
Reference and Local Studies Librarian Mrs A Thomas ALA (01437 775248)
Special Services Librarian Mrs E Evans ALA (01437 775246)

Community libraries
A   Pembroke Dock Library, Water Street, Pembroke Dock, Pembrokeshire SA72 6DW
      ☎(01646) 686356
      Community Librarian Ms L Holloway BA ALA
B   Milford Haven Library, Hamilton Terrace, Milford Haven, Pembrokeshire SA73 3HP
      ☎(01646) 692892
      Community Librarian Ms L Corey ALA
C   Fishguard Library, High Street, Fishguard, Pembrokeshire SA65 9AR
      ☎(01348) 872694
      Community Librarian Ms R Evans ALA
D   Tenby Library, Green Hill Avenue, Tenby, Pembrokeshire SA70 7LB
      ☎(01834) 843934
      Senior Library Assistant Mrs J Barber

POWYS
Headquarters Powys County Council, County Library HQ, Cefnllys Road, Llandrindod Wells, Powys LD1 5LD
☎(01597) 826860 (general enquiries)
Fax (01597) 826872
County Librarian Miss T L Adams BA ALA

Management/Administrative Centre, Community, Leisure and Recreation Department,

County Hall, Llandrindod Wells, Powys LD1 5LG
☎(01597) 826155
Fax (01597) 826243
Principal Librarian (Field Services) Mrs H Edwards BLib ALA
Principal Librarian (Support Services) Mrs M Mason BLib ALA
Principal Librarian (Education, Schools and Children) Mrs D Jones ALA

Main libraries
A   Newtown Library, Park Lane, Newtown, Powys SY16 1EJ
☎(01686) 626934
Fax (01686) 624935
Branch Librarian Mrs J Rimmer BLib ALA
B   Brecon Library, Ship Street, Brecon, Powys LD3 9AE
☎(01874) 623346
Fax (01874) 622818
Branch Librarian M Jones ALA

RHONDDA CYNON TAFF

Headquarters Rhondda Cynon Taff County Borough Council, Education Centre, Grawen Street, Porth, Rhondda Cynon Taff CF39 0BU
☎(01443) 687666
Fax (01443) 680286
County Borough Librarian (Cultural and Information Services) Mrs J A Jones BA ALA (01443 680255)
Principal Librarian (Reader Services) Mrs N Jones MSc ALA (01685 885319)
Area Librarian (North) Mrs R Williams MSc ALA (01685 885316)
Area Librarian (South) Mrs L Morris BA ALA (01443 486850)

Largest library
Aberdare Library, Green Street, Aberdare, Rhondda Cynon Taff CF44 7AG
☎(01685) 885318
Fax (01685) 881188
Branch Librarian Ms C Langdon BA ALA

Regional libraries
A   Pontypridd Library, Library Road, Pontypridd, Rhondda Cynon Taff CF37 2DY
☎(01443) 486850
Fax (01443) 493258
Branch Librarian Mrs C Morgan BA ALA
B   Treorchy Library, Station Road, Treorchy, Rhondda Cynon Taff CF42 6NN
☎(01443) 773204
Fax (01443) 777047
Branch Librarian Ms K Pugh BA ALA

SWANSEA

Headquarters Swansea City and County Council, County Library HQ, 12 Orchard Street, Swansea SA1 5AZ
☎(01792) 516720/516721
Fax (01792) 516737
e-mail: swanlib1@aol.com
County Librarian M Allen BA MSc ALA (01792 516735)
Assistant County Librarian, Systems and Development Mrs P Morris ALA (01792 516729)

Assistant County Librarian, Lending and Information Services Mrs K A Rowe BLib ALA
(01792 516725)

Central/largest library
Swansea Library, Alexandra Road, Swansea SA1 5DX
☎(01792) 516750/516751
Fax (01792) 516759
e-mail: swanlib2@aol.com
Librarian Vacant

Branch libraries
A   Clydach Library, High Street, Clydach, Swansea SA6 5LN
     ☎(01792) 843300
     Fax (01792) 843300
     Librarian Vacant
B   Gorseinon Library, 15 West Street, Gorseinon, Swansea SA4 4AA
     ☎(01792) 892945
     Fax (01792) 893971
     Librarian Mrs P Jenkins ALA ALAA
C   Morriston Library, Treharne Road, Morriston, Swansea SA6 7AA
     ☎(01792) 516770
     e-mail: morrlib@demon.co.uk
     Librarian Mrs J Clement BLib ALA
D   Oystermouth Library, Dunns Lane, Mumbles, Swansea SA3 4AA
     ☎(01792) 368380
     Librarian Mrs J James BA ALA
E   Pontarddulais Library, St Michael's Avenue, Pontarddulais, Swansea SA4 1TE
     ☎(01792) 882822
     Librarian Mrs G Jones
F   Sketty Library, Vivian Road, Sketty, Swansea SA2 0UN
     ☎(01792) 202024
     Librarian Mrs C Bonham

TORFAEN

Headquarters Torfaen County Borough Council, Torfaen Libraries HQ, Civic Centre,
Pontypool, Torfaen NP4 6YB
☎(01495) 766311
Fax (01495) 766317
Principal Librarian Ms S Johnson ALA

Central/largest library
Cwmbran Library, Gwent House, Cwmbran, Torfaen NP44 1XQ
☎(01633) 483240
Fax (01633) 838609
e-mail: gil48@dial.pipex.com
Senior Librarian Mrs R Chafer BA ALA

Group library
Pontypool Library, Hanbury Road, Pontypool, Torfaen NP4 6JL
☎(01495) 762820
Fax (01495) 752530
e-mail: xcr12@dial.pipex.com
Senior Librarian M Tanner BA DipLib

VALE OF GLAMORGAN

Headquarters Vale of Glamorgan Council, Directorate of Leisure and Cultural Services, Civic Offices, Holton Road, Barry, Vale of Glamorgan CF63 4RU
☎(01446) 709104
Chief Librarian Ms S E Jones BSc(Econ) MSc(Econ) ALA (e-mail: sjones@education.valeofglamorgan.gov.uk)
Principal Librarian C Edwards BA DipLib ALA

Central/largest library
Barry Library, King Square, Barry, Vale of Glamorgan CF63 4RW
☎(01446) 735722
Senior Librarian Ms S Wildsmith ALA

Main libraries
A   Penarth Library, Stanwell Road, Penarth, Vale of Glamorgan CF64 2YT
         ☎(01222) 708438
         Senior Librarian M Payne BA DipLib ALA
B   Cowbridge Library, Old Hall, Cowbridge, Vale of Glamorgan CF7 7AH
         ☎(01446) 773941
         Branch Librarian R Matthews
C   Dinas Powys Library, The Murch, Dinas Powys, Vale of Glamorgan CF64 4QU
         ☎(01222) 512556
         Branch Librarian Ms A Percival BA DipLib ALA
D   Llantwit Major Library, Boverton Road, Llantwit Major, Vale of Glamorgan CF61 9XZ
         ☎(01446) 792700
         Senior Librarian Ms H Price ALA

WREXHAM

Headquarters Wrexham County Borough Council, Library and Information Service, Roxburgh House, Hill Street, Wrexham LL11 1SN
☎(01978) 297430
Fax (01978) 297422
Chief Leisure, Libraries and Culture Officer A Watkin BA DipLib FLA MIM
Libraries Officer D Hughes BA DipLib ALA (01978 297442)

Central/largest library
Wrexham Library, Rhosddu Road, Wrexham LL11 1AU
☎(01978) 292090
Fax (01978) 292611
Community Librarian Mrs M Thomas ALA (01978 292600)

Group/branch libraries
A   Brynteg Library, Quarry Road, Brynteg, Wrexham LL11 6AB
         ☎(01978) 759523
         Community Librarian Ms K Mills BA(Hons) ALA
B   Rhosllanerchrugog Library, Princes Road, Rhos, Wrexham LL14 1AB
         ☎(01978) 840328
         Community Librarian Miss A L Hughes MA ALA

CROWN DEPENDENCIES

ALDERNEY

Headquarters Alderney Library, Island Hall, Royal Connaught Square, Alderney, Channel Islands GY9 3UE
☎(01481) 824178
Chairman, Alderney Library Committee Mrs E Mignot BA
Alderney Library is a voluntary organization

GUERNSEY

Headquarters Guille-Alles Library, Market Street, St Peter Port, Guernsey, Channel Islands GY1 1HB
☎(01481) 720392
Fax (01481) 712425
e-mail: gsylib@itl.net
Principal Librarian Miss M J Falla BA MA MLib ALA

Priaulx Library, Candie Road, St Peter Port, Guernsey, Channel Islands GY1 1UG
☎(01481) 721998
Fax (01481) 713804
Chief Librarian H Tomlinson MA(Hons) MEd PhD
The Priaulx Library is a reference and lending library specializing in local history and family history research in the Channel Islands

ISLE OF MAN

Headquarters Douglas Public Library, Ridgeway Street, Douglas, Isle of Man IM1 1EP
☎(01624) 623021
Fax (01624) 662792
e-mail: jrb@dpl.mcb.net
Librarian J R Bowring BA ALA

Onchan Library, 61-69 Main Road, Onchan, Isle of Man IM3 1AJ
☎(01624) 621228
Fax (01624) 663482
e-mail: oncpl@enterprise.net
url: http://homepages.enterprise.net/oncpl
Librarian Mrs P Hand

Ramsey Library, Parliament Square, Ramsey, Isle of Man IM8 1AB
☎(01624) 812228
Librarian P Boulton BA

Castletown Library, Farrants Way, Castletown, Isle of Man IM9 1NR
☎(01624) 825005
Librarian Mrs F Tasker

Ward Library, 38 Castle Street, Peel, Isle of Man IM5 1AL
☎(01624) 843533
Librarian Mrs C Horton

George Herdman Library, Bridson Street, Port Erin, Isle of Man IM9 6AL
☎(01624) 832365
Librarian Miss A Dryland BSc

JERSEY

Headquarters States of Jersey Library Service, Jersey Library, Halkett Place, St Helier, Jersey, Channel Islands JE2 4WH
☎(01534) 759991 (enquiries), (01534) 759992 (reference)
Fax (01534) 69444
e-mail: jsylib@itl.net
Chief Librarian Mrs M Corrigan ALA LLCM

Public Libraries in the Republic of Ireland

CARLOW COUNTY LIBRARY

Headquarters Carlow Central Library, Dublin Street, Carlow, Republic of Ireland
☎(00 353 503) 31126
Fax (00 353 503) 40548
County Librarian T King MA DipLib
Assistant Librarian Ms C Flahavan DipLib
Assistant Librarian Ms D Condron BComm DipLib

CAVAN COUNTY LIBRARY

Headquarters Cavan County Library, Farnham Street, Cavan, Republic of Ireland
☎(00 353 49) 31799
Fax (00 353 49) 31384
e-mail: cavancountylibrary@tinet.ie
County Librarian Ms J Brady BA DLIS
Assistant Librarians T Sullivan DLIS, M Doherty

CLARE COUNTY LIBRARY

Headquarters Clare County Library HQ, Mill Road, Ennis, Co Clare, Republic of Ireland
☎(00 353 65) 6821616/6842461
Fax (00 353 65) 6842462
County Librarian N Crowley FLAI

Central/largest library
De Valera Branch Library, Ennis, Co Clare, Republic of Ireland
☎(00 353 65) 6821616

Area libraries
A   Sean Lemass Library, Town Centre, Shannon, Co Clare, Republic of Ireland
         ☎(00 353 61) 364266
B   The Library, The Square, Ennistymon, Co Clare, Republic of Ireland
         ☎(00 353 65) 7071245
C   Kilrush Library, Kilrush, Co Clare, Republic of Ireland
         ☎(00 353 65) 9051504
D   The Library, Kilnasoolagh Park, Newmarket-on-Fergus, Co Clare, Republic of
         Ireland
         ☎(00 353 61) 368411
E   Sweeney Memorial Library, O'Connell Street, Kilkee, Co Clare, Republic of Ireland
         ☎(00 353 65) 9056034
F   The Library, The Lock House, Killaloe, Co Clare, Republic of Ireland
         ☎(00 353 61) 376062
G   The Library, Ballard Road, Miltown Malbay, Co Clare, Republic of Ireland
         ☎(00 353 65) 7084822
H   Local Studies Centre, The Manse, Harmony Row, Ennis, Co Clare, Republic of
         Ireland
         ☎(00 353 65) 6821616

CORK CITY LIBRARY

Headquarters Cork City Library, Grand Parade, Cork, Republic of Ireland
☎(00 353 21) 277110
Fax (00 353 21) 275684
e-mail: corkcity.library@indigo.ie
City Librarian Ms H O'Sullivan FLAI

Branch libraries

A   Douglas Library, Tesco Shopping Centre, Douglas, Cork, Republic of Ireland
e-mail: douglas.library@indigo.ie

B   Hollyhill Library, Shopping Centre, Hollyhill, Cork, Republic of Ireland
e-mail: hhill.library@indigo.ie

C   Mayfield Library, Old Youghal Road, Cork, Republic of Ireland
e-mail: mayfield.library@indigo.ie

D   St Mary's Road Library, Cork, Republic of Ireland
e-mail: stmarys.library@indigo.ie

E   Tory Top Road Library, Ballyphehane, Cork, Republic of Ireland
e-mail: torytop.library@indigo.ie

CORK COUNTY LIBRARY

Headquarters Cork County Library, Farranlea Road, Cork, Republic of Ireland
☎(00 353 21) 546499
Fax (00 353 21) 343254
County Librarian Ms R Flanagan BA DipLib ALAI

DONEGAL COUNTY LIBRARY

Headquarters Donegal County Library Admin. Centre, Rosemount, Letterkenny, Co
Donegal, Republic of Ireland
☎(00 353 74) 21968 (enquiries & administration)
Fax (00 353 74) 26402
e-mail: dglcolib@iol.ie
County Librarian L Ronayne BCL DipLib ALAI

Central/largest library
Central Library & Arts Centre, Oliver Plunkett Road, Letterkenny, Co Donegal, Republic of
Ireland
☎(00 353 74) 24950
Fax (00 353 74) 24950
e-mail: dglcolib@iol.ie
Assistant Librarian G McHugh BA DipLib

DUBLIN CORPORATION PUBLIC LIBRARIES

Headquarters Dublin Public Libraries, Central Department, 2nd Floor, Cumberland House,
Fenian Street, Dublin 2, Republic of Ireland
☎(00 353 1) 661 9000
Fax (00 353 1) 676 1628
e-mail: dublin.city.libs@iol.ie
City Librarian and Director Ms D Ellis-King BA DipLib ALAI MPhil
Acting Deputy City Librarian A Smeaton BA DipLib

Central/largest library
Central Public Library, ILAC Centre, Henry Street, Dublin 1, Republic of Ireland
☎(00 353 1) 873 4333
Fax (00 353 1) 872 1451
e-mail: dubcelib@iol.ie

DUN LAOGHAIRE/RATHDOWN COUNTY COUNCIL PUBLIC LIBRARY SERVICE

Headquarters Public Library Service, Duncairn House, 14 Carysfort Avenue, Blackrock, Co

Dublin, Republic of Ireland
☎(00 353 1) 278 1788
Fax (00 353 1) 278 1792
e-mail: dlrlibs@iol.ie
County Librarian M Ó Raghaill BSc(Econ) ALA
Senior Librarian, Staff and Administration Ms O Gallagher BSocSc DLT
Senior Librarian, Bibliographic Control and Computerization Ms J A Lloyd BA DLT
Librarian, Cataloguing J Keyes BSc DLIS
Librarian, Interlibrary Loans Ms G McHugh MA DLIS ALAI

Branch libraries
A   Blackrock Library, Main Street, Blackrock, Co Dublin, Republic of Ireland
        ☎(00 353 1) 288 8117
        Librarian Ms P Corish BA HDipEd DLIS
B   Cabinteely Library, Old Bray Road, Cabinteely, Dublin 18, Republic of Ireland
        ☎(00 353 1) 285 5363
        Librarian P Walsh BA HDipEd DLIS
C   Dalkey Library, Castle Street, Dalkey, Co Dublin, Republic of Ireland
        ☎(00 353 1) 285 5277
        Librarian Ms M Mitchell DLIS
D   Deansgrange Library, Clonkeen Drive, Deansgrange, Dublin 18, Republic of Ireland
        ☎(00 353 1) 285 0860
        Senior Librarian Ms K Guinan BA DLIS
E   Dundrum Library, Upper Churchtown Road, Dublin 14, Republic of Ireland
        ☎(00 353 1) 298 5000
        Senior Librarian T Curran BA DLIS
F   Dun Laoghaire Library, Lower George's Street, Dun Laoghaire, Co Dublin, Republic
        of Ireland
        ☎(00 353 1) 280 1147
        Librarian Ms E Prout BA DLIS
G   Sallynoggin Library, Senior College, Sallynoggin, Co Dublin, Republic of Ireland
        ☎(00 353 1) 285 0127
        Librarian Ms A Finn BA DLIS
H   Shankill Library, Library Road, Shankill, Co Dublin, Republic of Ireland
        ☎(00 353 1) 282 3081
        Librarian Ms M Boyle BSocSc
I   Stillorgan Library, St Laurence's Park, Stillorgan, Co Dublin, Republic of Ireland
        ☎(00 353 1) 288 9655
        Senior Librarian D Griffin BA DLT

FINGAL COUNTY LIBRARIES
Headquarters Fingal County Libraries, 11 Parnell Square, Dublin 1, Republic of Ireland
☎(00 353 1) 872 7777 ext 2875 (enquiries), ext 2868 (administration)
Fax (00 353 1) 873 2021
e-mail: fincolib@iol.ie
County Librarian P Harris DipLib ALAI
Senior Librarian (Personnel & Finance) Ms E Conway
Senior Librarian (Circulations & Development) Ms M Sliney
Archivist Ms T Hynes
Other services: Local Studies Dept (address etc as HQ)

Area libraries
A   Blanchardstown Library, Fingal County Libraries, Roselawn Shopping Centre,

Blanchardstown, Dublin 15, Republic of Ireland
☎(00 353 1) 821 2701
Fax (00 353 1) 820 5066
Senior Librarian M R Farrell
B   Balbriggan Library, Fingal County Libraries, St George's Square, Balbriggan. Co Dublin, Republic of Ireland
☎(00 353 1) 841 1128
Senior Librarian J Walsh
C   Malahide Library, Fingal County Libraries, Main Street, Malahide, Co Dublin, Republic of Ireland
☎(00 353 1) 845 2026
Senior Librarian Ms C Keane
D   Rathbeale Library, Fingal County Libraries, Rathbeale Shopping Centre, Swords, Co Dublin, Republic of Ireland
☎(00 353 1) 840 4179
Senior Librarian Ms C M Mullett
E   Howth Library, Fingal County Libraries, Main Street, Howth, Co Dublin, Republic of Ireland
☎(00 353 1) 832 2130
Librarian Ms C P McKeown
F   Mobile Library Service (HQ), Fingal County Libraries, Unit 34, Coolmine Industrial Estate, Coolmine, Dublin 15, Republic of Ireland
☎(00 353 1) 822 1564
Fax (00 353 1) 822 1568
Librarian Ms M Coakley

GALWAY COUNTY LIBRARIES

Headquarters Galway County Library HQ, Island House, Cathedral Square, Galway, Republic of Ireland
☎(00 353 91) 562471
Fax (00 353 91) 565039
e-mail: gallibr@indigo.ie
url: http://indigo.ie/~gallibr/
County Librarian P McMahon DipLib
Deputy Librarian Ms M Moran
Librarian, Branch System P Rabbitt
Librarian, Schools Library Service M Keating
Librarian ICT J Fitzgibbon

Central/largest library
Galway City Library, Hynes Building, St Augustine Street, Galway, Republic of Ireland
☎(00 353 91) 561666
Executive Librarian Mrs B Kelly BA DipLib
Assistant Librarian Mrs J Vahey

Branch libraries
A   Public Library, Fairgreen, Ballinasloe, Co Galway, Republic of Ireland
☎(00 353 905) 43464
Assistant Librarian Mrs M Dillon
B   Public Library, Tuam, Co Galway, Republic of Ireland
☎(00 353 93) 24287
Senior Library Assistant Vacant
C   Public Library, Clifden, Co Galway, Republic of Ireland

☎(00 353 95) 21092
Senior Library Assistant P Keogh
D Public Library, Portumna, Co Galway, Republic of Ireland
 ☎(00 353 509) 41261
 Library Assistant Ms T Tierney
E Public Library, Athenry, Co Galway, Republic of Ireland
 Branch Librarian Ms A Boyle
F Public Library, Gort, Co Galway, Republic of Ireland
 Branch Librarian Mrs J Hickey
G Public Library, Loughrea, Co Galway, Republic of Ireland
 Branch Librarian Mrs M Jennings

KERRY COUNTY LIBRARY

Headquarters Kerry County Library HQ, Moyderwell, Tralee, Co Kerry, Republic of Ireland
☎(00 353 66) 21200
Fax (00 353 66) 29202
Chief Librarian Mrs K Browne FLAI

Area libraries
A Killarney Branch Library, Killarney, Co Kerry, Republic of Ireland
 ☎(00 353 64) 32972
 Fax (00 353 64) 36065
B Ballybunion Branch Library, Ballybunion, Co Kerry, Republic of Ireland
 ☎(00 353 68) 27615
C Cahirciveen Branch Library, Cahirciveen, Co Kerry, Republic of Ireland
 ☎(00 353 66) 72287
D Castleisland Branch Library, Castleisland, Co Kerry, Republic of Ireland
 ☎(00 353 66) 41485
E Dingle Branch Library, Dingle, Co Kerry, Republic of Ireland
 ☎(00 353 66) 51499
F Kenmare Branch Library, Kenmare, Co Kerry, Republic of Ireland
 ☎(00 353 64) 41416
G Killorglin Branch Library, Killorglin, Co Kerry, Republic of Ireland
 ☎(00 353 66) 61272
H Listowel Branch Library, Listowel, Co Kerry, Republic of Ireland
 ☎(00 353 68) 23044

KILDARE COUNTY LIBRARY

Headquarters Kildare County Library Service, Athgarvan Road, Newbridge, Co Kildare,
Republic of Ireland
☎(00 353 45) 431109/431486 (enquiries)
Fax (00 353 45) 432490
County Librarian Ms B Gleeson

Main branch libraries
A Community Library, Town Hall, Athy, Co Kildare, Republic of Ireland
 ☎(00 353 507) 31144
B Branch Library, Celbridge, Co Kildare, Republic of Ireland
 ☎(00 353 1) 627 2207
C Branch Library, Newtown House, Leixlip, Co Kildare, Republic of Ireland
 ☎(00 353 1) 624 4240
D Branch Library, Main Street, Maynooth, Co Kildare, Republic of Ireland
 ☎(00 353 1) 628 5530

E   Branch Library, Canal Harbour, Naas, Co Kildare, Republic of Ireland
     ☎(00 353 45) 879111
F   Branch Library, Athgarvan Road, Newbridge, Co Kildare, Republic of Ireland
     ☎(00 353 45) 431486/431109

KILKENNY COUNTY LIBRARY

Headquarters Kilkenny County Library, 6 John's Quay, Kilkenny, Co Kilkenny, Republic of Ireland
☎(00 353 56) 22021 (enquiries), 22606 (administration)
Fax (00 353 56) 70233
e-mail: katlibs@iol.ie
County Librarian J Fogarty DLIS ALAI

Central/largest library
Kilkenny City Library, John's Quay, Kilkenny, Co Kilkenny, Republic of Ireland
☎(00 353 56) 22021 (enquiries), 22606 (administration)
Fax (00 353 56) 70233
e-mail: katlibs@iol.ie
Assistant Librarians D Macaulay BSc DLIS, D O'Reilly

Area libraries
A   Graiguenamanagh Library, Convent Road, Graiguenamanagh, Co Kilkenny,
     Republic of Ireland
     ☎(00 353 503) 24224
     Assistant Librarian Ms B Ward BA DLIS
B   Urlingford Library, The Courthouse, Urlingford, Co Kilkenny, Republic of Ireland
     ☎(00 353 56) 31656
C   Castlecomer Library, Main Street, Castlecomer, Co Kilkenny, Republic of Ireland
     ☎(00 353 56) 40055
     Senior Assistant Ms M Morrissey

LAOIS COUNTY LIBRARY

Headquarters Laois County Library, Library HQ, County Hall, James Fintan Lalor Avenue,
Portlaoise, Co Laois, Republic of Ireland
☎(00 353 502) 22044
Fax (00 353 502) 22313
County Librarian E Phelan FLAI

Central/largest library
Portlaoise Branch Library, Dunamase House, Portlaoise, Co Laois, Republic of Ireland
☎(00 353 502) 22333
Assistant Librarian Mrs C Kavanagh

Branch libraries
A   Abbeyleix Branch Library, Abbeyleix, Co Laois, Republic of Ireland
     ☎(00 353 502) 30020
     Branch Librarian Ms E Sutton
B   Mountmellick Branch Library, Mountmellick, Co Laois, Republic of Ireland
     ☎(00 353 502) 24733
     Branch Librarian Ms E Broomfield
C   Mountrath Branch Library, Mountrath, Co Laois, Republic of Ireland
     ☎(00 353 502) 56046
     Branch Librarian Ms J Phelan

D   Portarlington Branch Library, Portarlington, Co Laois, Republic of Ireland
     ☎(00 353 502) 43751
     Branch Librarian Ms B Doris
E   Rathdowney Branch Library, Rathdowney, Co Laois, Republic of Ireland
     ☎(00 353 505) 46852
     Branch Librarian Ms C Fitzpatrick
F   Stradballly Branch Library, Stradbally, Co Laois, Republic of Ireland
     Branch Librarian Ms M O'Callaghan

LEITRIM COUNTY LIBRARY
Headquarters Leitrim County Library, Ballinamore, Co Leitrim, Republic of Ireland
☎(00 353 78) 44012
Fax (00 353 78) 44425
e-mail: leitrimlibrary@tinet.ie
County Librarian S O Suilleabhain DLT FLAI ALAI

LIMERICK CITY LIBRARY
Headquarters Limerick City Library, The Granary, Michael Street, Limerick, Republic of Ireland
☎(00 353 61) 415799 (general enquiries), 314668 (direct line)
Fax (00 353 61) 415266
City Librarian Ms D Doyle BA FLAI ALAI (e-mail: ddoyle@citylib.limerickcorp.ie)

LIMERICK COUNTY LIBRARY
Headquarters Limerick County Library, 58 O'Connell Street, Limerick, Republic of Ireland
☎(00 353 61) 318477 (enquiries & administration)
Fax (00 353 61) 318478
County Librarian D Brady BA LAI DLIS
Executive Librarian Ms H Walsh DLIS LAI

Central/largest library
Dooradoyle Branch Library, Crescent Shopping Centre, Dooradoyle Road, Limerick, Republic of Ireland
☎(00 353 61) 301101
Assistant Librarian Ms A Bennett BA DLIS

Branch libraries
A   Adare Branch Library, Adare, Co Limerick, Republic of Ireland
     ☎(00 353 61) 396822
     Assistant Librarian Ms M O'Reilly BA DLIS
B   Newcastlewest Branch Library, Newcastlewest, Co Limerick, Republic of Ireland
     ☎(00 353 69) 62273
     Assistant Librarian Ms A Dillane BA DLIS
C   Foynes Branch Library, Foynes, Co Limerick, Republic of Ireland
     ☎(00 353 69) 65365
     Assistant Librarian Ms I Kelly
D   Abbeyfeale Branch Library, Bridge Street, Abbeyfeale, Co Limerick, Republic of Ireland
     ☎(00 353 68) 32488
     Senior Library Assistant M McInerney

LOUTH COUNTY LIBRARY

Headquarters Louth County Library, Roden Place, Dundalk, Co Louth, Republic of Ireland
☎(00 353 42) 35457 (enquiries), (00 353 42) 35458 (administration)
Fax (00 353 42) 34549
e-mail: louthcl@iol.ie
County Librarian Miss A Ward BA DLT

MAYO COUNTY LIBRARY

Headquarters Mayo County Library, Library HQ, Mountain View, Castlebar, Co Mayo, Republic of Ireland
☎(00 353 94) 24444 (enquiries & administration)
Fax (00 353 94) 24774
County Librarian A Vaughan DLIS

Central/largest library
Mayo Central Library, The Mall, Castlebar, Co Mayo, Republic of Ireland
☎(00 353 94) 24444
Fax (00 353 94) 24774
e-mail: mayolib@cbar.lolipop.ie

MEATH COUNTY LIBRARY

Headquarters Meath County Library, Railway Street, Navan, Co Meath, Republic of Ireland
☎(00 353 46) 21134/21451
County Librarian Vacant
Executive Librarian Ms G Donnelly

Branch libraries
A   Ashbourne Library, Killegland, Ashbourne, Co Meath, Republic of Ireland
     Branch Librarian Ms P Synnott
B   Athboy Library, Main Street, Athboy, Co Meath, Republic of Ireland
     ☎(00 353 46) 32539
     Branch Librarian Ms T Doherty
C   Duleek Library, Courthouse, Duleek, Co Meath, Republic of Ireland
     ☎(00 353 41) 988 0700
     Branch Librarian Ms M Rafferty
D   Dunboyne Library, Castleview, Dunboyne, Co Meath, Republic of Ireland
     ☎(00 353 1) 825 1248
     Branch Librarian Ms C Cunningham
E   Dunshaughlin Library, Main Street, Dunshaughlin, Co Meath, Republic of Ireland
     ☎(00 353 1) 825 0504
     Branch Librarian Ms F Keaney
F   Kells Library, Maudlin Street, Kells, Co Meath, Republic of Ireland
     ☎(00 353 46) 41592
     Branch Librarian Ms R Grimes
G   Laytown Library, Laytown, Co Meath, Republic of Ireland
     Branch Librarian Ms I Cunningham
H   Nobber Library, Nobber, Co Meath, Republic of Ireland
     Branch Librarian Ms I Griffin
I   Oldcastle Library, Millbrook Road, Oldcastle, Co Meath, Republic of Ireland
     Branch Librarian Ms K Dally
J   Slane Library, Castle Hill, Slane, Co Meath, Republic of Ireland
     Branch Librarian Ms M Morgan
K   Trim Library, High Street, Trim, Co Meath, Republic of Ireland

☎(00 353 46) 36014
Branch Librarian P Crinion

MONAGHAN COUNTY LIBRARY
Headquarters Monaghan County Library, The Diamond, Clones, Co Monaghan, Republic of Ireland
☎(00 353 47) 51143
Fax (00 353 47) 51863
e-mail: moncolib@tinet.ie
County Librarian J McElvaney

Central/largest library
Monaghan Branch Library, North Road, Monaghan Town, Republic of Ireland
☎(00 353 47) 81830
e-mail: monaghan@tinet.ie
Senior Library Assistant Ms M MacKenna

Branch libraries
A   Clones Branch Library, The Diamond, Clones, Co Monaghan, Republic of Ireland
     ☎(00 353 47) 51143
     Fax (00 353 47) 51863
     Senior Library Assistant Ms J Ryan
B   Carrickmacross Branch Library, Market Square, Carrickmacross, Co Monaghan, Republic of Ireland
     ☎(00 353 42) 61148
     e-mail: cmxlibrary@tinet.ie
     Library Assistant Ms B Moore
C   Castleblaney Branch Library, Market Square, Castleblaney, Co Monaghan, Republic of Ireland
     ☎(00 353 42) 40281
     Branch Librarian B McDonald
D   Ballybay Library, Main Street, Ballybay, Co Monaghan, Republic of Ireland
     ☎(00 353 42) 41256
     Branch Librarian Mrs A Leonard

OFFALY COUNTY LIBRARY
Headquarters Offaly County Library, O'Connor Square, Tullamore, Co Offaly, Republic of Ireland
☎(00 353 506) 46834
Fax (00 353 506) 52769
e-mail: colibrar@offalycoco.ie
County Librarian Miss A M Coughlan DLT ALA

ROSCOMMON COUNTY LIBRARY
Headquarters Roscommon County Library, Abbey Street, Roscommon, Republic of Ireland
☎(00 353 903) 37272/37273 (enquiries & administration)
Fax (00 353 903) 25474
e-mail: roslib@iol.ie
County Librarian Mrs H Kilcline BA ALAI FLAI (00 353 903 37271)

Central/largest library
Roscommon Branch Library, Abbey Street, Roscommon, Republic of Ireland
☎(00 353 903) 37277

Fax (00 353 903) 25474
Assistant Librarian i/c E Bolger

Branch libraries

A   Boyle Branch Library, The King House, Boyle, Co Roscommon, Republic of Ireland
     ☎(00 353 79) 62800
     Branch Librarian W O'Dowd

B   Ballaghaderreen Branch Library, Barrack Street, Ballaghaderreen, Co Roscommon, Republic of Ireland
     ☎(00 353 907) 60940
     Branch Librarian Ms O Feely

C   Castlerea Branch Library, Main Street, Castelrea, Co Roscommon, Republic of Ireland
     ☎(00 353 907) 20745
     Branch Librarian Ms M Carroll

D   Elphin Branch Library, Main Street, Elphin, Co Roscommon, Republic of Ireland
     ☎(00 353 78) 35091
     Branch Librarian Ms M Walsh

E   Strokestown Branch Library, Elphin Street, Strokestown, Co Roscommon, Republic of Ireland
     ☎(00 353 78) 33016
     Branch Librarian Ms M Lane

F   Ballyforan Branch Library, Ballyforan, Co Roscommon, Republic of Ireland
     Branch Librarian Ms M Kelly

SLIGO COUNTY LIBRARY

Headquarters Sligo County Library, The Westward Town Centre, Bridge Street, Sligo, Republic of Ireland
☎(00 353 71) 47190
Fax (00 353 71) 46798
e-mail: sligolib@iol.ie
County Librarian D Tinney BA DLIS ALAI
Assistant Librarian P Gannon BA DLIS

Central/largest library
Sligo City Library, Stephen Street, Sligo, Republic of Ireland
☎(00 353 71) 42212
Fax (00 353 71) 46798
Assistant Librarian F Hegarty FLAI
Senior Library Assistant Ms C Morgan DipLib

TIPPERARY JOINT LIBRARIES COMMITTEE

Headquarters Tipperary County Library, Castle Avenue, Thurles, Co Tipperary, Republic of Ireland
☎(00 353 504) 21555
Fax (00 353 504) 23442
e-mail: tipplibs@iol.ie url: http://www.iol.ie/~tipplibs
County Librarian M Maher

Branch libraries

A   Borrisokane Library, Main Street, Borrisokane, Co Tipperary, Republic of Ireland
     Branch Librarian Mrs F O'Carroll

B   Cahir Library, The Square, Cahir, Co Tipperary, Republic of Ireland
    ☎(00 353 52) 42075
    Branch Librarian Mrs A Tuohy

C   Carrick-on-Suir Library, Fair Green, Carrick-on-Suir, Co Tipperary, Republic of Ireland
    ☎(00 353 51) 640591
    Senior Library Assistant O Corbett

D   Cashel Library, The Green, Cashel, Co Tipperary, Republic of Ireland
    ☎(00 352 62) 62977
    Branch Librarian Ms S Meskell

E   Clonmel Library, Emmet Street, Clonmel, Co Tipperary, Republic of Ireland
    ☎(00 353 52) 24545
    e-mail: clonmlib@iol.ie
    Assistant Librarian Mrs M Boland

F   Cloughjordan Library, Main Street, Cloughjordan, Co Tipperary, Republic of Ireland
    Branch Librarian Mrs M Brady

G   Fethard Library, Main Street, Fethard, Co Tipperary, Republic of Ireland
    Branch Librarian Mrs A Curtin

H   Killenaule Library, Bailey Street, Killenaule, Thurles, Co Tipperary, Republic of Ireland
    Branch Librarian Mrs R Lahart

I   Nenagh Library, O'Rahilly Street, Nenagh, Co Tipperary, Republic of Ireland
    ☎(00 353 67) 34404
    Fax (00 353 67) 34405
    e-mail: nenalib@iol.ie
    Assistant Librarian Ms C Kennedy

J   Roscrea Library, Birr Road, Roscrea, Co Tipperary, Republic of Ireland
    ☎(00 353 505) 22032
    Assistant Librarian Ms A Beausang

K   Templemore Library, Town Hall, Templemore, Co Tipperary, Republic of Ireland
    Branch Librarian Mrs B Kennedy

L   Thurles Library, Castle Avenue, Thurles, Co Tipperary, Republic of Ireland
    ☎(00 353 504) 21555
    Assistant Librarian Vacant

M   Tipperary Library, Dan Breen House, Tipperary, Co Tipperary, Republic of Ireland
    ☎(00 353 62) 51761
    Branch Librarian Ms N Butler, Ms G Hughes

WATERFORD COUNTY LIBRARY

Headquarters Waterford County Library, West Main Street, Lismore, Co Waterford, Republic of Ireland
☎(00 353 58) 54128
Fax (00 353 58) 54877
e-mail: cbhqcirc@iol.ie
County Librarian D Brady
Systems Administrator E Byrne (e-mail: ebhqcirc@iol.ie)

Central/largest library
Dungarvan Branch Library, Davitt's Quay, Dungarvan, Co Waterford, Republic of Ireland
☎(00 353 58) 41231
Librarian Ms M O'Brien

Area libraries
A   Tramore Branch Library, Market Square, Waterford, Republic of Ireland

☎(00 353 51) 381479
e-mail: tramore@iol.ie
Librarian Ms K Murphy
B   Cappoquin Branch Library, Cappoquin, Waterford, Republic of Ireland
     Branch Librarian Mrs M Tobin
C   Dunmore Branch Library, Dunmore East, Waterford, Republic of Ireland
     ☎(00 353 51) 383211
     Branch Librarian .Ms C O Mullain
D   Lismore Branch Library, Main Street, Lismore, Waterford, Republic of Ireland
     ☎(00 353 58) 54128
     Branch Librarian Ms N Tobin
E   Portlaw Branch Library, The Square, Portlaw, Waterford, Republic of Ireland
     ☎(00 353 51) 387402
     Branch Librarian Ms L Kinsella
F   Stradbally Branch Library, Stradbally, Waterford, Republic of Ireland
     Branch Librarian Mrs K Gough

WATERFORD MUNICIPAL LIBRARY

Headquarters Waterford Municipal Library, Lady Lane, Waterford, Republic of Ireland
☎(00 353 51) 309975
Fax (00 353 51) 850031
City Librarian R Fennessy BA HDE DLIS
Assistant Librarian Ms K Moran BA DLIS

WESTMEATH COUNTY LIBRARY

Headquarters Westmeath County Library HQ, Dublin Road, Mullingar, Co Westmeath, Republic of Ireland
☎(00 353 44) 40781/2/3 (enquiries & administration)
Fax (00 353 44) 41322
County Librarian Miss M Farrell BA HDE DLIS ALAI
Librarian, Reference Services T Cox DLT

Branch libraries
A   Mullingar Library, Church Avenue, Mullingar, Co Westmeath, Republic of Ireland
     ☎(00 353 44) 48278
     Senior Library Assistant Ms P Shaw
B   Athlone Library, Father Matthew Hall, Athlone, Co Westmeath, Republic of Ireland
     ☎(00 353 902) 92166
     Librarian G O'Brien DLIS FLAI
C   Castlepollard Library, Town Hall, Castlepollard, Co Westmeath, Republic of Ireland
     ☎(00 353 44) 61646
     Branch Librarian Ms R Moran
D   Kilbeggan Library, Main Street, Kilbeggan, Co Westmeath, Republic of Ireland
     Branch Librarian Ms E Gorman
E   Killucan Library, St Joseph's Hall, Killucan, Co Westmeath, Republic of Ireland
     Branch Librarian Ms G Corroon
F   Moate Library, The Courthouse, Main Street, Moate, Co Westmeath, Republic of Ireland
     ☎(00 353 902) 81888
     Fax (00 353 902) 81888
     Branch Librarian Ms N Brennan-Gavin

WEXFORD COUNTY LIBRARY

Headquarters Management Services and Administrative HQ, Ardcavan, Co Wexford, Republic of Ireland
☎(00 353 53) 24922
Fax (00 353 53) 21097
County Librarian Ms F Hanrahan BA DLIS MLIS ALA ALAI

Central/largest library
Wexford Library, Skeffington Street, Wexford, Republic of Ireland
☎(00 353 53) 21637
e-mail: library.wexford@tinet.ie
Assistant Librarian J Glynn BA DLIS

Area libraries
A   New Ross Branch Library, Barrack Lane, New Ross, Co Wexford, Republic of Ireland
☎(00 353 51) 421877
Senior Library Assistant Ms A Griffin DLIS
B   Enniscorthy Branch Library, Lymington Road, Enniscorthy, Co Wexford, Republic of Ireland
☎(00 353 54) 36055
Senior Library Assistant Ms A Parle BA

WICKLOW COUNTY LIBRARY

Headquarters Wicklow County Library, UDC Offices, Boghall Road, Bray, Co Wicklow, Republic of Ireland
☎(00 353 1) 286 6566 (enquiries & administration)
Fax (00 353 1) 286 5811
e-mail: wcclhq@tinet.ie
County Librarian G Maher LLB(Hons) DLIS
Executive Librarian Ms C Moore DLIS
Assistant Librarian Ms N Ringwood BA DLIS

Largest library
Bray Public Library, Eglinton Road, Bray, Co Wicklow, Republic of Ireland
☎(00 353 1) 286 2600
Assistant Librarian M Maguire BA DLIS

Area library
Greystones Public Library, Church Road, Greystones, Co Wicklow, Republic of Ireland
☎(00 353 1) 287 3548
Assistant Librarian Ms U Campbell DLIS

Children's, Youth and Schools Library Services in the United Kingdom

(listed under public library authority)

England
Scotland
Wales
Crown Dependencies

For Northern Ireland, please see entries under Northern Ireland Education and Library Boards in the Public Libraries Section.

ENGLAND

BARKING AND DAGENHAM

London Borough of Barking and Dagenham, Children's/Youth Library Service, Central
Library, Barking, Essex IG11 7NB
☎020 8227 3611 (School Library Service 020 8227 3614)
Fax 020 8227 3699
Community and Education Manager Ms S Leighton MA ALA

BARNET

London Borough of Barnet, Cultural Services, The Old Town Hall, 1 Friern Barnet Lane,
London N11 3DL
☎020 8359 3164
Adviser for Children and Youth Mrs V Ross BA ALA (020 8359 2867)

School Library Resources Service, Grahame Park Library, The Concourse, Grahame Park,
London NW9 5XL
☎020 8200 8948 (Tel/Fax)
Joint Heads of Service M Crosse BA ALA, N Angrave BA ALA

BARNSLEY

Barnsley Metropolitan Borough Council, Central Library, Shambles Street, Barnsley, South
Yorkshire S70 2JF
☎(01226) 773952 (messages 773911)
Fax (01226) 773955
e-mail: special@barnsley.ac.uk
Head of Department, Children's Services Mrs J E Moore BLib(Hons) ALA

BATH AND NORTH EAST SOMERSET

Bath and North East Somerset Council, Central Library, The Podium, Northgate Street,
Bath BA1 5AN
☎(01225) 480110
Fax (01225) 331839
Learning Services Manager Ms A Jordan BA(Hons) ALA

BEDFORDSHIRE

Bedfordshire County Council, Department of Education, Arts and Libraries, Kempston
Library, Halsey Road, Kempston, Beds MK42 8AU
☎(01234) 853092
Fax (01234) 841476
Principal Librarian, Youth Services Ms K O'Neil BA(Hons) ALA (e-mail:
oneilk@bedfordshire.gov.uk)

Department of Education, Arts and Libraries, Schools Library Service, The Pilgrim Centre,
20 Brickhill Drive, Bedford MK41 7PZ
☎(01234) 316030
Fax (01234) 342681
Senior Librarian, Schools Library Service Ms S Arkle BA ALA (e-mail:
arkles@bedfordshire.gov.uk)

Department of Education, Arts and Libraries, Leighton Buzzard Library, Lake Street, Leighton Buzzard, Beds LU7 8RX
☎(01525) 371788
Fax (01525) 851368
Senior Librarian, Youth Services Ms V Fox ALA (e-mail: foxv@bedfordshire.gov.uk)

BEXLEY
London Borough of Bexley, Library, Hill View, Hill View Drive, Welling, Kent DA16 3RY
☎020 8303 7777
Fax 020 8308 4926
Senior Children's Librarian Vacant
Youth Services Librarian Vacant

BIRMINGHAM
Birmingham Metropolitan District Council, Central Library, Chamberlain Square, Birmingham B3 3HQ
☎0121 303 2418
Fax 0121 233 9702
Head of Children's, Youth and Education Services Mrs P Heap BA ALA (e-mail: patsy.heap@birmingham.gov.uk)

Schools Library Service, Ellen Street, Hockley, Birmingham B18 6QZ
☎0121 515 3939/515 1900
Fax 0121 515 1852
Managers, Schools Library Service Mrs S Rogers BA ALA, Mrs S Needham ALA

BLACKBURN WITH DARWEN
Blackburn with Darwen Borough Council, Children's and Schools' Service, The Education Centre, 103 Preston New Road, Blackburn BB2 6BJ
☎(01254) 679565
Fax (01254) 679565
Senior Librarian, Children's and Schools' Service Ms J Gabbatt BLib ALA (01254 587937)

BLACKPOOL
Blackpool Borough Council, Community and Tourism Services, Cultural Services Division, Central Library, Queen Street, Blackpool, Lancs FY1 1PX
☎(01253) 478111 (enquiries), (01253) 478107 (administration)
Fax (01253) 478071
Senior Librarian, Youth and Community Services Ms M Bowker ALA DMS (01253 478112)
Senior Librarian, Schools' Library Services Miss D Stanway BA ALA (01253 476627)

BOLTON
Bolton Metropolitan Borough Council, Children's and Schools' Library Service, Castle Hill Centre, Castleton Street, Bolton BL2 2JW
☎(01204) 525372
Fax (01204) 385381
e-mail: boltonsls@dial.pipex.com
url: http://dspace.dial.pipex.com/boltonsls/
Special Services Librarian Ms M Keane BA(Hons) DipLib ALA

BOURNEMOUTH

Bournemouth Borough Council, Children and Learning, Lansdowne Library, Meyrick Road, Bournemouth, Dorset BH1 3DJ

☎(01202) 556603

Fax (01202) 251781

Libraries Officer, Children and Learning Ms H Young BA ALA

(Bournemouth has joint provision with Dorset for school library services: see Dorset)

BRACKNELL FOREST

Bracknell Forest Borough Council, Bracknell Library, Town Square, Bracknell, Berks RG12 1BH

☎(01344) 352401

Fax (01344) 352420

Library and Information Manager Ms K Chambers BA ALA (e-mail: k.chambers@bracknell-forest.gov.uk)

Education Library Resource Centre (Berkshire authorities), 2-4 Darwin Close, Reading, Berks RG2 0TB

☎0118 901 5989

Fax 0118 901 5988

Head of Centre J Saunders BA ALA (0118 901 5990)

BRADFORD

City of Bradford Metropolitan Council, Central Library, Princes Way, Bradford BD1 1NN

☎(01274) 753643

Fax (01274) 395108

e-mail: public.libraries@bradford.gov.uk

Librarian, Children's Services and Xchange Ms C Binns

Education Library Service, 36 Spencer Road, Bradford BD7 2EU

☎(01274) 578898

Fax (01274) 522043

Principal Education Librarian R Wilkes BEd FLA

BRENT

London Borough of Brent, Library Service, Chesterfield House, 9 Park Lane, Wembley, Middlesex HA9 7RW

☎020 8937 3146

Fax 020 8937 3023

Head of Library Service Ms K Tyerman BA DipLib ALA (e-mail: karen.tyerman@brent.gov.uk)

Children's Services, Willesden Green Library, 95 High Road, London NW10 2ST

☎020 8937 3403

Principal Librarian J Verstraete

BRIGHTON AND HOVE

Brighton and Hove Council, Brighton Central Library, Church Street, Brighton, East Sussex BN1 1UE

☎(01273) 290800 (enquiries)

Fax (01273) 296951

Professional Services Manager, Lending, Stock and Community N Imi BA DipLib ALA

(01273 296953)

(Brighton and Hove has joint provision with East Sussex for schools library services: see East Sussex)

BRISTOL

Bristol City Council, Children's and Young People's Library Service, Cheltenham Road Library, Cheltenham Road, Bristol BS6 5QX
☎0117 924 7513
Fax 0117 922 1081
Children's and Young People's Adviser Mrs J Randall ALA

Bristol School Library Service, Nelson Parade, Bedminster, Bristol BS3 4HY
☎0117 966 2471
Fax 0117 953 2751
Service Manager Mrs B Newman

BROMLEY

London Borough of Bromley, Central Library, High Street, Bromley, Kent BR1 1EX
☎020 8460 9955 ext 211
Fax 020 8313 9975
Service Manager (Children and Young People) Mrs P Jones ALA

BUCKINGHAMSHIRE

Buckinghamshire County Council, County Library, Walton Street, Aylesbury, Bucks HP20 1UU
☎(01296) 383206
Fax (01296) 382259
e-mail: library@buckscc.gov.uk
Chief Youth Services Librarian Ms S A Hyland BA ALA DPSE(EdTech) (01296 383273; e-mail: shyland@buckscc.gov.uk)

Library and Information Service for Schools
☎ (01296) 382273
Fax (01296) 382405

BURY

Bury Metropolitan District Council, Library Service, Bury Central Library, Manchester Road, Bury, Greater Manchester BL9 0DG
☎0161 253 5873
Fax 0161 253 5857
e-mail: information@bury.gov.uk
url: http://www.bury.gov.uk/culture.htm
Principal Librarian Mrs D Sorrigan BA ALA (0161 253 7217)

Schools Library Service, Geoffrey Kershaw Centre, Maxwell Street, Bury, Greater Manchester BL9 7QF
☎0161 253 6440
Schools Librarian Ms J E Hamer ALA

CALDERDALE

Calderdale Metropolitan Borough, Children's and Schools' Library Service, Central Library, Northgate, Halifax HX1 1UN

☎(01422) 392618
Fax (01422) 392615
Principal Librarian, Children's Services Mrs H Cerroti BA ALA (e-mail:
helen.cerroti@calderdale.gov.uk)

CAMBRIDGESHIRE
Cambridgeshire County Council, Schools Library Service, Units 1-3, Springwater Business
Park, Station Road, Whittlesey, Peterborough, Cambs PE7 2EU
☎(01733) 758010
Fax (01733) 758015
Head of Service Mrs M Smith ALA (e-mail: margaret.smith@education.camcnty.gov.uk)

CAMDEN
London Borough of Camden, Children's and Youth Service, Swiss Cottage Library, 88
Avenue Road, London NW3 3HA
☎020 7413 6509
Fax 020 7413 6532
Principal Librarians, Children and Youth Ms N Innocent BA ALA, Ms F Page BA ALA

Schools Library Service, Swiss Cottage Library, 88 Avenue Road, London NW3 3HA
☎020 7413 6510
Fax 020 7413 6521
Schools Library Service Manager Ms J Andrew BA ALA

CHESHIRE
Cheshire County Council, Libraries and Archives, Goldsmith House, Hamilton Place,
Chester CH1 1SE
☎(01244) 606023
Fax (01244) 602805
Resources and Development Manager A Bell ALA

Education Library Service, Browning Way, Woodford Park Industrial Estate, Winsford,
Cheshire CW7 2JN
☎(01606) 557126
Fax (01606) 861412
Young People's Services Manager Ms S Maddocks BA ALA
Young People's Specialist, West Cheshire Ms S Wilkinson/Ms C Mapledon (Ellesmere
Port Library; 0151 355 8101)
Young People's Specialist, Mid Cheshire Ms A Warden (Winsford Library; 01606 552065)
Young People's Specialist, East Cheshire Ms J Roberts (Wilmslow Library; 01625 528977)

CORNWALL
Cornwall County Council, Information Services Group, Education Library and Resource
Centre, Unit 17, Threemilestone, Truro, Cornwall TR4 9LD
☎(01872) 323456
Fax (01872) 323819
Young People's Services Manager Ms B Wheeler

COVENTRY
Coventry City Council, Services to Children, Central Library, Smithford Way, Coventry
CV1 1FY
☎024 7683 2338/7683 2358

Fax 024 7683 3163
Children's and Schools' Librarian Ms W Wardle BA(Hons) ALA (e-mail: wendy@covsls.demon.co.uk)

CROYDON

London Borough of Croydon, Central Library, Katharine Street, Croydon CR9 1ET
☎020 8760 5400 ext 1051
Fax 020 8253 1004
url: http://www.croydon.gov.uk
Children's Services Manager Ms M Fraser MA ALA (e-mail: lbmf@croydon.gov.uk), Ms G McElwee BA(Hons) DipLib ALA (e-mail: lbgm@croydon.gov.uk) (job-share)

Education Resources Library, Davidson Professional Centre, Davidson Road, Croydon CR0 6DD
☎020 8655 1299
Fax 020 8656 1544
Senior Librarian Mrs S Smith BA(Hons) PGDipLib

CUMBRIA

Cumbria County Council, Heritage Services, Arroyo Block, The Castle, Cumbria CA3 8UR
☎(01228) 607278
Fax (01228) 607299
Young People's Library Services Manager Mrs A Singleton ALA (e-mail: a.singleton@dial.pipex.com)

Young People's Library Service HQ, Botchergate, Carlisle, Cumbria CA1 1RZ
☎(01228) 607277
Fax (01228) 607275
e-mail: pp10@dial.pipex.com
Young People's Library Services Manager Mrs A Singleton ALA (e-mail: a.singleton@dial.pipex.com)

DARLINGTON

Darlington Borough Council, Libraries and Museums, Darlington Library and Art Gallery, Crown Street, Darlington, DL1 1ND
☎(01325) 462034
Fax (01325) 381556
e-mail: library@dbc-lib.demon.co.uk
Special Services Librarian Mrs H Thompson BA(Hons)
(School Library Service in partnership with Durham: see Durham)

DERBY

Derby City Council, Leisure Services Department, Celtic House, Heritage Gate, Derby DE1 1QX
☎(01332) 716605
Fax (01332) 715549
e-mail: libraries@derby-city-council.gov.uk
Senior Librarian, Children and Education Ms F Renwick MA
(Derby has joint provision with Derbyshire for schools library services: see Derbyshire)

DERBYSHIRE

Derbyshire County Council, Libraries and Heritage: Services to Young People, County

Library HQ, County Hall, Matlock, Derbyshire DE4 4EH
☎(01629) 580000
Fax (01629) 585363
Coordinator of Services to Schools and Young People Ms T Kings BA ALA (01629 580000 ext 6587)

School Library Service: Derbyshire and Derby, Kedleston Road Centre, 184 Kedleston Road, Derby
☎(01332) 371921
Coordinator of Services to Schools and Young People Ms T Kings BA ALA (01629 580000 ext 6587; e-mail: tricia.kings@derbyshire.gov.uk)

DEVON
Devon County Council, North Devon Library and Record Office, Tuly Street, Barnstaple, Devon EX31 1EL
☎(01271) 388622
Fax (01271) 388619
Group Librarian, North & West Devon (i/c Children's Services) I Tansley ALA

Devon Library Services, Barley House, Isleworth Road, Exeter EX4 1RQ
☎(01392) 384304
Fax (01392) 384316
Head of School Library Service Ms L Medlock BEd ALA (e-mail: lmedlock@mf.devon-cc.gov.uk)

DONCASTER
Doncaster Metropolitan District Council, Education and Young People's Service, Top Road, Barnby Dun, Doncaster, South Yorkshire DN3 1DB
☎(01302) 881787
Fax (01302) 881787
Principal Librarian T W Finch ALA

DORSET
Dorset County Council, Dorset Library Service, Blandford Library – North Divisional Office, The Tabernacle, Blandford Camp, Blandford, Dorset DT11 7DW
☎(01258) 454744
Fax (01258) 459644
Senior Manager (North) Mrs V Chapman ALA (e-mail: v.chapman@dorset-cc.gov.uk)
School Library Manager Ms A Burgess BA DipLib ALA MLib

DUDLEY
Dudley Metropolitan Borough Council, Schools Library and Information Service, Milton Crescent, off Longfellow Road, The Straits, Lower Gornal, Dudley DY3 3EE
☎(01384) 812850
Fax (01384) 812851
e-mail: edlibpls@mbc.dudley.gov.uk
Principal Librarian Mrs D Ward ALA

DURHAM
Durham County Council, Arts, Libraries and Museums Department, County Hall, Durham DH1 5TY
☎0191 383 4459

Fax 0191 383 3694
Youth Services Manager P Burns ALA (e-mail: peter.burns@durham.gov.uk)

EALING

London Borough of Ealing, Central Library, Ealing Broadway Centre, Ealing, London W5 5JY
☎020 8567 3670
Fax 020 8840 2351
Children's Librarian Ms K Girling BALib ALA

West Ealing Library, Melbourne Avenue, London W13 9BA
☎020 8758 8837
Fax 020 8567 1736
Schools Librarian Mrs P A Jefferies ALA DMS

EAST RIDING OF YORKSHIRE

East Riding of Yorkshire Council, Library HQ, 10 Lord Roberts Road, Beverley HU17 9BE
☎(01482) 885087
Fax (01482) 881752
Senior Librarian, Schools Library Service A Kurvits BSc MPhil DipLib (01482 885270)

EAST SUSSEX

East Sussex County Council, Libraries, Information and Arts, 44 St Anne's Crescent, Lewes, East Sussex BN7 1SQ
☎(01273) 481329
Fax (01273) 481716
Head of Special Client Services Mrs V Warren BA ALA

Schools Library Service, Hammonds Drive, Lottbridge Drove, Hampden Park, Eastbourne, East Sussex BN23 6PW
☎(01323) 416324
Fax (01323) 412806
Manager, Schools Library Service Ms R Drever ALA

ENFIELD

London Borough of Enfield, PO Box 58, Civic Centre, Silver Street, Enfield EN1 3XJ
☎020 8379 3748
Fax 020 8379 3777
Principal Librarian, Children and Education Ms L Love BA(Hons) DipLib ALA

Library Resources Unit, Southgate Town Hall, Green Lanes, London N13 4XD
☎020 8379 2708
Fax 020 8379 2761
url: http://www.enfield.gov.uk
Schools Library Service Librarian Ms S Smith BSc MA ALA

ESSEX

Essex County Council, County Library HQ, Goldlay Gardens, Chelmsford, Essex CM2 0EW
☎(01245) 284981
Fax (01245) 492780
url: http://www.essexcc.gov.uk/libraries/
Children's Services Manager Mrs M Tarrant (e-mail: moirat@essexcc.gov.uk)

School Library Service Manager H Roberton (01245 353149, Fax 01245 353206, e-mail: essexsls@dial.pipex.com)

GATESHEAD
Gateshead Metropolitan Borough Council, Youth Services Team, Dryden PDC, Evistones Road, Low Fell, Gateshead NE9 5UR
☎0191 487 1895
Fax 0191 491 1394
Youth Services Manager Mrs B Wood BA ALA

GLOUCESTERSHIRE
Gloucestershire County Council, County Library, Arts and Museums Service, Quayside House, Shire Hall, Gloucester GL1 2HY
☎(01452) 425020
Fax (01452) 425042
e-mail: clams@gloscc.gov.uk
Principal Librarian, Learning and Literacy Mrs E Dubber BA ALA (01452 425030; e-mail: edubber@gloscc.gov.uk)

Schools Library Service, Churchdown House, Hucclecote, Gloucester GL3 3QL
☎(01452) 427240
Fax (01452) 427443
e-mail: glossls@dial.pipex.com
Principal Librarian, Learning and Literacy Mrs E Dubber BA ALA (01452 425030; e-mail: edubber@gloscc.gov.uk)

GREENWICH
London Borough of Greenwich, Children's and Young People's Service, Eltham Library, Eltham High Street, London SE9 1TS
☎020 8850 2268
Fax 020 8850 1368
Senior Library Manager Ms L Donnelly BA ALA

The Project Loans Service, West Greenwich Library, Greenwich High Road, London SE10 8NN
☎020 8853 1691
Fax 020 8858 3512
Education Librarian Ms S Saunders DMS BA ALA

HACKNEY
London Borough of Hackney, Young People's Services, Stamford Hill Library, Portland Avenue, London N16 6SB
☎020 8356 2573
Fax 020 8809 5986
Library Manager H Coffey

HALTON
Halton Borough Council, Halton Lea Library, Halton Lea, Runcorn, Cheshire WA7 3PF
☎(01928) 715351
Fax (01928) 790231
Young Persons Officer Mrs A Watt BA(Hons) ALA
(Schools library services provided by Education Library Service, Cheshire: see Cheshire)

HAMMERSMITH AND FULHAM

London Borough of Hammersmith and Fulham, Children's Library Service, Hammersmith Library, Shepherds Bush Road, Hammersmith, London W6 7AT
☎020 8576 5055 ext 3811
Fax 020 8576 5022
Principal Librarian, Public Services D A Herbert BA MLS ALA (e-mail: d.herbert@libs.lbhf.gov.uk)

Schools' Library Service, Teachers' Resource Centre, Clem Attlee Court, Lillie Road, Fulham, London SW6 7PU
☎020 8576 5256
Fax 020 8576 5022
Senior Librarian, Community Services Ms A Stirrup BA ALA (020 8576 5055)

HAMPSHIRE

Hampshire County Council, County Library, 81 North Walls, Winchester, Hants SO23 8BY
☎(01962) 846084
Fax (01962) 856615
e-mail: libsjd@hants.gov.uk
url: http://www.hants.gov.uk/library/index.html
Assistant County Librarian, Children's, Schools and Community Services J Dunne BA ALA

HARINGEY

London Borough of Haringey, Wood Green Central Library, High Road, Wood Green, London N22 6XD
☎020 8888 1292
Fax 020 8889 0110
Neighbourhood Librarian Ms J Harvey

Schools Library Service, Professional Development Centre, Downhills Park Road, London N17 6AR
☎020 8829 5043
Fax 020 8365 8253
School Services Librarian Ms C Collingborn

HARROW

London Borough of Harrow, Young People's and School Library Services Department, Civic Centre Library, PO Box 4, Harrow, Middlesex HA1 2UU
☎020 8424 1052
Fax 020 8424 1971
Principal Librarian, Young People's and School Library Services Mrs S Bussey BA ALA

HARTLEPOOL

Hartlepool Borough Council, Central Library, 124 York Road, Hartlepool TS26 9DE
☎(01429) 272905
Fax (01429) 275685
Children's Services Officer Ms D Sparrowhawk
Children's Librarian Ms P Turner
Schools Resources Service: see Redcar & Cleveland (cooperative service with Middlesbrough, Redcar & Cleveland and Stockton-on-Tees)

HAVERING

London Borough of Havering, Central Library, St Edwards Way, Romford, Essex RM1 3AR
☎(01708) 772397
Fax (01708) 772391
Principal Librarian, School Library Service Mrs J Shoush ALA

HEREFORDSHIRE

Herefordshire Council, Libraries and Information Service, Young People's Library Service, Shirehall, Hereford HR1 2HY
☎(01432) 359830
Young People's Library Services Manager Mrs J Radburn BA PGCE DipLib ALA
Young People's Library Services Librarian Mrs D Probert BLib ALA

HERTFORDSHIRE

Hertfordshire County Council, Community Information Directorate: Libraries, New Barnfield, Travellers Lane, Hatfield, Herts AL10 8XG
☎(01707) 281583
Fax (01707) 281589
Young People's Services Manager Ms C Hall BA ALA (e-mail: christine.hall@hertscc.gov.uk)
Joint Heads of Schools Library Service Ms H Boothroyd BA ALA, Ms S Jones MA ALA (01707 281630; fax 01707 281611)

HILLINGDON

London Borough of Hillingdon, Central Library, 14-15 High Street, Uxbridge, Middlesex UB8 1HD
☎See below
Fax (01895) 811164/239794 (Hillingdon Libraries)
e-mail: clibrary@lbhill.gov.uk
url: http://www.hillingdon.gov.uk
Children and Youth Services Manager Ms H Lorusso ALA (01895 250703; e-mail: hlorusso@lbhill.gov.uk)
Children and Schools Manager Ms E Smyth ALA (01895 250715; e-mail: esmyth@lbhill.gov.uk)

HOUNSLOW

London Borough of Hounslow, Young People's Library Service, Centrespace, 24 Treaty Centre, High Street, Hounslow, Middlesex TW3 1ES
☎020 8862 6922
Fax 020 8862 5669
Principal Librarian, Library Management Group Ms F Stanbury ALA (e-mail: frances-stanbury@cip.org.uk)

ISLE OF WIGHT

Isle of Wight Council, Children's Library Service, Upper St James' Street, Newport, Isle of Wight PO30 1LQ
☎(01983) 529463
Fax (01983) 825972
e-mail: s&c@sclibiow.demon.co.uk
Children's Library Service Manager Miss G Wanless BA ALA
School Library Service Manager Vacant

ISLINGTON

London Borough of Islington, Central Library, 2 Fieldway Crescent, London N5 1PF
☎020 7689 7962
Fax 020 7689 7995
Principal Librarian, Services to Children and Young People Ms M Snook BLib ALA

Education Library Service, Block D, Barnsbury Complex, Barnsbury Park, London N1 1QG
☎020 7457 5827
Fax 020 7457 5564
e-mail: lb@iels.demon.co.uk
Head of Education Library Service Ms P Dix

KENSINGTON AND CHELSEA

Royal Borough of Kensington and Chelsea, Chelsea Library, Old Town Hall, Kings Road, London SW3 5EE
☎020 7361 4053
Fax 020 7351 1294
Youth Services Librarian Ms A T Cahill BSc DipLib ALA

Schools Library Service, Isaac Newton Centre for Professional Development, 108A Lancaster Road, London W11 1QS
☎020 7221 4078
Fax 020 7243 1570
Schools' Librarian Ms S Riley MLS ALA

KENT

Kent County Council, Arts and Libraries, Gibson Drive, Kings Hill, West Malling, Kent ME19 4AL
☎(01622) 605213
Fax (01622) 605221
Principal Young People's Librarian and Learning Resources Manager Ms L Prestage BA MA ALA DipMgmt (01622 605211; e-mail: lindsay.prestage@kent.gov.uk)

KINGSTON UPON HULL

Kingston upon Hull City Council, Hull Central Library, Albion Street, Kingston upon Hull HU1 3TF
☎(01482) 616806
Fax (01482) 616827
url: http://www.hullcc.gov.uk
Senior Librarian Ms L Benton

Schools Library Service, James Reckitt Library, Holderness Road, Kingston upon Hull HU1 1EA
☎(01482) 225587
Head of Libraries and Arts B Chapman

KINGSTON UPON THAMES

Royal Borough of Kingston upon Thames, New Malden Library, Kingston Road, New Malden, Surrey KT3 3LY
☎020 8547 6543
Fax 020 8547 6545
url: http://www.kingston.gov.uk

Manager M Treacy (e-mail: mike@lucy4013.co.uk)

Schools Library Service, Fairfield Centre, Fairfield East, Kingston upon Thames, Surrey KT1 2PT
☎020 8408 9100
Schools Library Service Manager Ms A Tozer, Ms K Priestley (job-share)

KIRKLEES
Kirklees Metropolitan District Council, Cultural Services HQ, Red Doles Lane, Huddersfield HD2 1YF
☎(01484) 226325 (direct), (01484) 226300
Fax (01484) 226342
e-mail: books.plus-kirklees@btinternet.com
Manager (Books+) and Principal Children's and Young People's Librarian Ms J Madden BA ALA

KNOWSLEY
Knowsley Metropolitan Borough Council, Page Moss Library, Stockbridge Lane, Huyton, Knowsley, Merseyside L36 3SA
☎0151 482 1306
Fax 0151 482 1304

School Library Service, Kirkby Library, Newtown Gardens, Kirkby, Knowsley, Merseyside L32 8RR
☎0151 443 4285
Fax 0151 443 4283
School Library Service Manager Ms P Jones BA ALA

LAMBETH
London Borough of Lambeth, Children and Young People's Service, Carnegie Library, 188 Horne Hill Road, London SE24 0AG
☎020 7926 0750
Fax 020 7926 0751
Children's and Young People's Services Manager S Garner BA DipLib ALA (020 7926 6060, fax 020 7926 6072)

LANCASHIRE
Lancashire County Council, School Library Service, Bowran Street, Preston, Lancs PR1 2UX
☎(01772) 264041
Fax (01772) 263391
e-mail: maninfo@library.org.uk
County Library Manager D G Lightfoot MA DLIS ALA
Manager, Young People's Services Mrs J Wolstenholme DMS ALA (01772 264040)

LEEDS
Leeds City Council, Library and Information Services HQ, 32 York Road, Leeds LS9 8TD
☎0113 214 3310
Fax 0113 214 3312
url: http://www.leeds.gov.uk
Head of Children's Services Vacant

School Library Service, Foxcroft Close, Leeds LS6 3NT
☎0113 214 4531

Fax 0113 214 4532
School Library Service Manager Mrs M Drinkwater MA ALA

LEICESTER
Leicester City Council, Libraries and Information Services, Beaumont Leys Library,
Beaumont Way, Leicester LE4 1DS
☎0116 299 5460
Fax 0116 234 0078
Area Librarian N Morgan (0116 299 5472)
(Leicester has joint provision for schools library services with Leicestershire: see
Leicestershire)

LEICESTERSHIRE
Leicestershire County Council, Leicestershire Libraries and Information Service, County
Hall, Glenfield, Leicester LE3 8SS
☎0116 265 7388
Fax 0116 265 7370
Senior Adviser, Children's, Youth and Community Mrs C Dyer BA ALA (e-mail:
cdyer@leics.gov.uk)

Library Services for Education, Rothley Cross Road, 929-931 Loughborough Road,
Rothley, Leicester LE7 7NH
☎0116 267 8000
Fax 0116 267 8039
County Education Librarian Mrs G Willars MA ALA (e-mail: gwillars@leics.gov.uk)

LEWISHAM
London Borough of Lewisham, Lewisham Education and Community Services, The Library
Service, 3rd Floor, Laurence House, 1 Catford Road, Catford, London SE6 4RU
☎020 8695 6000 ext 8027
Fax 020 8314 3039
Acting Head of Library Service Ms J Newton

LINCOLNSHIRE
Lincolnshire County Council, Education and Cultural Services Directorate, County Offices,
Newland, Lincoln LN1 1YL
☎(01522) 552804
Fax (01522) 552811
Special Services Manager G Elgar BA(Hons) DipLib ALA

LIVERPOOL
Liverpool City Council, Central Library, William Brown Street, Liverpool L3 8EW
☎0151 233 5841
Fax 0151 233 5842
e-mail: central@lvpublib.demon.co.uk
Coordinator for Children's Support Services Vacant

LONDON, City of
Corporation of London, Barbican Library, Barbican Centre, London EC2Y 8DS
☎020 7628 9447
Fax 020 7638 2249
Children's Librarian Mrs M-A Stevens BA ALA

LUTON

Luton Borough Council, Children & Young People's Service, Leagrave Library, Marsh Road, Luton LU3 2NL
☎(01582) 597851
Fax (01582) 560012
Principal Librarian (Children, Young People and Schools Library Service) Mrs J Hair ALA

Schools Library Service, Leagrave Library, Marsh Road, Luton LU3 2NL
☎(01582) 598065
Fax (01582) 847077
Senior Librarian, Schools Library Service R Luscombe BA MLS ALA

MANCHESTER

Manchester City Council, North District Libraries, Abraham Moss Centre, Crescent Road, Manchester M8 5UF
☎0161 721 4555
Fax 0161 721 4927
e-mail: libbyt@libraries.manchester.gov.uk
Senior Librarian, Children's Services Ms L Tempest MA ALA

MEDWAY

Medway Council, Children's and Young People's Services, Gillingham Library, High Street, Gillingham, Kent ME7 1BG
☎(01634) 281066
Children's and Young People's Librarian D Mead BA ALA (Librarian for under-8s)

Children's and Young People's Services, Strood Library, Bryant Road, Strood, Rochester, Kent ME2 3EP
☎(01634) 718161 (tel/fax)
Children's and Young People's Librarian Mrs G Paterson MA DipLib ALA (Librarian for over-8s)
(Medway shares a schools library service provided by Kent: see Kent)

MERTON

London Borough of Merton, Libraries and Heritage Services, Merton Civic Centre, London Road, Morden, Surrey SM4 5DX
☎020 8545 3773
Fax 020 8545 3629
e-mail: fm047@viscount.org.uk
Principal Librarian: Lending, Information and Children's Services G Brewin ALA
Senior Young People's Schools' Librarian Ms J Graves BA ALA

MIDDLESBROUGH

Middlesbrough Borough Council, Education Support Service, c/o Berwick Hills Library, Crossfell Road, Berwick Hills, Middlesbrough TS3 7RP
☎(01642) 246947
Fax (01642) 218112
Senior Librarian, Education Support Ms P Holt
(Schools Resources Service: see Redcar and Cleveland. Cooperative service with Hartlepool, Redcar & Cleveland and Stockton-on-Tees)

MILTON KEYNES

Milton Keynes Council, Children's Service, Central Library, 555 Silbury Boulevard, Central
Milton Keynes MK9 3HL
☎(01908) 254050
Fax (01908) 254089
Children's Librarian Mrs E Carrick BA ALA, Mrs M Herriman BA DipLib ALA (job share)
(01908 254081)
School Library Service, Bletchley Library, Westfield Road, Bletchley, Milton Keynes
MK2 2RA
☎(01908) 647611
Fax (01908) 645562
Schools Librarian Mrs R Marks MA ALA

NEWCASTLE UPON TYNE

Newcastle upon Tyne City Council, Priority Services, Byker Library, Brinkburn Street,
Newcastle upon Tyne NE6 2AR
☎0191 265 5510/0191 224 3277
Fax 0191 265 5553
Priority Services Manager Mrs J Hall ALA

NEWHAM

London Borough of Newham, Stratford Reference Library, Water Lane, London E15 4NJ
☎020 8557 8727/020 8519 6346
Fax 020 8503 1525
Acting Principal Advisory Services Librarian (Children, Local Studies and Reference)
Ms J Davies BSc DipLib

Schools Library Services, Canning Town Library, Barking Road, London E16 4HQ
☎020 7476 2925
Fax 020 7511 8693
Resources Manager Ms J Stannard

NORFOLK

Norfolk County Council, Library and Information Service, County Hall, Martineau Lane,
Norwich NR1 2DH
☎(01603) 222271
Fax (01603) 222422
Assistant Director Mrs J Holland BA ALA (01603 222272; e-mail:
jennifer.holland.lib@norfolk.gov.uk)
Senior Librarian, Young People's Services Dr D Fraser BA ALA (01603 222270; e-mail:
dorne.fraser.lib@norfolk.gov.uk)

School Library Service, County Hall, Martineau Lane, Norwich NR1 2DH
☎(01603) 222266
Fax (01603) 222422
Principal Area Librarian Mrs J Emerson BA ALA (tel./fax: 01603 439981; e-mail:
joan.emerson.lib@norfolk.gov.uk)
School Library Service Manager P Cocker (01603 222266; e-mail:
philip.cocker.lib@norfolk.gov.uk)

NORTH EAST LINCOLNSHIRE

North East Lincolnshire Council, Schools Library Service, Broadway, Grimsby, North East

Lincolnshire DN34 5RS
☎(01472) 323654
Fax (01472) 323653
Senior Librarian Mrs J M Sargent BA DipLib (01472 323614)
Schools Service Librarian Mrs V Marson

NORTH LINCOLNSHIRE
North Lincolnshire Council, Scunthorpe Central Library, Carlton Street, Scunthorpe, North
Lincolnshire DN15 6TX
☎(01724) 860161
Fax (01724) 859737
e-mail: scunthorpe.ref@central.library.demon.co.uk
Senior Librarian, Young People's Services C Brabazon BA ALA

Schools Library Service, Frodingham Library, Trent Street, Scunthorpe, North Lincolnshire
DN16 1UE
☎(01724) 865420
Fax (01724) 859737
Librarian, Young People's Services Mrs R Scotting

NORTH SOMERSET
North Somerset Council, Service for Children and Young People, Weston Library, The
Boulevard, Weston-super-Mare, Somerset BS23 1PL
☎(01934) 620373/636638
Fax (01934) 413046
Librarian for Services to Children and Young People (South Area) Mrs M M Coleman
ALA

NORTH TYNESIDE
North Tyneside Metropolitan District Council, Children and Young People's Service, St
Edmund's Building, Station Road, Backworth, Tyne and Wear NE27 0RU
☎0191 200 8223
Fax 0191 200 8231
Manager Ms J Clements MBE BA ALA
(Includes a support service to schools)

NORTH YORKSHIRE
North Yorkshire County Council, Special Services, County Library, 21 Grammar School
Lane, Northallerton, North Yorkshire DL6 1DF
☎(01609) 776271
Fax (01609) 780793
e-mail: nycl@dial.pipex.com
Special Services Adviser Mrs B J Scatchard ALA

School Library Service, County Library, 21 Grammar School Lane, Northallerton, North
Yorkshire DL6 1DF
☎(01609) 776271/776162
Fax (01609) 780793
Acting Principal Librarian, School Library Service Mrs B Hooper ALA

NORTHAMPTONSHIRE
Northamptonshire County Council, Library Headquarters, PO Box 259, 27 Guildhall Road,
Northampton NN1 1BA

☎(01604) 620262
Fax (01604) 632443
Principal Libraries and Information Officer (Service Development) Ms E L Jarvis BA
MA DipLib ALA DMS (e-mail: ejarvis@northamptonshire.gov.uk)
Assistant County Librarian, Children and Young People Ms L Saunders BA DipLib ALA
(e-mail: lsaunders@northamptonshire.gov.uk)

Learning Resources for Education, Northamptonshire Libraries and Information Service, PO
Box 259, 27 Guildhall Road, Northampton NN1 1BA
☎(01604) 620262
Fax (01604) 626789
Principal Libraries and Information Officer (Service Delivery) N L Matthews BA ALA
DMS (e-mail: nmatthews@northamptonshire.gov.uk)
Learning Resources Manager Ms K Harrison MA DipLib ALA DMS (e-mail:
kharrison@northamptonshire.gov.uk)

NORTHUMBERLAND
Northumberland County Council, Amenities Division, County Library HQ, The Willows,
Morpeth, Northumberland NE61 1TA
☎(01670) 534507
Fax (01670) 534521
e-mail: amenities@northumberland.gov.uk
Principal Library and Archive Officer C Baker ALA

Schools Library Service, Hepscott Park, Stannington, Morpeth, Northumberland NE61 6NF
☎(01670) 534354
Fax (01670) 533591
Principal Library and Archive Officer C Baker ALA

NOTTINGHAM
City of Nottingham Council, Department of Leisure and Community Services, Libraries,
Information and Museums Services, 14 Hounds Gate, Nottingham NG1 7BD
☎0115 915 7241
Children's Services Librarian Ms D Sheppard ALA, Ms E Dykes BA ALA (job share)
(Schools Library Service offered in partnership with Nottinghamshire County Council: see
Nottinghamshire)

NOTTINGHAMSHIRE
Nottinghamshire County Council, Education Library Service, Glaisdale Parkway,
Nottingham NG8 4GP
☎0115 985 4200/1
Fax 0115 928 6400
Principal Libraries Officer (Resources and Commissioning) P Marshall BA DipLib ALA

Education Library Service, Units 4-6, Glaisdale Parkway, Glaisdale Drive, Bilborough,
Nottingham NG8 4GP
☎0115 985 4200
Fax 0115 928 6400
e-mail: elsg@nottscc.gov.uk
Principal Librarian (Advisory) Mrs C Brittain MA ALA
Principal Librarian (Resources) Mrs J Huffer BA DipLib ALA

OLDHAM

Oldham Metropolitan District Council, Children's Library Service, Oldham Library, Union Street, Oldham, Lancs OL1 1DN
☎0161 911 4634
Fax 0161 911 4630
Community Children's Librarian C Dunn BA(Hons) (0161 911 4635), B Fitzsimons (0161 911 4639)

Schools Library Service, Fitton Hill Library, Fir Tree Avenue, Fitton Hill, Oldham, Lancs OL8 2QP
☎0161 678 6539
Senior Library Assistant Ms R Radcliffe

OXFORDSHIRE

Oxfordshire County Council, Cultural Services, South Area Libraries, Wantage Library, Stirlings Road, Wantage, Oxford OX12 7BB
☎(01235) 771131
Fax (01235) 770951
Assistant County Librarian Mrs V Angel BA DipLib ALA (e-mail: veronica.angel.occ@dial.pipex.com)

PETERBOROUGH

Peterborough City Council, Children's Library Services, Central Library, Broadway, Peterborough PE1 1RX
☎(01733) 348343
Fax (01733) 319140
Senior Librarian, Children's Services Ms A Rowson BA MA ALA
(Schools Library Service shared with Cambridgeshire County Council: see Cambridgeshire)

PLYMOUTH

Plymouth City Council, Schools Library Service, Schools Library Centre, Chaucer Way, Manadon, Plymouth PL5 3EJ
☎(01752) 780713
Fax (01752) 767623
Coordinator of Library Services to Young People Ms S Whittle (e-mail: whittles@plymouth.gov.uk)
Schools Librarian Ms M Wild

POOLE

Borough of Poole, Children's Services, Central Library, Dolphin Centre, Poole BH15 1QE
☎(01202) 673910 ext 238
Fax (01202) 676401
Children's Services Librarian Mrs E Ireland BEd DipILM ALA
(School library service provided by Dorset: see Dorset)

PORTSMOUTH

Portsmouth City Council, Children's Library Service, Central Library, Guildhall Square, Portsmouth PO1 2DX
☎023 9281 9311
Fax 023 9283 9855
City Children's Librarian Ms E Stevenson BSc ALA (e-mail: estevenson@portsmouth.gov.uk)

School Library Service, King Richard School, Allaway Avenue, Paulsgrove, Portsmouth
PO6 4QP
☎023 9232 6612
Fax 023 9237 5245
City Schools Librarian P Bone BA ALA (e-mail: pbone@portsmouth.gov.uk)

READING

Reading Borough Council, Central Library, Abbey Square, Reading, Berks RG1 3BQ
☎0118 901 5950
Senior Lending Librarian Mrs E Delaney ALA
Shared Education Library Resource Centre: see Bracknell Forest

REDBRIDGE

London Borough of Redbridge, Central Library, Clements Road, Ilford, Essex IG1 1EA
☎020 8478 7145
Fax 020 8553 4185
Senior Children's and Schools' Librarian Ms C Pountney BA ALA (e-mail:
Christine.Pountney@redbridge.gov.uk)

REDCAR AND CLEVELAND

Redcar and Cleveland Borough Council, Library Service, Redcar and Cleveland House, PO
Box 86, Kirkleatham Street, Redcar TS10 1XX
☎(01642) 444319
Fax (01642) 444341
Children's and Special Services Officer Ms S Anderson BA(Lib)

Schools Resources Service, The Cooper Centre, Beech Grove, South Bank, Middlesbrough
TS6 6SU
☎(01642) 289199
Fax (01642) 289199
Schools Resources Officer Mrs C Rimmington
(Cooperative service with Hartlepool, Middlesbrough and Stockton-on-Tees)

RICHMOND UPON THAMES

London Borough of Richmond upon Thames, Young People's Services, The Cottage, Little
Green, Richmond TW9 1QL
☎020 8940 0590
Fax 020 8940 8030
e-mail: yps@richmond.gov.uk
Young People's Services Manager Ms H M O'Brien BA(Hons) DipLib ALA

ROCHDALE

Rochdale Metropolitan District Council, Children's Library Service, Wheatsheaf Library,
Baillie Street, Rochdale, Greater Manchester OL16 1JZ
☎(01706) 864972
Fax (01706) 864992
Bibliographical and Special Services Librarian Mrs F Fletcher ALA (01706 864964)

ROTHERHAM

Rotherham Metropolitan Borough Council, Education and Young People's Services, Maltby
Library, High Street, Maltby, Rotherham, South Yorkshire S66 8LA
☎(01709) 813034

Fax (01709) 798269
Senior Librarian, Education and Young People's Services S J Hird BA ALA

RUTLAND

Rutland County Council, Children and Young People's Service, Oakham Library, Catmos Street, Oakham, Rutland LE15 6HW
☎(01572) 722918
Fax (01572) 724906
Children and Young People's Librarian Ms D Wright BA(Hons) ALA

ST HELENS

Metropolitan Borough of St Helens, The Rivington Centre, Rivington Road, St Helens, Merseyside WA10 4ND
☎(01744) 455403
Fax (01744) 455350
East District Manager, Libraries Ms S Thomas BA DMS

Central Library, Gamble Building, Victoria Square, St Helens, Merseyside WA10 1DY
☎(01744) 456989
Fax (01744) 20836
Children's Services Ms S Thomas (01744 456956)
Schools Library Service Manager Ms J Lilley BA(Hons) DipLib (01744 455412)

SALFORD

Salford City Council, Children's Services, Swinton Library, Chorley Road, Swinton, Manchester M27 4AE
☎0161 793 3568
Fax 0161 727 7071
Senior Librarian, Children and Young People Mrs P Manley BA MLS PGDipLib MA(Ed)

Schools Library Service, Salford Education Centre, London Street, Salford M6 6DT
☎0161 743 4207

SANDWELL

Sandwell Metropolitan Borough Council, Resource Matters, Sandwell Education Library Service, Popes Lane, Oldbury, West Midlands B69 4PJ
☎0121 569 4415
Fax 0121 569 4481
e-mail: resource.matters@sandwell.gov.uk
url: http://www.earl.org.uk/earl/members/sandwell
Principal Libraries Officer (Youth and Education) Ms H Vickerman BA ALA

SEFTON

Sefton Council, Schools and Children's Library Services, Crosby Library, Crosby Road North, Waterloo, Merseyside L22 0LQ
☎0151 257 6403/0151 330 5771
Fax 0151 934 5770
Schools and Children's Officer Ms J H Briscoe JP ALA (e-mail: j.briscoeseflib@merseymail.com)

SHEFFIELD

Sheffield City Council, Libraries, Archives and Information Department, Learning and Young People's Unit, Bannerdale Education Centre, Bannerdale Road, Sheffield S7 2EW
☎0114 250 6840
Fax 0114 250 6841
Group Manager A Milroy BA DipLib ALA (0114 250 6839)

SHROPSHIRE

Shropshire County Council, Children's and Schools Library Services, Column House, 7 London Road, Shrewsbury SY2 6NW
☎(01743) 255030
Fax (01743) 255050
County Education and Young People's Librarian G Dickins BA ALA (01743 255005)

SLOUGH

Slough Borough Council, Community Services Dept, Slough Library, High Street, Slough SL1 1EA
☎(01753) 535166
Fax (01753) 825050
Senior Librarian Mrs D Flood BA(Hons) DMS ALA (01753 787506)
Children's and Outreach Librarian Ms K Croll BA(Hons) MSc ALA (01753 787530)
Shared Education Library Resource Centre: see Bracknell Forest

SOLIHULL

Solihull Metropolitan Borough Council, Central Library, Homer Road, Solihull, West Midlands B91 3RG
☎0121 704 6969
Fax 0121 704 6991
Head of Children's and Schools Services Ms T Scragg MA BLS(Hons)

Schools Library Service, Central Library, Homer Road, Solihull, West Midlands B91 3RG
☎0121 704 6984
Schools Librarian Mrs S Laurence BA(Hons) ALA

SOMERSET

Somerset County Council, Resources for Learning, Parkway, Bridgwater, Somerset TA6 4RL
☎(01278) 421015
Fax (01278) 444284
Assistant County Librarian, Children's Learning and Special Services Miss R Boyd BA ALA (e-mail: rboyd@somerset.gov.uk)

SOUTH GLOUCESTERSHIRE

South Gloucestershire Council, Downend Library, Buckingham Gardens, Downend, South Gloucestershire BS16 5TW
☎(01454) 868451
Children and Young People's Librarian Ms W Nicholls ALA

SOUTH TYNESIDE

South Tyneside Metropolitan Borough Council, Central Library, Prince George Square, South Shields, Tyne and Wear NE33 2PE

☎0191 427 1717 ext 2141
Fax 0191 455 8085
Young People's Services Librarian Ms K Armstrong

School Library Service, Chuter Ede Education Centre, Goldsworthy Road, South Shields,
Tyne and Wear NE34 9UG
☎0191 519 1909 ext 405
Fax 0191 519 0600
Schools Librarian Miss K Hall

SOUTHAMPTON
Southampton City Council, Central Children's Library, Civic Centre, Southampton SO14 7LW
☎020 8083 2598
Fax 020 8033 6305
e-mail: e.whale@southampton.gov.uk
url: http://www.southampton.gov.uk/libraries/
Principal Children's Librarian C Barnes BA ALA

School Library Service Centre, Warren Crescent, Shirley Warren, Southampton SO16 6AY
☎020 8078 0507
Fax 020 8070 2783
Senior Schools Librarian Miss C Thomas ALA

SOUTHEND ON SEA
Southend on Sea Borough Council, Children's and Access Services, Southend Library,
Victoria Avenue, Southend on Sea, Essex SS2 6EX
☎(01702) 612621
Fax (01702) 469241
e-mail: sos@dial.pipex.com
Head of Children's and Access Services M Thres BA ALA

SOUTHWARK
London Borough of Southwark, Southwark Education & Leisure, 15 Spa Road, London
SE16 3QW
☎020 7525 1582
Fax 020 7525 1536
Young People's Services Librarian J Hurst BA(Hons) DipLib (e-mail:
jhurst@dial.pipex.com)
Service Development Librarian, Children and Young People Vacant (020 7525 1581,
Fax 020 7525 1568)

The Education Library Service, Education Resource Centre, Cator Street, London SE15
6AA
☎020 7525 2830
Fax 020 7525 2837
Librarian i/c Ms E Brumant

STAFFORDSHIRE
Staffordshire County Council, Library and Information Services, Friars Terrace, Stafford
ST17 4AY
☎(01785) 278587
Fax (01785) 278319

Assistant County Librarian, Young People's Services Mrs M Williams MA(Hons) DipLib ALA (e-mail: morna.williams@staffordshire.gov.uk)

STOCKPORT
Stockport Metropolitan Borough Council, Dialstone Centre, Lisburne Lane, Stockport SK2 7LL
☎0161 474 2253
Fax 0161 483 0950
Head of Services to Children Ms A Ellison BA MA

STOCKTON-ON-TEES
Stockton-on-Tees Borough Council, Priority Services Section, Bedale Library, Bedale Avenue, Billingham, Stockton-on-Tees TS23 1AJ
☎(01642) 397597
Fax (01642) 393924
Priority Services Officer Mrs L King BA(Hons)
Senior Children's Officer T Quantrill BSc(Hons)
Children's Librarian Miss A Lockwood MA
Schools Resources Service: see Redcar & Cleveland (cooperative service with Middlesbrough, Redcar & Cleveland and Hartlepool)

STOKE-ON-TRENT
Stoke-on-Trent City Council, Children's and Youth Service, Bentilee Library, Ubberley Road, Bentilee, Stoke-on-Trent ST2 0EW
☎(01782) 238496
Senior Children's Librarian Ms C Lovatt BA, Ms E Grainger-Jarvis BSc (job share)

Schools Library Service, Staffordshire Library and Information Service, Friars Terrace, Stafford ST17 4AY
☎(01785) 278340
Fax (01785) 278319
e-mail: sls@staffordshire.gov.uk
Principal Librarian, SLS Mrs B Kettle ALA

SUFFOLK
Suffolk County Council, Schools Library Service, 3 Holywells Close, Ipswich, Suffolk IP3 0AW
☎(01473) 583507
Fax (01473) 583509
url: http://www.suffolkcc.gov.uk/libraries_and_heritage/
Schools Library Service Manager Vacant

SUNDERLAND
City of Sunderland Metropolitan District Council, Service to Young People, City Library and Arts Centre, 28-30 Fawcett Street, Sunderland SR1 1RE
☎0191 514 1235
Fax 0191 514 8444
Principal Officer, Young People and Special Services Mrs A Scott ALA

Schools Library Service, Broadway Centre, Springwell Road, Sunderland SR4 8NW
☎0191 553 5645/6 (tel./fax)
Senior Assistant Librarian Ms E Dowley BA ALA

SURREY
Surrey County Council, Runnymede Centre, Chertsey Road, Addlestone, Surrey KT15 2EP

Tel (01932) 582700
Fax (01932) 582727
Library Service Manager, North West Surrey Ms R Wilson (01932 582707; e-mail: r.wilson@surreycc.gov.uk)

SUTTON
London Borough of Sutton, Children's Library Service, Central Library, St Nicholas Way, Sutton, Surrey SM1 1EA
☎020 8770 4766
Fax 020 8770 4777
Children's Services Manager Mrs P Deakin BA ALA , Mrs J Allen BA ALA (020 8770 4622) (job share)

Schools Library Service, Central Library, St Nicholas Way, Sutton, Surrey SM1 1EA
☎020 8770 4754
Fax 020 8770 4666/4777
Schools Library Service Manager Mrs C Sawyer ALA

SWINDON
Swindon Borough Council, Central Library, Regent Circus, Swindon SN1 1QG
☎(01793) 463238
Fax (01793) 541319
Principal Librarian D Allen (01793 463230; e-mail: davidallen@swindon.gov.uk)

School Library Service, Wiltshire and Swindon Learning Resources, c/o Wiltshire County Council Libraries HQ, Bythesea Road, Trowbridge, Wilts BA14 8BS
☎(01225) 713700
Fax (01225) 713993
Head Ms S McCulloch

TAMESIDE
Tameside Metropolitan District Council, Children's/Youth Service, Denton Library, Peel Street, Denton, Manchester M34 3JX
☎0161 336 8234/320 3202
Fax 0161 337 8931
Principal Officer, Area Services Mrs C Simensky ALA

Schools Library Service, Education Development Centre, Lakes Road, Dukinfield, Tameside SK16 4TR
☎0161 343 5935
Fax 0161 339 8994
Librarian and Information Officer Ms L Parkin ALA

TELFORD AND WREKIN
Telford and Wrekin Council, Telford and Wrekin Libraries, Telford Library, St Quentin Gate, Town Centre, Telford, Shropshire TF3 4JG
☎(01952) 292151
Fax (01952) 292078
Lead Specialist, Children and Young People Mrs B Taylor BA ALA (01952 814541)
(Schools library service offered in partnership with Shropshire County Council: see Shropshire)

THURROCK
Thurrock Borough Council, Children's Services, Leisure, Libraries and Cultural Services

Department, Grays Library, Orsett Road, Grays, Essex RM17 5DX
☎(01375) 383611 (enquiries), (01375) 382555 ext 221 (administration)
Fax (01375) 370806
Children's Services Manager Miss R Jones BA(Hons) DipLib

TORBAY

Torbay Council, Children's Service, Torquay Central Library, Lymington Road, Torquay, Devon TQ1 3DT
☎(01803) 208300
Fax (01803) 208311
Children's Services Librarian Miss T West BA(Hons) ALA (01803 208289)

Schools Library Service, Torquay Central Library, Lymington Road, Torquay, Devon TQ1 3DT
☎(01803) 208293
Fax (01803) 208311
Centre Manager Miss M Granata
Senior Schools Librarian Mrs J Patridge

TOWER HAMLETS

London Borough of Tower Hamlets, Children's Library Services, Whitechapel Library, 77 Whitechapel High Street, London E1 7QX
☎020 7247 9510
Fax 020 7247 5731
Coordinator, Children's Library Services G Harrison BSc(Econ) MSc ALA

Tower Hamlets Professional Development Centre, English Street, London E3 4TA
☎020 7364 6428
Fax 020 7334 6422
Library Adviser Ms G Harris

TRAFFORD

Trafford Metropolitan District Council, Schools Library Service, Davyhulme Library, Hayeswater Road, Davyhulme, Greater Manchester M41 7BL
☎0161 912 2981/2982/2983
Fax 0161 912 2895
Education Services Librarian Miss S Kift BA ALA

WAKEFIELD

Wakefield Metropolitan District Council, Library HQ, Balne Lane, Wakefield WF2 0DQ
☎(01977) 722745
Fax (01924) 302245
Senior Librarian, Children's Services Mrs C Hayes BA ALA

Library HQ, Balne Lane, Wakefield WF2 0DQ
☎(01924) 302238
Fax (01924) 302245
Senior Librarian, Schools Library Services Mrs K Smith BA ALA

WALSALL

Walsall Metropolitan Borough Council, Central Library, Lichfield Street, Walsall WS1 1TR
☎(01922) 653108
Fax (01922) 722687

url: http://www.earl.org.uk/earl/members/walsall/
Children and Youth Library Services Manager Vacant

Schools Library Support Services, Education Development Centre, Pelsall Lane, Rushall, Walsall WS4 1NG
☎(01922) 685812
Fax (01922) 685813
e-mail: slss@walsalledc.rmplc.co.uk
School Library Services Manager P S Thompson BA ALA

WALTHAM FOREST
London Borough of Waltham Forest, Young People's Library Service, Leytonstone Library, 6 Church Lane, Leytonstone, London E11 1HG
☎020 8556 8600
Fax 020 8556 1026
e-mail: ypls@a.l.lbwf.gov.uk
Young People's Library Services Manager Miss H Manning MA ALA (e-mail: hilary.manning@a.l.lbwf.gov.uk)

WANDSWORTH
London Borough of Wandsworth, Children's Library Service, Battersea Library, Lavender Hill, London SW11 1JB
☎020 8871 7466
Fax 020 7978 4376
Senior Children's Librarian Ms N Finn BA(Hons) DipInfStud ALA

WARRINGTON
Warrington Borough Council, Young People's Services, Warrington Library, Museum Street, Warrington, Cheshire WA1 1JB
☎(01925) 442889 (switchboard), (01925) 442892 (specialist services)
Fax (01925) 411395
Managers of Young People's Services Mrs K Syder BA DipLib ALA, Mrs A Cowsill BA DipLib ALA
(Schools library services provided by Education Library Service, Cheshire: see Cheshire)

WARWICKSHIRE
Warwickshire County Council, County Library, Barrack Street, Warwick CV34 4TH
☎(01926) 412657
Fax (01926) 412471
e-mail: warcolib@dial.pipex.com
Head of Children's and Youth Services Mrs W Leek MA ALA CertEd

Schools Library Service, Unit 11b, Montague Road, Warwick CV34 5SX
☎(01926) 413462/413461
Fax (01926) 413438
e-mail: warwickshiresls@dial.pipex.com
Senior Adviser, Warwickshire Schools Library Service Miss C Merriman BA ALA
Resource Manager Mrs K Jones BA ALA

WEST BERKSHIRE
West Berkshire District Council, Newbury Library, Carnegie Road, Newbury RG14 5DW
☎(01635) 40972
Fax (01635) 35463

Children's Librarians Mrs S Deering-Punshon Blib(Hons) ALA, Mrs B Magee BA MA ALA, Mrs P Harper BA(Hons) ALA, Mrs R Preuss BA ALA
Shared Education Library Resource Centre: see Bracknell Forest

WEST SUSSEX
West Sussex County Council, Library Service, Bibliographical Support Services, Tannery Annexe, Westgate, Chichester, West Sussex PO19 3RT
☎(01243) 752370
Fax (01243) 752373
Head of Services to Children and Young People Ms L Sim BA ALA (e-mail: lsim@westsussex.gov.uk)

School Library Services Administration Centre, Tannery Annexe, Westgate, Chichester, West Sussex PO19 3RT
☎(01243) 752371
Fax (01243) 752373
Head of Schools Library Service Ms S A Heyes BA(Hons) CertEd ALA (e-mail: susan.heyes@westsussex.gov.uk)

WESTMINSTER
Westminster City Council, Children and Schools Library Service, Charing Cross Library, 4 Charing Cross Road, London WC2H 0HG
☎020 7641 6571
Fax 020 7641 6551
Children's and Schools Services Manager Ms S Wilkie BLib(Hons) ALA

Schools Library Service, 62 Shirland Road, London W9 2EH
☎020 7641 4321/0
Fax 020 7641 4322
Schools Library Service Manager N Fuller BA(Hons) AgDipLib ALA

WIGAN
Wigan Metropolitan Borough Council, Atherton Library, York Street, Atherton, Wigan M46 9JH
☎(01942) 404815
District Manager Mrs S Underwood BA

Schools Library Service, Shevington Library, Gathurst Lane, Shevington, Wigan WN6 8HA
☎(01257) 253269
Senior Schools Librarian Ms L Gavin

WILTSHIRE
Wiltshire County Council, Wiltshire and Swindon Learning Resources, Libraries and Heritage HQ, Bythesea Road, Trowbridge, Wiltshire BA14 8BS
☎(01225) 713742
Fax (01225) 350029
Head, Wiltshire and Swindon Learning Resources Mrs S McCulloch BA ALA

WINDSOR AND MAIDENHEAD
Royal Borough of Windsor and Maidenhead Council, Children's Library Services, Maidenhead Central Library, St Ives Road, Maidenhead, Berks SL6 1QU
☎(01628) 796969
Fax (01628) 796971
Senior Librarian, Young People Mrs P Dobby ALA
Shared Education Library Resource Centre: see Bracknell Forest

WIRRAL

Metropolitan Borough of Wirral, Children's Library Services, Bebington Central Library, Civic Way, Bebington, Wirral CH63 7PN
☎0151 643 7222
Fax 0151 643 7231
Librarian i/c, Young People's Services Ms S Powell Ba ALA

Wirral Schools Library Service, Wirral Education Centre, Acre Lane, Bromborough, Wirral CH62 7BZ
☎0151 346 1184
Fax 0151 334 0080
Schools' Librarian Ms M Bryning BA DipLib

WOKINGHAM

Wokingham District Council, Woodley Library, Headley Road, Woodley, Reading RG5 4JA
☎0118 969 9421
Team Leader, Children and Youth Services Mrs H Barnes BA ALA

WOLVERHAMPTON

Wolverhampton Metropolitan Borough Council, Central Library, Snow Hill, Wolverhampton WV1 3AX
☎(01902) 552023
Fax (01902) 552024
e-mail: wolverhampton.libraries@dial.pipex.com
Children and Young People's Service Manager Ms M Cockin ALA

Education Library Service, Jennie Lee Centre, Lichfield, Wednesfield, Wolverhampton WV11 3H7
☎(01902) 555906
Fax (01902) 555366
Senior Librarian, Children's and Young People's Services Ms S Lester BA(Hons)

WORCESTERSHIRE

Worcestershire County Council, School Library Service, Cultural Services, County Hall, Spetchley Road, Worcester WR5 2NP
☎(01905) 766233
Fax (01905) 766244
Principal Librarian, North and Services to Young People Ms C Reed BA ALA (e-mail: creed@worcestershire.gov.uk)

YORK

City of York Council, Children's and Youth Service, Acomb Library, Front Street, Acomb, York YO24 3BZ
☎(01904) 791135
Special Services Librarians C Appleton BA ALA, Ms F Postlethwaite BA ALA, Ms A Masters BA ALA (e-mail: spec.svcs.librarians@york.gov.uk)

SCOTLAND

ABERDEEN

Aberdeen City Council, Arts & Recreation Department (Libraries), Central Library, Rosemount Viaduct, Aberdeen AB25 1GW
☎(01224) 652501
Fax (01224) 641985
e-mail: centchild@globalweb.co.uk
Children's Services Librarian Ms A Stephen BEd ALA
Assistant Librarian, Central Children's Library Ms M Wands MA

Curriculum Resources and Information Service, Summerhill Education Centre, Stronsay Drive, Aberdeen AB15 6JA
☎(01224) 346114
Fax (01224) 208845
e-mail: slsacc@dial.pipex.com
url: http://www.rmplc.co.uk/eduweb/sites/acityed/services/s&c/cris/crisf
Principal Officer Mrs A Turriff BA MEd FLA (01224 346110; e-mail: a.turriff@dial.pipex.com)

ABERDEENSHIRE

Aberdeenshire Council, Library & Information Service, Meldrum Meg Way, The Meadows Industrial Estate, Old Meldrum, Aberdeen AB51 0GN
☎(01651) 872707
Fax (01651) 872142
Children's and Schools' Resources Librarian Miss M Wilson BEd DipLib ALA DMS (e-mail: mwilson.ed@aberdeenshire.gov.uk)
Primary School Librarian Mrs A Hogg BA

ANGUS

Angus Council, Cultural Services Department, County Buildings, Market Street, Forfar, Angus DD8 3WF
☎(01307) 461460
Fax (01307) 465920
e-mail: cultural@angus.gov.uk
Director, Cultural Services G N Drummond ALA

Educational Resource, Bruce House, Wellgate, Arbroath, Angus DD11 1TL
☎(01241) 435045
Educational Resources Librarian Ms M Hood BA ALA

ARGYLL AND BUTE

Argyll and Bute Council, Library HQ, Highland Avenue, Sandbank, Dunoon, Argyll PA23 8PB
☎(01369) 703214
Fax (01369) 705797
e-mail: andyewan@abc-libraries.demon.co.uk
Youth Services Librarian Ms D McLennan MA(Hons) ALA

CLACKMANNANSHIRE

Clackmannanshire Council, Library Services, 26-28 Drysdale Street, Alloa FK10 1JL
☎(01259) 722262
Fax (01259) 219469
e-mail: clack.lib@mail.easynet.co.uk
Library Services Manager D Hynd ALA (ext 27)
Team Leader (Childrens Services) Ms A Fulton BSc ALA (ext 24)
Team Leader (Community Services) J Blake BSc DipLib DipEdTech ALA (ext 24)
Children's Librarian Ms R Bruce BA ALA (ext 25)

COMHAIRLE NAN EILEAN SIAR (formerly Western Isles)

Comhairle Nan Eilean Siar, Leabharlainn Nan Eilean Siar, Public Library, Cromwell Street, Stornoway, Isle of Lewis HS1 2DA
☎(01851) 703064
Fax (01851) 705657
Senior Librarian, Youth Services Mrs J Robson ALAA ALA

Education Resource Centre, Kenneth Street, Stornoway, Isle of Lewis HS1 2DA
☎(01851) 703564
Fax (01851) 704709
Senior Librarian, Youth Services Mrs J Robson ALAA ALA

DUMFRIES AND GALLOWAY

Dumfries and Galloway Council, Libraries, Information and Archives, Central Support Unit, Catherine Street, Dumfries DG1 1JB
☎(01387) 253820
Fax (01387) 260294
e-mail: libs&i@dumgal.gov.uk
Section Librarian, Children and Young People's Services Ms G Swales BA ALA DipLib
Section Librarian, Schools Support Service Ms J Goldie BA DipLib ALA

DUNDEE

Dundee City Council, Children's Department, Central Library, The Wellgate, Dundee DD1 1DB
☎(01382) 434328
Fax (01382) 434642
Resource Worker Ms S Donaldson BSc

Neighbourhood Resources and Development Department, Development and QA Team, Arthurstone Neighbourhood Library, Arthurstone Terrace, Dundee DD4 6RT
☎(01382) 438888
Fax (01382) 436881
Senior Youth Resource Worker Ms L Moy BA ALA

School Library Service, Central Library, The Wellgate, Dundee DD1 1DB
☎(01382) 434335
Fax (01382) 434642
Resource Worker S Syme BA ALA (01382 434373; e-mail: stuart.syme@dundeecity.gov.uk)

EAST AYRSHIRE

East Ayrshire Council, The Dick Institute, 14 Elmbank Avenue, Kilmarnock KA1 3BU
☎(01563) 526401
Fax (01563) 529661
e-mail: libraries@east-ayrshire.gov.uk
Young People's Services (North) G Downie

Council Offices, Lugar, Cumnock KA18 3JQ
☎(01563) 555457
Fax (01563) 555400
Education Liaison Officer Ms P Standen (01563 555451; e-mail:
pat.standen@east-ayrshire.gov.uk)
Young People's Services (South) Ms M Patterson/Ms A McInnes

EAST DUNBARTONSHIRE

East Dunbartonshire Council, Cultural Services HQ, 2 West High Street, Kirkintilloch
G66 1AD
☎0141 776 5666
Fax 0141 776 0408
Acting Librarian, Young People's Services F MacArthur MA ALA
Assistant Librarian, Young People's Services I Gibson BA ALA

Education Dept, Curriculum Support Unit, Castlehill Primary School, Rosslyn Road,
Bearsden, Glasgow G61 4DL
☎0141 943 1689
Fax 0141 943 1688
Principal Curriculum Resources Officer Ms S Barron
Curriculum Resources Officer Ms L Owens
Curriculum Resources Officer Ms L Farrar

EAST LOTHIAN

East Lothian Council, Library and Museum HQ, Dunbar Road, Haddington, East Lothian
EH41 3PJ
☎(01620) 828212 (Senior Librarian), (01620) 828213 (Librarian)
Fax (01620) 828201
e-mail: hq@elothlib.demon.co.uk
url: http://www.earl.org.uk/partners/eastlothian/index.html
Senior Librarian, Young People's Services Ms A Hunter BA DipLib ALA
Librarian, Young People's Services Ms E Young ALA

EAST RENFREWSHIRE

East Renfrewshire Council, Cultural Services, Glen Street, Barrhead
G78 1QA
☎0141 577 3502 (Youth & Community Services Manager), 0141 557 3504 (Children's
Librarian)
Fax 0141 577 3501
Youth & Community Services Manager M Wright
Children's Librarian Mrs J Watt

EDINBURGH

City of Edinburgh Council, Central Library, George IV Bridge, Edinburgh EH1 1EG
☎0131 225 5584 ext 243/244/245

Fax 0131 225 8783
Principal Library Officer, Youth Services Ms B Rowan BA ALA

School Library Service, St Bernard's Education Centre, Dean Park Street, Edinburgh
EH4 1JS
☎0131 311 5600
Fax 0131 332 3848
Principal Officer, Libraries & Resources Ms A Ross BA(Hons) ALA
Service Librarian Ms V Walker ALA

FALKIRK

Falkirk Council, Library Services, Victoria Buildings, Queen Street, Falkirk FK2 7AF
☎(01324) 506800
Fax (01324) 506801
e-mail: falkirk-libsuprt@falkirk-libsuprt.demon.co.uk
Convenor, Young People's Services Working Group Ms Y Manning MA DipLib ALA

FIFE

Fife Council, East Area Library Services, Library HQ, St Catherine Street, Cupar, Fife KY15
4TA
☎(01334) 412285
Fax (01334) 412467
e-mail: info@cupar.fifelib.net
Children's Librarian Ms S J Deas

West Area Library Services, Central Library, 1 Abbot Street, Dunfermline KY12 7NL
☎(01383) 312600
Fax (01383) 312608
Senior Librarian, Young People's Services Ms F Craig

Schools Library Service, Auchterderran Staff Development and Resources Centre,
Woodend Road, Cardenden, Fife KY5 0NE
☎(01592) 414612
Schools Service Librarian Mrs M Gray

GLASGOW

Glasgow City Council, City Libraries and Archives, The Mitchell Library, North Street,
Glasgow G3 7DN
☎0141 287 2867
Fax 0141 287 2815/2871
Children's Services Co-ordinator Ms P McClean BA ALA

Education Resource Service, St Teresa's Primary RC School, 97 Scone Street, Glasgow
G21 1JF
☎0141 336 7407
Fax 0141 336 7412
e-mail: ersglasgow@easynet.co.uk
Principal Resources Development Officer Ms F Walker
Resource Centre Manager Ms M Ward
Educational Resource Librarians Ms C Edwards, Ms E Galt

HIGHLAND

Highland Council, Cultural and Leisure Services, c/o Library Support Unit, 31A Harbour Road, Inverness IV1 1UA
☎(01463) 235713
Fax (01463) 236986
Area Libraries Officer, Sutherland Ms A Forrest

INVERCLYDE

Inverclyde Council, Central Library, 1 Clyde Square, Greenock PA15 1NA
☎(01475) 712323
Fax (01475) 712334
Children's Services Librarian Ms J Skimming

Education Resource Service, Central Library, Clyde Square, Greenock, Renfrewshire PA15 1NA
☎(01475) 712333
Fax (01475) 712334
Education Resource Service Librarian Mrs I Gilchrist MA(Hons) DipLib ALA

MIDLOTHIAN

Midlothian Council, Library HQ, 2 Clerk Street, Loanhead, Midlothian EH20 9DR
☎0131 271 3980
Fax 0131 440 4635
e-mail: library.hq@midlothian.gov.uk
Senior Librarian, Young People's Services Vacant
Assistant Librarian, School Library Service Ms R Dryburgh MA DipLib ALA
Junior Mobile Librarian A A Scobbie BA(Hons) ALA

MORAY

Moray Council, Technical and Leisure Services, Community Development Service, Elgin Library, Cooper Park, Elgin IV30 1HS
☎(01343) 562611
Fax (01343) 562630
e-mail: lib_support@techleis.moray.gov.uk
Principal Librarian, Young People's Services Ms H Adair BA(Hons) ALA (e-mail: helen.adair@techleis.moray.gov.uk)

NORTH AYRSHIRE

North Ayrshire Council, Library HQ, 39-41 Princes Street, Ardrossan KA22 8BT
☎(01294) 469137
Fax (01294) 604236
e-mail: reference@naclibhq.prestel.co.uk
Children's Librarian Ms M Craik MA ALA

Education Resource Service, Greenwood Centre, Dreghorn, Irvine KA11 4HL
☎(01294) 212716
Fax (01294) 222430
Principal Resources Development Officer Ms M McLarty

NORTH LANARKSHIRE
North Lanarkshire Council, Community Services Dept, Buchanan Tower, Buchanan
Business Park, Cumbernauld Road, Stepps, Glasgow G33 6HR
☎0141 304 1843
Fax 0141 304 1967
Libraries and Information Manager J Fox (e-mail: fox@northlan.gov.uk)

Education Department, Education Resource Service, 8 Kildonan Street, Coatbridge
ML5 3LP
☎(01236) 434377
Fax (01236) 436224
e-mail: nlaners@rmplc.co.uk
Principal Librarian Ms L Wilson MA(Hons) DipLib ALA
Senior Team Librarian R Brown BA(Hons) ALA

ORKNEY
Orkney Islands Council, The Orkney Library, Laing Street, Kirkwall, Orkney KW15 1NW
☎(01856) 873166
Fax (01856) 875260
Assistant Librarian Ms K Miller BSc(Econ) LibInfStud

PERTH AND KINROSS
Perth and Kinross Council, Leisure and Cultural Services, Libraries and Archives Division,
A K Bell Library, York Place, Perth PH2 8EP
☎(01738) 477039
Fax (01738) 477046
Senior Librarian, Children's Services Ms M Kelly MA DipLib ALA
Librarian, Children's Services Ms J Noble BA ALA

RENFREWSHIRE
Renfrewshire Council, Renfrewshire Libraries, 8A Seedhill Road, Paisley PA1 1AJ
☎0141 840 3003
Fax 0141 848 3004
Senior Librarian, Young People's Services M MacNeill ALA

Education Resource Service, Abbey House, Seedhill, Paisley PA1 1AG
☎0141 840 3008
Fax 0141 840 3004
e-mail: ersren@easynet.co.uk
Principal Resources Development Officer Miss M Kean BA ALA

SCOTTISH BORDERS
Scottish Borders Council, Library HQ, St Mary's Mill, Selkirk TD7 5EW
☎(01750) 20842
Fax (01750) 22875
e-mail: library1@netcomuk.co.uk
Principal Librarian, Youth Services Ms R D M Collin BA ALA
Alternative address: Melrose Education Centre (01896 823517; fax: 01896 823422)

SHETLAND ISLANDS
Shetland Islands Council, Children's and Schools Library Services, Shetland Library, Lower Hillhead, Lerwick, Shetland ZE1 0EL
☎(01595) 693868
Fax (01595) 694430
e-mail: info@shetland-library.gov.uk
Chief Librarian J G Hunter ALA (01950 422364; e-mail: john@shetland-library.gov.uk)

SOUTH AYRSHIRE
South Ayrshire Council, Carnegie Library, 12 Main Street, Ayr KA8 8AD
☎(01292) 286385
Fax (01292) 611593
Children's Services Librarian Ms E McMahon

Library HQ, 26 Green Street, Ayr KA8 8AD
☎(01292) 2888820
Fax (01292) 618777
Libraries and Galleries Manager C Deas

SOUTH LANARKSHIRE
South Lanarkshire Council, East Kilbride Central Library, The Olympia, East Kilbride G74 1PG
☎(01355) 243652/220046
Fax (01355) 229365
Youth Services Manager Ms M Cowan ALA

Central Library, Cadzow Street, Hamilton ML3 6HQ
☎(01698) 452410/452447
Fax (01698) 286334
Youth Services Librarians Ms J Haldane BA DipLib ALA, Ms E Patrick ALA

STIRLING
Stirling Council, Libraries, Heritage and Cultural Services, Library HQ, Borrowmeadow Road, Stirling FK7 7TN
☎(01786) 432390
Fax (01786) 432395
Head of Libraries, Heritage and Culture A Gillies ALA

Educational Resources and Information Service, Resource Centre, Modan Road, Stirling FK7 9BS
☎(01786) 474974
Fax (01786) 474980
Principal Librarian Ms M Murray BA ALA

WEST DUNBARTONSHIRE
West Dunbartonshire Council, West Dunbartonshire Libraries, Levenford House, Helenslee Road, Dumbarton G82 4AH
☎(01389) 738328
Fax (01389) 734204
Children's Librarian Ms M McLean MA

Education Resource Service, Edinbarnet Primary School Campus, Faifley Road, Faifley,

Clydebank G81 5BQ
☎(01389) 890011
Fax (01389) 891414
Team Librarians Ms P Davy, Ms S Carragher BA ALA

WEST LOTHIAN

West Lothian Council, Library HQ, Connolly House, Hopefield Road, Blackburn, West Lothian EH47 7HZ
☎(01506) 776336
Fax (01506) 776345
url: http://www.westlothian.gov.uk/libraries
Library Services Manager B Walker BA ALA (e-mail: william.walker@westlothian.gov.uk)
Schools Library Liaison Officer Mrs J Barnes ALA

WALES

ANGLESEY, ISLE OF
Isle of Anglesey County Council, Children and Young People's Library Services, Llangefni
Library, Lôn-y-Felin, Llangefni, Anglesey LL77 7RT
☎(01248) 752096
Fax (01248) 750197
Children and Young People's Librarian Ms N Gruffydd BA MLib ALA

BLAENAU GWENT
Blaenau Gwent County Borough Council, Ebbw Vale Library, 21 Bethcar Street, Ebbw Vale,
Blaenau Gwent NP3 6HH
☎(01495) 303069
Fax (01495) 350547
Library Manager Ms S White (01495 301122)
(Blaenau Gwent has joint provision with Caerphilly for schools library services: see
Caerphilly)

BRIDGEND
Bridgend County Borough Council, Bridgend Library and Information Service, Coed Parc,
Park Street, Bridgend, South Wales CF31 4BA
☎(01656) 767451
Fax (01656) 645719
e-mail: blis@bridgendlib.gov.uk
Children's/Promotions Librarian Mrs M A Griffiths BLib ALA

CAERPHILLY
Caerphilly County Borough Council, Youth and Schools, Library HQ, Unit 4, Woodfieldside
Business Park, Penmaen Road, Pontllanfraith, Blackwood, Caerphilly NP2 2DG
☎(01495) 235565
Fax (01495) 235565
e-mail: caer.sls@dial.pipex.com
Library Manager, Youth and Schools Ms S Titcombe BLib MEd ALA (01495 235561)
Principal Librarian, Schools Library Service Ms C Selby MSc(Econ) ALA (01495
235563)
Youth Services Librarian Ms L Case ALA (01495 235562)

CARDIFF
Cardiff County Council, Central Library, St David's Link, Frederick Street, Cardiff CF1 4DU
☎029 2038 2116
Fax 029 2087 1599
Chief Librarian P Sawyer (e-mail: p.sawyer@cardiff.gov.uk)
Head of Children and School Services Mrs H Noble

CARMARTHENSHIRE
Carmarthenshire County Council, Area Library, St Peter's Street, Carmarthen SA31 1LN
☎(01267) 224832
Fax (01267) 221839
Children's/Schools Librarian K Bowen BA ALA

CEREDIGION

Ceredigion County Council, Public Library, Corporation Street, Aberystwyth, Ceredigion
SY23 2BU
☎(01970) 617464
Fax (01970) 625059
Assistant Librarian, Primary Schools Mrs H Jones BLib ALA

CONWY

Conwy County Borough Council, Services to Children and Young People, Llanrwst Library
and Offices, Plas yn Dre, Station Road, Llanrwst, Conwy LL26 0DF
☎(01492) 640043
Fax (01492) 642316
e-mail: llyfrwst@dircon.co.uk
Community Librarian, Services to Children and Young People Ms T Jones ALA
BA(Hons)
School Library Service: see Flintshire (cooperative service with Denbighshire, Flintshire and
Wrexham)

DENBIGHSHIRE

Denbighshire County Council, Library and Information Service, Yr Hen Garchar, 46 Clwyd
Street, Ruthin LL15 1HP
☎(01824) 708207
Fax (01824) 708202
e-mail: library.services@denbighshire.gov.uk
Children and Young People and Welsh Services Library Adviser Ms B Hughes BA
DipLib ALA
Schools Library Service: see Flintshire (cooperative service with Flintshire, Conwy and
Wrexham)

FLINTSHIRE

Flintshire County Council, Library HQ, County Hall, Mold, Flintshire CH7 6NW
☎(01352) 704405
Fax (01352) 753662
e-mail: flintslib@dial.pipex.com
Children's Services and Adult Education Librarian Ms L E Courtney ALA (e-mail:
lesley_courtney@flintshire.gov.uk)

North East Wales Schools Library Service, c/o Library and Information HQ, County Hall,
Mold, Flintshire CH7 6NW
☎(01352) 704431
Fax (01352) 753662
Schools Library Service Manager D Barker
(Cooperative service with Conwy, Denbighshire and Wrexham)

GWYNEDD

Gwynedd Council, Schools Library Service, Caernarfon Library, Pavilion Hill, Caernarfon,
Gwynedd LL55 1AS
☎(01286) 679465
Fax (01286) 671137
e-mail: llyfrgell@gwynedd.gov.uk
Principal Librarian H James BA DipLib ALA (e-mail: hyweljames@gwynedd.gov.uk)

MERTHYR TYDFIL

Merthyr Tydfil County Borough Council, Central Library, High Street, Merthyr Tydfil CF47 8AF
☎(01685) 723057
Fax (01685) 370690
e-mail: library@merthyrgov.bt.internet.com
Libraries and Arts Officer G James BA ALA

MONMOUTHSHIRE

Monmouthshire County Council, Leisure Community and Culture Department, Fifth Floor,
County Hall, Cwmbran NP44 2XH
☎(01633) 644552
Fax (01633) 644545
url: http://www.earl.org.uk/partners/monmouthshire/
Principal Librarian, Community and Youth Ms A Jones MLib ALA (e-mail:
annjones@monmouthshire.gov.uk)

Schools Library Service, County Hall, Cwmbran NP44 2XH
☎(01633) 644560
Fax (01633) 644545
Schools Library Service Manager Ms A Noble BA DipLib ALA
Librarian, Schools Library Service Vacant
(Schools library service in partnership with Newport and Torfaen)

NEATH PORT TALBOT

Neath Port Talbot County Borough Council, Library HQ, Reginald Street, Velindre, Port
Talbot SA13 1YY
☎(01639) 899829
Fax (01639) 899152
Senior Assistant Librarian (Children's Services) Ms J O'Brien

Education, Library and Resource Service, Glanafan Lower School, Reginald Street,
Velindre, Port Talbot SA13 1YY
☎(01639) 899829
Fax (01639) 899152
Assistant County Librarian/Head of Education, Library and Resource Service C
Biscoe ALA
(School library service in partnership with Swansea)

NEWPORT

Newport County Borough Council, Library and Information Service, Central Library, John
Frost Square, Newport, South Wales NP20 1PA
☎(01633) 265539
Fax (01633) 222615
Children's Services Librarian Ms L Thomas
(Schools library service in partnership with Monmouthshire and Torfaen: see
Monmouthshire)

PEMBROKESHIRE

Pembrokeshire County Council, Special Services, County Library, Dew Street,
Haverfordwest, Pembrokeshire SA61 1SU
☎(01437) 775246
Fax (01437) 769218
Special Services Librarian Mrs E Evans ALA

POWYS

Powys County Council, Education, Schools' and Children's Services, County Library HQ, Cefnllys Road, Llandrindod Wells, Powys LD1 5LD
☎(01597) 826866
Fax (01597) 826872
Principal Librarian Mrs D Jones ALA (01597 826867; e-mail: diannej@powys.gov.uk)

RHONDDA CYNON TAFF

Rhondda Cynon Taff County Borough Council, Children's and Youth Service, Mountain Ash Library, Knight Street, Mountain Ash, Rhondda Cynon Taff CF45 3EY
☎(01443) 478463
Fax (01443) 477270
Senior Librarian, Children's/Youth Services Ms C Roberts ALA DipEd

Schools Library Service, Mountain Ash Library, Knight Street, Mountain Ash, Rhondda Cynon Taff CF45 3EY
☎(01443) 478463
Fax (01443) 477270
Librarian, Schools and Related Services Ms M Lile ALA BA

SWANSEA

Swansea City and County Council, Library HQ, 12 Orchard Street, Swansea SA6 5AZ
☎(01792) 516728
Fax (01792) 516737
Children's Services Librarian Mrs R Rees ALA
(Schools library service in partnership with Neath Port Talbot: see Neath Port Talbot)

TORFAEN

Torfaen County Borough Council, Pontypool Library, Hanbury Road, Pontypool, Torfaen NP4 6JL
☎(01495) 735722/762820
Fax (01495) 752530
e-mail: xcr12@dial.pipex.com
Senior Librarian M Tanner BA(Hons) DipLib ALA
(Schools library service in partnership with Newport and Monmouthshire: see Monmouthshire)

VALE OF GLAMORGAN

Vale of Glamorgan Council, Barry Library, King Square, Barry, Vale of Glamorgan CF63 4RW
☎(01446) 735722/735591
Fax (01446) 734427
Librarian, Services to Children and Young People Mrs M Holt MA DipLib

WREXHAM

Wrexham County Borough Council, Children's and Young People's Service, Wrexham Library, Rhosddu Road, Wrexham LL11 1AU
☎(01978) 292643
Fax (01978) 292611
Children's Librarian Vacant
Schools Library Service: see Flintshire (cooperative service with Conway, Denbighshire and Flintshire)

CROWN DEPENDENCIES

GUERNSEY
Schools' Library Service, Guille-Allès Library, Market Street, St Peter Port, Guernsey GY1 1HB
☎(01481) 714098
Fax (01481) 714436
e-mail: slsguern@guernsey.net
Head of Services to Education and Young People Mrs M E R Harris ALA CMS

Guille-Allès Library, Market Street, St Peter Port, Guernsey GY1 1HB
☎(01481) 720392
Fax (01481) 712425
e-mail: gsylib@itl.net
Children's Librarian Ms S A Ball BA MA ALA

ISLE OF MAN
IOM Government, Junior and Mobile Library, Nobles Hall, Westmoreland Road, Douglas, Isle of Man IM1 1RL
☎(01624) 671043
Fax (01624) 673123
Mobile Librarian Vacant
Junior Librarian Ms M Cousins
Library Assistant Mrs L Strickett

JERSEY
States of Jersey Library Service, Jersey Library, Halkett Place, St Helier, Jersey, Channel Islands JE2 4WH
☎(01534) 759991
Fax (01534) 769444
e-mail: jsylib@itl.net
Principal Librarian, Young People's Services Ms J Graham ALA
Younger Readers' Librarian Ms K Powell BA DipLib ALA

Children's, Youth and Schools Library Services in the Republic of Ireland
(listed under public library authority)

In the Republic of Ireland, local authority public library services generally provide a service to primary schools on an agency basis for the Department of Education (there is no similar service for second level schools). Within public libraries it is not usual for staff to be appointed with specific responsibility for children's or youth libraries. Please contact the appropriate library authority as listed in the Public Libraries in the Republic of Ireland Section for information. The exceptions that follow are Dublin, Dun Laoghaire, Fingal, Galway and Wexford.

DUBLIN

Dublin Corporation Public Libraries, Children's and Schools' Section, Kevin Street Library, Lower Kevin Street, Dublin 8, Republic of Ireland
☎(00 353 1) 475 8791
e-mail: schollib@iol.ie
Senior Librarian, Children's and Schools' Section Ms E Turley BA HDipEd DPLIS

DUN LAOGHAIRE/RATHDOWN

Public Library Service, Duncairn House, 14 Carysfort Avenue, Blackrock, Co Dublin, Republic of Ireland
☎(00 353 1) 278 1788
Fax (00 353 1) 278 1792
e-mail: dlrlibs@iol.ie
Librarian, Schools and Young People's Services Ms S Trappe BA HDip DLIS

FINGAL

Schools Library Service, 2nd Floor, Unit 34, Coolmine Industrial Estate, Coolmine, Dublin 15
☎(00 353 1) 822 5056
Fax (00 353 1) 822 1568
e-mail: finsclib@indigo.ie
Librarian Ms A Griffin BSocSc(InfSt)

GALWAY

Galway County Library HQ, Island House, Cathedral Square, Galway, Republic of Ireland
☎(00 353 91) 562471
Fax (00 353 91) 565039
Schools Librarian M Keating

WEXFORD

Wexford County Library, Ardcavan, Co Wexford, Republic of Ireland
☎(00 353 53) 42211
Fax (00 353 53) 21097
County Librarian Ms F Hanrahan BA DipLib MLIS ALA ALAI
Schools and Children's Librarian E O'Brien BA DLIS

Libraries in Academic Institutions in the United Kingdom

ABERDEEN UNIVERSITY

Directorate of Information Systems and Services: Heritage Division, Aberdeen University, King's College, Aberdeen AB24 3SW
☎(01224) 272598 (enquiries)
Fax (01224) 273891
e-mail: speclib@abdn.ac.uk
url: http://www.abdn.ac.uk/diss/heritage
Manager, Heritage Division A G Knox BSc PhD

Directorate of Information Systems and Services: Library Division, Aberdeen University, Queen Mother Library, Meston Walk, Aberdeen AB24 3UE
☎(01224) 272579 (enquiries), (01224) 272573 (administration)
Fax (01224) 487048
e-mail: library@abdn.ac.uk
url: http://www.abdn.ac.uk/diss
Associate Director and Librarian C A McLaren BA MPhil DipArchAdm FSAScot
Library Services Manager Ms C I Munro MA DipLib (01224 273321; e-mail: c.munro@abdn.ac.uk)

Site libraries
A   MacRobert Library, Aberdeen University, MacRobert Building, 581 King Street, Aberdeen AB24 5UA
        ☎(01224) 272600 (enquiries & administration)
        Site Services Manager M Sommer BA DipLib ALA (e-mail: m.sommer@abdn.ac.uk)
B   Medical School Library, Aberdeen University, Polwarth Building, Foresterhill, Aberdeen AB25 2ZD
        ☎(01224) 681818 ext 52488 (enquiries), ext 52403 (administration)
        Fax (01224) 685157
        e-mail: medlib@abdn.ac.uk
        Site Services Manager W Pirie MA ALA
C   Taylor Library and European Documentation Centre, Aberdeen University, Taylor Building, Aberdeen AB24 3UB
        ☎(01224) 272601 (enquiries & administration)
        Fax (01224) 273893
        e-mail: lawlib@abdn.ac.uk
        Site Services Manager Ms V Stevenson BA MIInfSc

UNIVERSITY OF ABERTAY DUNDEE

Information Services, University of Abertay Dundee, Bell Street, Dundee DD1 1HG
☎(01382) 308866
Fax (01382) 308880
Head of Information Services I G Lloyd BA DipLib MLib ALA (e-mail: i.g.lloyd@abertay-dundee.ac.uk)

ANGLIA POLYTECHNIC UNIVERSITY

University Librarian Ms N Kershaw (based at Rivermead Campus, Chelmsford)
Deputy University Librarian Ms F Parsons (based at East Road, Cambridge)

A   Library, Anglia Polytechnic University, East Road, Cambridge CB1 1PT
        ☎(01223) 363271 ext 2312
        Fax (01223) 352973
        Librarian Ms J Wells BA(Hons) ALA (e-mail: j.wells@anglia.ac.uk)
B   Library, Anglia Polytechnic University, Rivermead Campus, Bishop Hall Lane,

Chelmsford, Essex CM1 1SQ
☎(01245) 493131 ext 3757
Fax (01245) 495920
Librarian Ms J Parmenter BA ALA DMS (e-mail: j.r.parmenter@anglia.ac.uk)
C   Library, Anglia Polytechnic University, Danbury Park Conference Centre, Main
Road, Danbury, Essex CM3 4AT
☎(01245) 225511 ext 3864
Fax (01245) 224331 (incoming only)
Librarian Ms D M Garfield BA (e-mail: d.m.garfield@anglia.ac.uk)

ASTON UNIVERSITY

Library & Information Services, Aston University, Aston Triangle, Birmingham B4 7ET
☎0121 359 3611 ext 4412 (enquiries), ext 4398 (administration)
Fax 0121 359 7358
e-mail: library@aston.ac.uk
url: http://www.aston.ac.uk/lis/
Director of Library and Information Services Dr N R Smith
Team Leader and Head of Human Resources Mrs J Brocklebank, Mrs H Whitehouse
Team Leader and Head of Public Services Mrs J Lambert

UNIVERSITY OF BATH

Library and Learning Centre, University of Bath, Bath BA2 7AY
☎(01225) 826835 (enquiries), (01225) 826084 (administration)
Fax (01225) 826229
e-mail: library@bath.ac.uk
University Librarian H D Nicholson MA ALA

BATH SPA UNIVERSITY COLLEGE

Library, Bath Spa University College, Newton Park, Newton St Loe, Bath BA2 9BN
☎(01225) 875490
Fax (01225) 875493
Director of Library and Information Services Mrs J Parry MLib ALA (01225 875634;
e-mail: j.parry@bathspa.ac.uk)
Head of Academic Services N Drew BA MLib ALA (01225 875477; e-mail:
n.drew@bathspa.ac.uk)
Head of Library Systems Ms A Siswell BA DipLib ALA (01225 875678; e-mail:
a.siswell@bathspa.ac.uk)
Information Managers Mrs B Molloy BA ALA (01225 875430; e-mail:
b.molloy@bathspa.ac.uk), Mrs M Floyd ALA (01225 875476; e-mail: m.floyd@bathspa.ac.uk)

Campus library
Library, Bath Spa University College, 8 Somerset Place, Bath BA1 5SF
☎(01225) 875648
Fax (01225) 427080
Campus Librarians Ms H Rayner BA(Hons) DipInf, Ms C Tylee MA ALA (01225 875648;
e-mail: h.rayner@bathspa.ac.uk), (01225 875648; e-mail: c.tylee@bathspa.ac.uk)

UNIVERSITY OF BIRMINGHAM

Main Library, Information Services, University of Birmingham, Edgbaston, Birmingham
B15 2TT
☎0121 414 5817 (enquiries), 0121 414 6572 (administration)
Fax 0121 471 4691

e-mail: library@bham.ac.uk
url: http://www.bham.ac.uk/is
Librarian and Director of Information Services C D Field MA DPhil

Site libraries

A   Barber Fine Art Library, University of Birmingham, Edgbaston, Birmingham B15 2TT
     ☎0121 414 7334
     Librarian Ms C Summerill

B   Barber Music Library, University of Birmingham, Edgbaston, Birmingham B15 2TT
     ☎0121 414 5852
     Librarian A Greig BA MSc

C   Barnes Library (Medicine, Health Sciences, Life Sciences), University of
     Birmingham, Edgbaston, Birmingham B15 2TT
     ☎0121 414 3567
     Librarian J Scott BA DipLib ALA

D   Baykov Library, Centre for Russian and East European Studies, University of
     Birmingham, Edgbaston, Birmingham B15 2TT
     ☎0121 414 3614
     Librarian G A Dix BA MA ALA

E   Chemical Engineering Library, University of Birmingham, Edgbaston, Birmingham
     B15 2TT
     ☎0121 414 5321
     Librarian P A Beasley BA DipTEFL

F   Ronald Cohen Dental Library, Birmingham Dental Hospital, University of
     Birmingham, St Chad's Queensway, Birmingham B4 6NN
     ☎0121 237 2859
     Librarian G R Price ALA

G   Education Library, University of Birmingham, Edgbaston, Birmingham B15 2TT
     ☎0121 414 4869
     Librarian E Lewis BA MA ALA

H   Electronic and Electrical Engineering Library, University of Birmingham, Edgbaston,
     Birmingham B15 2TT
     ☎0121 414 4321
     Librarian P A Beasley BA DipTEFL

I   Harding Law Library, University of Birmingham, Edgbaston, Birmingham B15 2TT
     ☎0121 414 5865
     Librarian D Abit BA DipLib ALA

J   Shakespeare Institute Library, University of Birmingham, Shakespeare Institute,
     Mason Croft, Church Street, Stratford upon Avon, Warwicks CV37 6HP
     ☎(01789) 293384
     Librarian J Shaw BA MA ALA

K   Learning and Media Resource Centre, University of Birmingham, Edgbaston,
     Birmingham B15 2TT
     ☎0121 414 5960
     Librarian L C Priestley BA MA ALA

BISHOP GROSSETESTE COLLEGE

Sibthorp Library, Bishop Grosseteste College, Newport, Lincoln LN1 3DY
☎(01522) 530771/527347
Librarian J C Child BA ALA (ext 312; e-mail: c.child@bgc.ac.uk)
Deputy Librarian P Jones MA (ext 227; e-mail: p.l.jones@bgc.ac.uk)

BOLTON INSTITUTE

Learning Support Centre, Bolton Institute, Chadwick Campus, Chadwick Street, Bolton, Greater Manchester BL2 1JW
☎(01204) 903262 (enquiries), (01204) 903279 (administration)
Fax (01204) 903373
url: http://www.lss.bolton.ac.uk
Library Manager Mrs K Senior BA ALA MLib (01204 903278; e-mail: k.senior@bolton.ac.uk)
Academic Services Librarian Mrs W Carley MA BA ALA (01204 903090; e-mail: wc1@bolton.ac.uk)
Reader Services Librarian Ms C Smith BA ALA (01204 903090; e-mail: cs4@bolton.ac.uk)
Acquisitions Librarian Mrs S Ward MA ALA PGCE (01204 903098; e-mail: sw2@bolton.ac.uk)

Eagle Learning Support Centre, Bolton Institute, Deane Road, Bolton, Greater Manchester BL3 5AB
☎(01204) 903092
Fax (01204) 903373
Senior library staff as above

BOURNEMOUTH UNIVERSITY

Dorset House Library, Bournemouth University, Talbot Campus, Fern Barrow, Poole, Dorset BH12 5BB
☎(01202) 595083 (enquiries), (01202) 595044 (administration)
Fax (01202) 595475
e-mail: sgrant@bournemouth.ac.uk
url: http://www.bournemouth.ac.uk
Associate Head of Academic Services (University Librarian) D Ball MA(Oxon) DipLib MLitt MIInfSc MIMgt

Site library
Bournemouth House Library, Bournemouth University, Bournemouth House, 19 Christchurch Road, Bournemouth, Dorset BH1 3LG
☎(01202) 504297 (site librarian), (01202) 504301 (enquiries)
Fax (01202) 504298
Site Librarian Mrs P Dale BA ALA

UNIVERSITY OF BRADFORD

J B Priestley Library, University of Bradford, Bradford, West Yorkshire BD7 1DP
☎(01274) 233370 (enquiries), (01274) 233400 (administration)
Fax (01274) 233398
e-mail: library@bradford.ac.uk
url: http://www.brad.ac.uk/library/
Chief Librarian M B Stevenson BSc PhD MA

BRETTON HALL

Library, Bretton Hall, West Bretton, Wakefield, West Yorkshire WF4 4LG
☎(01924) 832020
Fax (01924) 832077
e-mail: llr@bretton.ac.uk
url: http://www.bretton.ac.uk (college); http://talis.bretton.ac.uk:8001 (library catalogue)
Head of Library and Learning Resources Ms P Cullen BA(Hons) DipLib FLA PGCE (01924 830261 ext 2301; e-mail: pcullen@bretton.ac.uk)
College Librarian Ms J Morton BA ALA (ext 2303; e-mail: jmorton@mailhost.bretton.ac.uk)

UNIVERSITY OF BRIGHTON

Learning Resources, University of Brighton, Moulsecoomb, Brighton, Sussex BN2 4GJ
☎(01273) 600900
Fax (01273) 642988
url: http://www.bton.ac.uk/library
Head of Learning Resources Miss C E Moon BA ALA

Central/largest library
The Aldrich Library, Learning Resources, University of Brighton, Cockcroft Building, Lewes
Road, Brighton, Sussex BN2 4GJ
☎(01273) 642760
Fax (01273) 642988
Librarian i/c Ms L Turpin MA ALA

Site libraries
A   Learning Resources, University of Brighton, St Peter's House, 16-18 Richmond Place,
     Brighton, Sussex BN2 2NA
     ☎(01273) 643220
     Librarian i/c Mrs H L Tucker BA ALA
B   Learning Resources, University of Brighton, Falmer, Brighton, Sussex BN1 9PH
     ☎(01273) 643568
     Librarian i/c K Baxter BA ALA
C   Learning Resources, University of Brighton, The Welkin, Carlisle Road, Eastbourne,
     Sussex BN20 7SN
     ☎(01273) 643822
     Librarian i/c M J R Ainscough BA ALA

UNIVERSITY OF BRISTOL

Arts and Sciences Library, University of Bristol, Tyndall Avenue, Bristol BS8 1TJ
☎0117 928 9000 ext 8017, 0117 928 8004 (administration)
Fax 0117 925 5334
e-mail: library@bris.ac.uk
url: http://www.bris.ac.uk/depts/library
University Librarian M G Ford MSc ALA

Site libraries
A   Biological Sciences Library, University of Bristol, Woodland Road, Bristol BS8 1UG
     ☎0117 928 7943
B   Canynge Hall Library (Social Medicine), University of Bristol, Whiteladies Road, Bristol
     BS8 2PR
     ☎0117 928 7366
C   Chemistry Library, University of Bristol, School of Chemistry, Cantocks Close, Bristol
     BS8 1TS
     ☎0117 928 7947
D   Continuing Education Library, University of Bristol, 10 Berkeley Square, Bristol
     BS8 1HH
     ☎0117 928 7177
E   Dental Library, University of Bristol, Lower Maudlin Street, Bristol BS1 2LY
     ☎0117 928 4419
F   Education Library, University of Bristol, 35 Berkeley Square, Bristol BS8 1JA
     ☎0117 928 7062
G   Geography Library, University of Bristol, University Road, Bristol BS8 1SS
     ☎0117 928 9000 ext 3823

H   Medical Library, University of Bristol, Medical School, University Walk, Bristol BS1 1TD
☎0117 928 7945

I   Physics Library, University of Bristol, H. H. Wills Physics Laboratory, Tyndall Avenue, Bristol BS8 1TL
☎0117 928 7960

J   Queen's Library (Engineering, Mathematics, Computer Science), University of Bristol, Queen's Building, University Walk, Bristol BS8 1TR
☎0117 928 7785

K   Veterinary Science Library, University of Bristol, School of Veterinary Science, Churchill Building, Langford, Bristol BS40 5DU
☎0117 928 9205

L   Wills Memorial Library, (Law, Geology, EDC), University of Bristol, Wills Memorial Building, Queen's Road, Bristol BS8 1RJ
☎0117 954 5398

BRUNEL UNIVERSITY
Library, Brunel University, Uxbridge, Middlesex UB8 3PH
☎(01895) 274000 ext 2787 (enquiries), (01895) 274000 ext 2782 (administration)
Fax (01895) 203263
e-mail: library@brunel.ac.uk
url: http://www.brunel.ac.uk/depts/lib
Director of Information Services Dr L C Y Lee Bsc PhD MInstP CPhys FBCS FRSA
(e-mail: louis.lee@brunel.ac.uk)
Head of Library Services Mrs B A Thompson BSc DipLib ALA (e-mail:
beryl-anne.thompson@brunel.ac.uk)

Campus libraries
A   Osterley Campus Library, Brunel University, Borough Road, Isleworth, Middlesex TW7 5DU
☎020 8891 0121
Fax 020 8891 8251
Librarian i/c R Elves BSc MSc (e-mail: robert.elves@brunel.ac.uk)

B   Runnymede Campus Library, Brunel University, Coopers Hill, Englefield Green, Egham, Surrey TW20 0JZ
☎(01784) 431341
Fax (01784) 470342
Librarian i/c J Aanonson BSc MSc ALA (e-mail: john.aanonson@brunel.ac.uk)

C   Twickenham Campus Library, Brunel University, 300 St Margaret's Road, Twickenham, Middlesex TW1 1PT
☎020 8891 0121
Fax 020 8891 8240
Librarian i/c J Langridge (e-mail: james.langridge@brunel.ac.uk)

UNIVERSITY OF BUCKINGHAM
University Library, University of Buckingham, Hunter Street, Buckingham MK18 1EG
☎(01280) 814080
Fax (01280) 820312
e-mail: library@buckingham.ac.uk
url: http://www.buckingham.ac.uk
Chief Librarian J L Holah BA MLib MIInfSc

Site libraries
A   Franciscan Library, University of Buckingham, London Road, Buckingham MK18 1EG

☎(01280) 814080
Fax (01280) 828288
Assistant Librarian L M Hammond BSc ALA
B   Hunter Street Library, University of Buckingham, Hunter Street, Buckingham
MK18 1EG
☎(01280) 814080
Fax (01280) 820312
Assistant Librarians B J Clifton BA MSc FLA AIMgt, S H Newell BA DipLib ALA

BUCKINGHAMSHIRE CHILTERNS UNIVERSITY COLLEGE
Library, Buckinghamshire Chilterns University College, Queen Alexandra Road, High
Wycombe, Bucks HP11 2JZ
☎(01494) 522141 ext 5107 (enquiries), ext 3270 (administration)
Fax (01494) 450774
Head of Library and Media Services Mrs D A Biggs BA MLib FLA DipEdTech (e-mail:
d.biggs@buckscol.ac.uk)
Resources Librarian Mrs A Peters ALA (ext 3293; e-mail: a.peters@buckscol.ac.uk)

Campus libraries
A   Campus Library, Buckinghamshire Chilterns University College, Queen Alexandra
Road, High Wycombe, Bucks HP11 2JZ
☎(01494) 522141 ext 3465
Fax (01494) 450774
Campus Librarian Mrs I Sims ALA (ext 3294; e-mail: i.sims@buckscol.ac.uk)
B   Campus Library, Buckinghamshire Chilterns University College, Wellesbourne
Campus, Kingshill Road, High Wycombe, Bucks HP13 5BB
☎(01494) 522141 ext 4055
Fax (01494) 450774
Faculty Librarian Mrs M Collins BSc MSc ALA (e-mail: m.collins@buckscol.ac.uk)
C   Campus Library, Buckinghamshire Chilterns University College, Chalfont Campus,
Newland Park, Gorlands Road, Chalfont St Giles, Bucks HP8 4AD
☎(01494) 522141 ext 2333
Fax (01494) 603082
Campus Librarian Ms L Cooke BA MA ALA (ext 3081; e-mail:
l.cooke@buckscol.ac.uk)

UNIVERSITY OF CAMBRIDGE
University Library, University of Cambridge, West Road, Cambridge CB3 9DR
☎(01223) 333000
Fax (01223) 333160
e-mail: library@ula.cam.ac.uk
url: http://www.cam.ac.uk/libraries
Librarian P K Fox MA AKC ALA
Deputy Librarians D J Hall MA FSA, R W Welbourn MA ALA

Site libraries
A   Scientific Periodicals Library, University of Cambridge, Benet Street, Cambridge
CB2 3PY
☎(01223) 334744
Fax (01223) 334748
Librarian i/c M L Wilson MA
B   Squire Law Library, University of Cambridge, 10 West Road, Cambridge CB3 9DZ
☎(01223) 330077

Fax (01223) 330048
Librarian i/c D F Wills BA ALA

C   University Medical Library, University of Cambridge, Addenbrooke's Hospital, Hills
     Road, Cambridge CB2 2SP
     ☎(01223) 336757
     Fax (01223) 331918
     Librarian i/c P B Morgan MA ALA

UNIVERSITY OF CAMBRIDGE
(College, Institute and Departmental)

Cambridge Union Society
Keynes Library, Cambridge Union Society, 9(A) Bridge Street, Cambridge CB2 1UB
☎(01223) 566421
Fax (01223) 566444
Senior Librarian Miss C J E Guite MA ALA LCTC (01223 334950)
Assistant Librarian B High BA(Hons) PGDip MA(Lib)

Christ's College
Library, Christ's College, Cambridge CB2 3BU
☎(01223) 334950
Fax (01223) 334967
url: http://www.christs.cam.ac.uk
Librarian Dr V Cox PhD
Sub-Librarian Miss C J E Guite MA ALA LTCL (e-mail: cjeg2@cam.ac.uk)

Churchill College
Library, Churchill College, Storey's Way, Cambridge CB3 0DS
☎(01223) 336138
Fax (01223) 336160
Librarian Ms M Kendall MA ALA
(NB The Library is available to College Members only)

Clare College
Fellows' Library, Clare College, Cambridge CB2 1TL
☎(01223) 333267
Fax (01223) 333219
url: http://www.cam.ac.uk
Librarian Dr R Schofield (e-mail: rss1@cam.ac.uk)

Corpus Christi College
Parker Library, Corpus Christi College, Cambridge CB2 1RH
☎(01223) 338025
Fax (01223) 338041
e-mail: parker-library@corpus.cam.ac.uk
url: http://www.corpus.cam.ac.uk
Librarian Dr F W Ratcliffe CBE JP (Hon)FLA
Assistant Librarian Mrs G C Cannell

Darwin College
Library, Darwin College, Silver Street, Cambridge CB3 9EU

☎(01223) 335660 ext 35778
Fax (01223) 333450
Librarian Dr P F Friend

Department of Land Economy

Department of Land Economy, Laundress Lane, Cambridge CB2 1SD
☎(01223) 337110
Fax (01223) 337130
url: http://www.landecon.cam.ac.uk
Librarian Ms W Thurley BA ALAA (e-mail: wt10000@cam.ac.uk)

Downing College

The Maitland Robinson Library, Downing College, Regent Street, Cambridge CB2 1DQ
☎(01223) 334829 (enquiries), (01223) 335352 (administration)
Fax (01223) 363852
Fellow Librarian J H Scott BA PhD
College Librarian A Johnson BA MLib

Emmanuel College

Library, Emmanuel College, Cambridge CB2 3AP
☎(01223) 334233
Fax (01223) 334426
Librarian Dr A P McD Orchard
Acting Sub-Librarian C E P Bonfield BA

Faculty of Oriental Studies Library

Faculty of Oriental Studies Library, Sidgwick Avenue, Cambridge CB3 9DA
☎(01223) 335112 (enquiries), (01223) 335111 (administration)
Fax (01223) 335110
e-mail: caa1@cus.cam.ac.uk
url: http://www.oriental.cam.ac.uk
Librarian Mrs C A Ansorge MA ALA (01223 335111)

Fitzwilliam College

Library, Fitzwilliam College, Cambridge CB3 0DG
☎(01223) 332042
Fax (01223) 464162
Librarian Miss M A MacLeod MA DipLib (e-mail: mam1007@cam.ac.uk)

Girton College

Library, Girton College, Cambridge CB3 0JG
☎(01223) 338970
Fax (01223) 339890
Fellow and Librarian Ms F Gandy MA ALA (01223 338968; e-mail: fl10@cam.ac.uk)
Assistant Librarian Ms S Elsegood BSc ALA (e-mail: sae22@hermes.cam.ac.uk)
Archivist Mrs K Perry (01223 338897; e-mail: kp10011@cus.cam.ac.uk)

Gonville and Caius College

Library, Gonville and Caius College, Cambridge CB2 1TA
☎(01223) 332419
Fax (01223) 332430

e-mail: library@cai.cam.ac.uk
url: http://www.cai.cam.ac.uk/caius/library/lib-source.html
Librarian J H Prynne MA
Sub-Librarian L K Bailey BA MLib ALA
(Working library open to members of the College only. Old library open to scholars by appointment. All enquiries should be addressed to the Sub-Librarian)

Homerton College

The New Library, Homerton College, Hills Road, Cambridge CB2 2PH
☎(01223) 507259
College Librarian G Mizen (e-mail: gml0009@cam.ac.uk)

Institute of Criminology

Radzinowicz Library of Criminology, Institute of Criminology, 7 West Road, Cambridge CB3 9DT
☎(01223) 335375
Fax (01223) 335356
url: http://www.law.ac.uk/crim/iochpg.htm
Librarian Mrs H Krarup BA(Open) MSc (e-mail: hek10@cus.cam.ac.uk)
Assistant Librarian Mrs M Gower ALA

Jesus College

Quincentenary Library, Jesus College, Cambridge CB5 8BL
☎(01223) 339451
Fax (01223) 324910
Fellow Librarian Dr A Tooze
Quincentenary Librarian Ms R K Watson BA(Hons) ALA (e-mail: rkw10@cam.ac.uk)

The Old Library, Jesus College, Cambridge CB5 8BL
☎(01223) 339414
Keeper of the Old Library P R Glazebrook
Assistant to the Keeper Dr F H Willmoth (01223 339405)

King's College

Library, King's College, King's Parade, Cambridge CB2 1ST
☎(01223) 331232
Fax (01223) 331891
e-mail: library@kings.cam.ac.uk
url: http://www.kings.cam.ac.uk/library/library.htm
Librarian P Jones

Lucy Cavendish College

Library, Lucy Cavendish College, Lady Margaret Road, Cambridge CB3 0BU
☎(01223) 332183
Fax (01223) 332178
e-mail: lcc-admin@lists.cam.ac.uk
Librarian J M Sheppard MA PhD
Assistant Librarian J M Harris BA
(The Library is open only to the members of the College; it is essentially an undergraduate library)

Magdalene College

Libraries, Magdalene College, Cambridge CB3 0AG
☎(01223) 332100
Acting College Librarian N G Jones MA LLM PhD
Pepys Librarian R Luckett MA PhD
Undergraduate Library: available only to members of the College. The Old Library: readers by appointment in writing.The Pepys Library: readers by appointment in writing, and open to visitors during full term only in Oct–Mar 2.30–3.30; Apr–Aug 11.30–12.30 and 2.30–3.30; parties by appointment. Application for the Old and Pepys Libraries to R Luckett MA PhD (Fax 01223 332187)

New Hall

Rosemary Murray Library, New Hall, Huntingdon Road, Cambridge CB3 0DF
☎(01223) 762202
Fax (01223) 352941
e-mail: library@newhall.cam.ac.uk
url: http://www.newhall.cam.ac.uk
Librarian Ms A Wilson BA MLitt MSc ALA MIInfSc
(Admittance to New Hall members only; for special collections, please write to the Librarian)

Newnham College

Library, Newnham College, Cambridge CB3 9DF
☎(01223) 335740/335739
url: http://www.newn.cam.ac.uk/newnlib/nnmlib.html
Librarian Ms D Hodder MA ALA

Pembroke College

Library, Pembroke College, University of Cambridge, Cambridge CB2 1RF
☎(01223) 338100
Fax (01223) 338163
e-mail: lib@pem.cam.ac.uk
Librarian T R S Allan MA BCL(Oxon)
Assistant Librarian Mrs P Judd BA MA DipLib

Peterhouse

Ward and Perne Libraries, Peterhouse, Cambridge CB2 1RD
☎(01223) 338200
Ward Librarian M S Golding (ext 38218) (Members of Peterhouse only)
Perne Librarian Dr R W Lovatt (ext 38233) (Scholars' library: by appointment only)

Queens' College

Library, Queens' College, Cambridge CB3 9ET
☎(01223) 335549, (Porter's Lodge 01223 335511)
Fax (01223) 335522
e-mail: que1@ula.cam.ac.uk
url: http://www.quns.cam.ac.uk
Librarian M Williams BA (e-mail: jmw@cam.ac.uk)
Fellow Librarian C J Pountain MA PhD

Robinson College

Library, Robinson College, Cambridge CB3 9AN
☎(01223) 339124

College Librarian Ms L Read MA BA ALA

St Catharine's College
Library, St Catharine's College, Cambridge CB2 1RL
☎(01223) 338343
Fax (01223) 338340
Cambridge Unix cth1@ula.cam.ac.uk
url: http://www.lib.cam.ac.uk/university/collLibs/StCatharines.html
Librarian J R Shakeshaft MA PhD
Assistant Librarian Mrs S N T Griffiths MA ALA (e-mail: sntg100@cam.ac.uk)

St Edmund's College
Library, St Edmund's College, Mount Pleasant, Cambridge CB3 0BN
☎(01223) 336250 (enquiries)
Fax (01223) 336111
e-mail: edm1@ula.cam.ac.uk
Librarian Dr P Dunstan
(Please write in with enquiries)

St John's College
Library, St John's College, Cambridge CB2 1TP
☎(01223) 338661 (administration), (01223) 338662 (enquiries)
Fax (01223) 337035
e-mail:library@joh.cam.ac.uk
url: http://www.joh.cam.ac.uk
Librarian Vacant

School of Education
Library and Information Service, School of Education, Shaftesbury Road, Cambridge CB2 2BX
☎(01223) 369631 ext 208 (enquiries), ext 205 (administration)
Fax (01223) 324421
e-mail: educ-library@lists.cam.ac.uk
Librarian Ms A Cutts BA ALA
Site Librarian Miss E J Batchelor BA DipILS ALA

Site library
Library and Information Service, School of Education, University of Cambridge, 17 Brookside, Cambridge CB2 1JG
☎(01223) 336297
Fax (01223) 332894
Site Librarian Ms S Hakin ALA

Scott Polar Research Institute
Library, Scott Polar Research Institute, Lensfield Road, Cambridge CB2 1ER
☎(01223) 336552
Fax (01223) 336549
url: http://www.spri.cam.ac.uk/lib/libhome.htm
Keeper and Librarian W J Mills MA ALA CertEd (e-mail: wjm13@cam.ac.uk)

Selwyn College
Library, Selwyn College, Grange Road, Cambridge CB3 9DQ

☎(01223) 335880
Fax (01223) 335837
e-mail: lib@sel.cam.ac.uk
url: http://www.sel.cam.ac.uk/current/libguide.shtml
Fellow Librarian J D Ray MA (01223 335854; e-mail: jdr1000@cus.cam.ac.uk)
Assistant Librarian Mrs A G Eyres BA ALA
Rare Books Cataloguer Mrs J Gregory BA DipLib (01223 62014)

Sidney Sussex College

Library, Sidney Sussex College, Cambridge CB2 3HU
☎(01223) 338800 (enquiries), (01223) 338852 (administration)
Fax (01223) 338884
e-mail: librarian@sid.cam.ac.uk
url: http://www.sid.cam.ac.uk/library/library.htm
Librarian Mrs H E Lane MA(Oxon) DipLib ALA (e-mail: hel20@cus.cam.ac.uk)

Section library
Archive and Muniment Room, Sidney Sussex College, Cambridge CB2 3HU
☎(01223) 338824
Fax (01223) 338884
e-mail: sid1@ula.cam.ac.uk/archivist@sid.cam.ac.uk
Research Assistant N J Rogers MA MLitt (01223 338824; e-mail: njr1002@cus.cam.ac.uk)

Trinity College

Library, Trinity College, Cambridge CB2 1TQ
☎(01223) 338488
Fax (01223) 338532
e-mail: lacs1@cus.cam.ac.uk
Librarian Dr D J McKitterick FBA
(Undergraduate Library open to members of the College only. Wren Library: readers by
appointment. Visitors: Mon–Fri 12–2pm; Sat 10.30–12.30, full term only)

Trinity Hall

Library, Trinity Hall, Trinity Lane, Cambridge CB2 1TJ
☎(01223) 332546
Fax (01223) 332537
e-mail: trh1@ula.cam.ac.uk
Fellow Librarian Dr P Hutchinson
Assistant Librarian Dr A C Lacey MA

University Music School

Pendlebury Library of Music, University Music School, West Road, Cambridge CB3 9DP
☎(01223) 335182
Fax (01223) 335067
url: http://www.mus.cam.ac.uk
Librarian A Bennett BA MLitt DipLib ARCO

Wolfson College

The Lee Library, Wolfson College, Cambridge CB3 9BB
☎(01223) 335965 (direct), (01223) 335965 (main college line)
Fax (01223) 335937
Librarian C Holland MA

CANTERBURY CHRIST CHURCH UNIVERSITY COLLEGE

Library, Canterbury Christ Church University College, North Holmes Road, Canterbury, Kent CT1 1QU

☎(01227) 782514 (enquiries), (01227) 782403 (administration)

Fax (01227) 767530

e-mail: lib1@cant.ac.uk

url: http://www.cant.ac.uk

Director of Library Services Dr A Conyers MA PhD ALA (01227 782232; e-mail: a.d.conyers@cant.ac.uk)

Systems Librarian Mrs R Lewis ALA (01227 782231; e-mail: r.j.lewis@cant.ac.uk)

Academic Services Librarian Mrs M Crowther BA Mlib ALA (01227 782415; e-mail: m.crowther@cant.ac.uk)

Bibliographical Services Librarian D Dorman BEd DipLib (01227 782516; e-mail: d.dorman@cant.ac.uk)

Reader Services Librarian Ms K Pounder BA MLib ALA (01227 782573; e-mail: k.pounder@cant.ac.uk)

AV Services Manager J Marshall BA (01227 782816; e-mail: j.marshall@cant.ac.uk)

Salomons Library, Canterbury Christ Church University College, David Salomons Estate, Broomhill Road, Southborough, Tunbridge Wells, Kent TN3 0TG

☎(01892) 507717

Fax (01892) 539102

e-mail: salomons.library@salomons.org.uk

Librarian Mrs G Joye BA (e-mail: g.joye@salomons.org.uk)

CARDIFF UNIVERSITY

Information Services, Cardiff University, PO Box 430, Cardiff CF10 3XT

☎029 2087 4876

Fax 029 2037 1921

e-mail: library@cardiff.ac.uk

url: http://www.cf.ac.uk/uwcc/infos/

Director of Information Services J K Roberts MSc ALA

UNIVERSITY OF CENTRAL ENGLAND IN BIRMINGHAM

Information Services, University of Central England in Birmingham, Perry Barr, Birmingham B42 2SU

☎0121 331 5289 (enquiries), 0121 331 5300 (administration)

Fax 0121 356 2875

url: http://www.uce.ac.uk/library/public/

Director of Library Services Ms J Andrews MA DipLib ALA (e-mail: judith.andrews@uce.ac.uk)

(Information services includes all library, computing and telecommunications services)

UNIVERSITY OF CENTRAL LANCASHIRE

Library and Learning Resource Services, University of Central Lancashire, Preston, Lancs PR1 2HE

☎(01772) 892284 (enquiries), (01772) 892260 (administration)

Fax (01772) 892937

e-mail: l.library@uclan.ac.uk

url: http://www.ucan.ac.uk

Head of Library and Learning Resource Services K Ellard BA MA DMS ALA (01772 892261; e-mail: k.r.ellard@uclan.ac.uk)

Acting Head of Information Services J Andrew BSc (01772 892264; e-mail: j.s.andrew@uclan.ac.uk)

Acting Head of User Support A Marriott (01772 892127; e-mail: a.s.marriott@uclan.ac.uk)

Acting Head of Main Site Services Ms K Coulling (01772 892272; e-mail: k.r.coulling@uclan.ac.uk)

Head of Distributed Services Mrs J Hilton (01772 892106; e-mail: j.a.hilton@uclan.ac.uk)

Head of Central Services Mrs E Boaler (01772 892295; e-mail: e.boaler@uclan.ac.uk)

Acting Head of Systems Support D Miller-Crook (01772 892298; e-mail: d.crook:uclan.ac.uk)

Site libraries

A   Blackpool Site, Education Centre, University of Central Lancashire, Victoria Hospital, Whinney Heys Road, Blackpool, Lancs FY3 8NR
☎(01253) 303831
Fax (01253) 303566

B   Ormskirk Site, Education Centre, University of Central Lancashire, Ormskirk and District General Hospital, Ormskirk, Merseyside L39 2AZ
☎(01695) 583790
Fax (01695) 575359

C   The Library, Wigan Site, University of Central Lancashire, Bernard Surgeon Suite, The Elms, Royal Albert Edward Infirmary, Wigan Lane, Wigan, Lancs WN1 2NN
☎(01942) 822162
Fax (01942) 822444

D   The Library, Education Centre, University of Central Lancashire, Burnley General Hospital, Casterton Avenue, Burnley, Lancs BB10 2PQ
☎(01282) 474699

E   Blackburn Site, Education Centre, University of Central Lancashire, Blackburn Royal Infirmary, Bolton Road, Blackburn, Lancs BB2 3LR
☎(01254) 294312
Fax (01254) 294318

F   Library and Resource Centre, University of Central Lancashire, Newton Rigg College, Penrith, Cumbria CA11 0AH
☎(01768) 863791
Fax (01768) 867249

CENTRAL SCHOOL OF SPEECH AND DRAMA

Learning and Information Services, Central School of Speech and Drama, Embassy Theatre, 64 Eton Avenue, London NW3 3HY

☎020 7559 3942 (enquiries), 020 7559 3998 (library counter)

Fax 020 7722 4132

url: http://www.cssd.ac.uk

Head of Learning and Information Services J A Edwards BA MSc ALA (020 7559 3995; e-mail: a.edwards@cssd.ac.uk)

Library Services Manager P Collett BA PGDipLib ALA (020 7559 3995)

Computer Services Manager G Thomas BA (020 7559 3969)

Media Services Manager R West (020 7559 3934)

CHELTENHAM AND GLOUCESTER COLLEGE OF HIGHER EDUCATION

Learning Centre, Cheltenham and Gloucester College of Higher Education, PO Box 220, The Park, Cheltenham, Gloucestershire GL50 2QF

☎(01242) 543458

Fax (01242) 53492

url: http://infosource.chelt.ac.uk/

Learning Centres Manager Ms A E Mathie BA ALA (01242 532944; e-mail: amathie@chelt.ac.uk)

Site libraries

A   Learning Centre, Cheltenham and Gloucester College of Higher Education, Francis Close Hall, Swindon Road, Cheltenham, Gloucestershire GL50 4AZ

☎(01242) 532913

Information Services Team Leader Ms M Rowley (01242 532911; e-mail: mrowley@chelt.ac.uk)

B   Library, Cheltenham and Gloucester College of Higher Education, Pittville Learning Centre, Albert Road, Cheltenham, Gloucestershire GL52 3JG

☎(01242) 532259

User Services Team Manager T Smith (01242 532980; e-mail: tsmith@chelt.ac.uk)

CHESTER COLLEGE OF HIGHER EDUCATION

Library, Chester College of Higher Education, Parkgate Road, Chester CH1 4BJ

☎(01244) 375444 ext 3301 (enquiries), ext 3309 (administration)

Fax (01244) 392722

Director of Learning Resources Mrs C M Stockton BA MA ALA (ext 3300; e-mail: c.stockton@chester.ac.uk)

Deputy Librarian P F Williams BA MA ALA (ext 3305; e-mail: p.williams@chester.ac.uk)

Nursing and Midwifery Services Librarian Mrs W Fiander BSc MA ALA (ext 3307; e-mail: w.fiander@chester.ac.uk)

Media/Systems Librarian Ms J Millington BA MSc (ext 3311; e-mail: j.millington@chester.ac.uk)

Reader Services Librarian Mrs A Walsh BLib MA ALA (ext 3308; e-mail: a.walsh@chester.ac.uk)

Site libraries

A   Arrowe Park Hospital Site Library, Chester College of Higher Education, School of Nursing and Midwifery, Upton, Wirral L49 5PE

☎0151 678 5111 ext 2115

Fax 0151 604 7291

Librarian Mrs C Holly BSc (e-mail: c.holly@chester.ac.uk)

B   Countess of Chester Hospital Site Library, Chester College of Higher Education, School of Nursing and Midwifery, Countess of Chester Health Park, Liverpool Road, Chester CH2 1UL

☎(01244) 364664

Library Manager Mrs T Gibson (e-mail: t.gibson@chester.ac.uk)

C   JET (Joint Education and Training) Library, Chester College of Higher Education, Leighton Hospital, Middlewich Road, Crewe, Cheshire CW1 4QJ

☎(01270) 255141 ext 2538

e-mail: sbate@uccjet.u-net.com

Medical Libarian Miss E Thompson BA(Hons)

D   Library, Chester College of Higher Education, School of Nursing and Midwifery, Training Dept, K Block, West Park Hospital, Macclesfield, Cheshire SK10 3BL

☎(01625) 661986
Library Manager Mrs B Spencer

UNIVERSITY COLLEGE CHICHESTER
Library, University College Chichester, Bishop Otter Campus, College Lane, Chichester, West Sussex PO19 4PE
☎(01243) 816089 (enquiries), (01243) 816091 (administration)
Fax (01243) 816080
Head of Learning Resources S O Robertson MA MEd ALA (01243 816090; e-mail: s.robertson@chihe.ac.uk)
Information Services Librarian P E Verrill BA MA MLib (01243 816092; e-mail: p.verrill@chihe.ac.uk)
Circulation Librarian Mrs C Douglas BA ALA (01243 816093; e-mail: c.douglas@chihe.ac.uk)
Systems Librarian R Heron MA (01243 816098; e-mail: r.heron@chihe.ac.uk)

Campus library
Library, University College Chichester, Bognor Regis Campus, Upper Bognor Road, Bognor Regis, West Sussex PO21 1HR
☎(01243) 816099
Fax (01243) 816081
Campus Librarian Ms N Leigh BLib MA ALA (01243 816082; e-mail: n.leigh@chihe.ac.uk)

CITY UNIVERSITY
University Library, City University, Northampton Square, London EC1V 0HB
☎020 7477 8191 (enquiries)
Fax 020 7477 8194
e-mail: library@city.ac.uk
url: http://www.city.ac.uk/library/index.html
University Librarian J A McGuirk MA DipLib
Deputy Librarian B M Casey BA DipLib

Site libraries
A   Cyril Kleinwort Library, City University, Barbican, London EC2Y 8HB
       ☎020 7477 8787 (enquiries)
       Fax 020 7638 1080
       e-mail: cklib@city.ac.uk
       url: http://www.city.ac.uk/library/ckl/index.html
       Sub-Librarian L R Baldwin BA DipLib
B   St Bartholomew's School of Nursing and Midwifery Library, City University, West Smithfield Site, 20 Bartholomew Close, London EC1A 7QN
       ☎020 7505 5759 (enquiries)
       url: http://www.city.ac.uk/library/nursing/index.html
C   Whitechapel Site Library, City University, Alexandra Building, Philpot Street, London E1 2EA
       ☎020 7505 5859 (enquiries)
       Sub-Librarian M Lanigan MSc DipLib

COVENTRY UNIVERSITY
Lanchester Library, Coventry University, Much Park Street, Coventry CV1 2HF
☎024 7688 8708
Fax 024 7688 8686
url: http://www.coventry.ac.uk/library/

University Librarian P Noon BA MBA DipLib ALA

Departmental libraries
A   Art and Design Library, Coventry University, Gosford Street, Coventry, Warwicks CV1 5RZ
     ☎024 7688 7688
     Librarian Mrs S Silvester BA ALA
B   Performing Arts Library, Coventry University, Leasowes Avenue, Coventry, Warwicks CV3 6BH
     ☎024 7641 8868 ext 34
     Assistant Subject Librarian Ms J Thompson BA(Hons) PGDipLis

CRANFIELD UNIVERSITY
Kings Norton Library, Cranfield University, Cranfield, Bedford MK43 0AL
☎(01234) 754444 (general enquiries)
Fax (01234) 752391
url: http://www.cranfield.ac.uk/library/
University Librarian Dr H Woodward BA ALA MIInfSc (01234 754446)
Deputy University Librarian J S Town MA DipLib FLA MIInfSc MIMgt

Other libraries
A   Management Information Resource Centre, Cranfield University, Cranfield, Bedford MK43 0AL
     ☎(01234) 754440
     Fax (01234) 751806
     Head Ms L Edwards BA(Hons) DipLib MInstInfSci (e-mail: l.edwards@cranfield.ac.uk)
B   School of Agriculture, Food and Environment (SAFE), Cranfield University, Library, Silsoe, Bedford MK45 4DT
     ☎(01525) 863000 ext 3022
     Fax (01525) 863001
     Librarian C J Napper BA DipLib ALA (e-mail: c.napper@cranfield.ac.uk)
C   Royal Military College of Science, Cranfield University, Library, Shrivenham, Swindon, Wiltshire SN6 8LA
     ☎(01793) 785484 (general enquiries)
     Fax (01793) 785555
     e-mail: library2@rmcs.cranfield.ac.uk
     Director of Information Services J S Town MA DipLib FLA MIInfSc MIMgt (01793 785480; e-mail: stown@rmcs.cranfield.ac.uk)

CUMBRIA COLLEGE OF ART AND DESIGN
Library, Cumbria College of Art and Design, Brampton Road, Carlisle CA3 9AY
☎(01228) 400312
Fax (01228) 514491
College Librarian Ms C Daniel BA MA ALA (e-mail: cdaniel@cumbriacad.ac.uk)

DARTINGTON COLLEGE OF ARTS
Library, Dartington College of Arts, Totnes, Devon TQ9 6EJ
☎(01803) 861651 (enquiries), (01803) 862224 (administration)
Fax (01803) 863569
e-mail: library@dartington.ac.uk
url: http://www.dartington.ac.uk
Director of Academic Services Ms D Faulkner BA(Hons) DipLib MA ALA (01803 861652;

e-mail: d.faulkner@dartington.ac.uk)
Deputy Librarian R Taylor BA PGDip ALA (e-mail: r.taylor@dartington.ac.uk)

DE MONTFORT UNIVERSITY
Kimberlin Library, De Montfort University, The Gateway, Leicester LE1 9BH
☎0116 255 1551
Fax 0116 250 6360
url: http://www.library.dmu.ac.uk
Head of Library Services K J Arnold BA DipLib ALA (e-mail: karnold@dmu.ac.uk)
Library Services Manager (Leics) E S Loveridge MAMgt BA DipLib ALA (e-mail:
esl@dmu.ac.uk)
Quality and Staff Resources Manager M E Oldroyd BA(Hons) MLib ALA (e-mail:
meo@dmu.ac.uk)
Electronic Services Development Manager K H Black BA DipInsSysTech (e-mail:
khb@dmu.ac.uk)

Campus libraries
A   Information Centre, De Montfort University, Milton Keynes Campus, Hammerwood
        Gate, Kents Hill, Milton Keynes MK7 6HP
        ☎(01908) 834921
        Fax (01908) 834929
        Information Officer C Baker BA MSc ALA
B   Lansdowne Campus Library, De Montfort University, 37 Lansdowne Road, Bedford
        MK40 2BZ
        ☎(01234) 351966
        Fax (01234) 350833
        Campus Librarian L Droogmans BA(Hons) PGDipLib ALA HRM
C   Polhill Campus Library, De Montfort University, Polhill Avenue, Bedford MK41 9EA
        ☎(01234) 351671
        Fax (01234) 217738
        Library Services Manager (MK/Bedford) D Saulsbury BA MA PGDipLib CertEdFE
D   Information Centre, De Montfort University, School of Applied Arts and Design,
        Lindum Road, Lincoln LN2 1PK
        ☎(01522) 895080
        Fax (01522) 895147
        Library Services Manager (Lincoln) L A Bale BA DipLib ALA
E   Information Centre, De Montfort University, School of Agriculture and Horticulture,
        Caythorpe Court, Grantham, Lincs NG32 3EP
        ☎(01400) 275632
        Fax (01400) 272722
        Campus Librarian E G Kent BSc DipLib ALA
F   Information Centre, De Montfort University, School of Agriculture and Horticulture,
        Riseholme Hall, Lincoln CN2 2LG
        ☎(01522) 895310
        Fax (01522) 545436
        Campus Librarian J Maughan CertEd
G   Scraptoft Campus Library, De Montfort University, Scraptoft Lane, Leicester LE7 9SU
        ☎0116 257 7867
        Fax 0116 257 7866
        Campus Librarian M O Reynard MLS ALA (e-mail: mor@dmu.ac.uk)
H   Charles Frears Campus Library, De Montfort University, 266 London Road, Leicester
        LE2 1RQ
        ☎0116 270 0661

Fax 0116 270 9722
Campus Librarian Ms B Freeman BA ALA

UNIVERSITY OF DERBY
University Library, University of Derby, Kedleston Road, Derby DE22 1GB
☎(01332) 622222
Fax (01332) 622767
url: http://www.derby.ac.uk/library/homelib.html
Librarian J G Brewer BA MA ALA

DUNDEE UNIVERSITY
University Library, Dundee University, Small's Wynd, Dundee DD1 4HN
☎(01382) 344087 (enquiries), (01382) 344084 (administration)
Fax (01382) 229190
e-mail: username@dundee.ac.uk
url: http://www.dundee.ac.uk/Library/Welcome.htm
Librarian J M Bagnall MA DipLib MIInfSc

Site libraries
A   Archives & Manuscripts Department, Dundee University, Tower Building, Dundee
DD1 4HN
☎(01382) 344095
Fax (01382) 345523
e-mail: username@dundee.ac.uk
University Archivist Ms P Whatley BA(Hons)
B   Conservation Unit, Dundee University, Dundee DD1 4HN
☎(01382) 344094
Fax (01382) 345614
e-mail: username@dundee.ac.uk
Conservator Mrs Y M T Player-Dahnsjo MA AKC HND
C   Law Library, Dundee University, Scrymgeour Building, Dundee DD1 4HN
☎(01382) 344100
Fax (01382) 228669
e-mail: username@dundee.ac.uk
Librarian D R Hart MA ALA
D   Ninewells Medical Library, Dundee University, Ninewells Hospital and Medical School,
Dundee DD1 9SY
☎(01382) 60111 ext 2519
Fax (01382) 566179
e-mail: username@dundee.ac.uk
Librarian D A Orrock MA
E   School of Nursing and Midwifery Library, Fife Campus, Forth Avenue, Kirkcaldy, Fife
KY2 5YS
☎(01592) 268888 ext 5930
Fax (01592) 642910
e-mail: username@dundee.ac.uk
Librarian A Aiton MA DipLib ALA
F   Duncan of Jordanstone College Library, 13 Perth Road, Dundee DD1 4HT
☎(01382) 345255 (enquiries)
Fax (01382) 229283
e-mail: username@dundee.ac.uk
College Librarian Ms M C Simmons BA ALA
G   School of Nursing and Midwifery Library, Tayside Campus, Ninewells, Dundee
DD1 9SY

☎(01382) 632012
e-mail: username@dundee.ac.uk
Learning Resources Manager A Jackson BA(Hons) ALA

UNIVERSITY OF DURHAM

University Library, University of Durham, Stockton Road, Durham DH1 3LY
☎0191 374 3018
Fax 0191 374 7481
e-mail: main.library@durham.ac.uk
Chief Librarian J T D Hall BA PhD

Departmental libraries
A   Library, Education Section, University of Durham, Leazes Road, Durham DH1 1TA
      ☎0191 374 7867
      Librarian Mrs J R Adams BA MSc ALA
B   Library, University of Durham, Palace Green Section (Law, Music, Archives & Special
      Collections), Palace Green, Durham DH1 3RN
      ☎0191 374 3032
      Librarian Miss E M Rainey BA DipLibStds

UNIVERSITY OF EAST ANGLIA

Library, University of East Anglia, Norwich, Norfolk NR4 7TJ
☎(01603) 592421 (enquiries), (01603) 592407 (administration)
Fax (01603) 259490
e-mail: library@uea.ac.uk
url: http://www.lib.uea.ac.uk
Director of Library Services Mrs J C Steward BA MA ALA (01603 59242; e-mail:
j.steward@uea.ac.uk)
Office Manager Mrs C Christopher BA(Hons) PGCE (01603 592407; e-mail:
c.christopher@uea.ac.uk)
Subject Librarian (Arts and Humanities) A Noel-Tod MA DipLib (01603 592428; e-mail:
a.noel-tod@uea.ac.uk)
Subject Librarian (Social Sciences) J Marsh BSc(Econ) MA DipLib (01603 592431; e-mail:
j.marsh@uea.ac.uk)
Subject Librarian (Sciences) E B Clarke BSc PhD (01603 512412; e-mail:
e.clarke@uea.ac.uk)
Acquisitions Librarian Mrs A B Baker BA ALA (01603 592411; e-mail:
a.b.baker@uea.ac.uk)
Circulation Librarian Mrs J Crabtree BA MA (01603 592420; e-mail: j.crabtree@uea.ac.uk)
Head of Systems I Reeman (01603 592423; e-mail: i.reeman@uea.ac.uk)

Nursing library
NAM Library, Peddars Centre, University of East Anglia, Hellesdon, Drayton High Road,
Norwich, Norfolk NR6 5BE
☎(01603) 421527
e-mail: a.cook@uea.ac.uk
Branches Librarian Mrs S McGregor BA(Hons) (01603 421527; e-mail:
s.mcgregor@uea.ac.uk)

UNIVERSITY OF EAST LONDON

Learning Support Services, University of East London, Longbridge Road, Dagenham, Essex
RM8 2AS
☎020 8590 7722 ext 2610 (enquiries), ext 2617 (administration)

Fax 020 8849 3612
e-mail: library@uel.ac.uk
University Librarian and Head of Learning Support Services Mrs J Doust BA MA ALA
ALAA (ext 2620/2619)

Campus libraries
A   Learning Resource Centre, Barking, University of East London, Longbridge Road,
      Dagenham, Essex RM8 2AS
      ☎020 8590 7000 (enquiries ext 2614)
      Librarian Ms M March BA ALA
B   Learning Resource Centre, University of East London, Maryland House, Manbey Park
      Road, Stratford, London E15 1EY
      ☎020 8590 7000 (enquiries ext 4224)
      Librarian M Snelling BA ALA DMS
C   Learning Resource Centre, University of East London, Duncan House, High Street,
      Stratford, London E15 2JA
      ☎020 8590 7000 (enquiries ext 3346)
      Librarian B Nottage BA MA ALA
D   Learning Resource Centre, University of East London, Greengate House, Greengate
      Street, London E13 0BG
      ☎020 8590 7000 (enquiries ext 3434)
      Librarian Ms J Preece BA ALA
E   Learning Resource Centre, University of East London, Holbrook, Holbrook Road,
      London E15 3EA
      ☎020 8590 7000 (enquiries ext 3252)
      Librarian Ms J Preece

EDGE HILL COLLEGE OF HIGHER EDUCATION
Learning Resource Centre, Edge Hill College of Higher Education, St Helens Road, Ormskirk,
Lancs L39 4QP
☎(01695) 584298 (enquiries), (01695) 575171 (administration)
Fax (01695) 584592
Head of Library and Information Services Ms R Jenkinson MSc BA(Hons) DipLib ALA
(01695 584284; e-mail: jenkinsr@staff.ehche.ac.uk)
Learning Services Manager Ms S Roberts BA(Hons) DipLib MA ALA (01695 584297;
e-mail: robertss@staff.ehche.ac.uk)
Support Services Manager Ms C Black BA(Hons) (01695 584334; e-mail:
blackc@staff.ehche.ac.uk)

Site libraries
A   Learning Resource Centre, Edge Hill College of Higher Education,
      Woodlands Campus, Southport Road, Chorley, Lancs PR7 1QR
      ☎(01257) 239736
      Learning Resource Centre Manager Ms R Wilson BA DipLib ALA (01257 239737;
      e-mail: wilsonr@wood.ehche.ac.uk)
B   The Library, Edge Hill College of Higher Education, School of Health
      Studies, Aintree Complex, Fazakerley Hospital, Longmoor Lane, Liverpool L9 7AL
      Information Resource Manager Mrs M J Carney BA (0151 529 2648; e-mail:
      carneyj@staff.ehche.ac.uk)

EDINBURGH COLLEGE OF ART
Site libraries
A   Art and Design Library, Edinburgh College of Art, Lauriston Place, Edinburgh EH3 9DF

☎0131 221 6034
Fax 0131 221 6033
Principal Librarian W Smith MA DipLib

B   Environmental Studies Library, Edinburgh College of Art, 79 Grassmarket, Edinburgh
EH1 2HJ
☎0131 221 6180
Fax 0131 221 6159
Principal Librarian W Smith MA DipLib

UNIVERSITY OF EDINBURGH

Edinburgh University Library, University of Edinburgh, George Square, Edinburgh EH8 9LJ
☎0131 650 3384 (administration), 0131 650 3409 (Admissions and Lending Services),
0131 650 3374 (Catalogue, Reference and Information Services), 0131 650 8379 (Special
Collections)
Fax 0131 667 9780/650 3380
e-mail: library@ed.ac.uk
url: http://www.lib.ed.ac.uk/
Librarian I R M Mowat MA BPhil FLA FRSE (e-mail: ian.mowat@ed.ac.uk)
Deputy Librarian P B Freshwater MA ALA (e-mail: p.freshwater@ed.ac.uk)

Site libraries

A   Erskine Medical Library, University of Edinburgh, George Square, Edinburgh
EH8 9XE
☎0131 650 3684/5
Fax 0131 650 6841
Librarian Ms I McGowan BA ALA (e-mail: i.mcgowan@ed.ac.uk)

B   Law/Europa Library, University of Edinburgh, Old College, South Bridge, Edinburgh
EH8 9YL
☎0131 650 2044
Fax 0131 650 6343
Librarian K D Taylor BA (e-mail: keith.taylor@ed.ac.uk)

C   New College Library (Divinity), University of Edinburgh, Mound Place, Edinburgh
EH1 2LU
☎0131 650 8957
Fax 0131 650 6579
Librarian Mrs P M Gilchrist BA FLA (e-mail: p.gilchrist@ed.ac.uk)

D   Reid Music Library, University of Edinburgh, Alison House, Nicolson Square,
Edinburgh EH8 9DF
☎0131 650 2436
Fax 0131 650 2425
Librarian J C Upton BMus MA ALA (e-mail: j.upton@ed.ac.uk)

E   Science Libraries, University of Edinburgh, West Mains Road, Edinburgh EH9 3JF
☎0131 650 5205
Fax 0131 650 6702
Librarian R Battersby BA DipLib ALA (e-mail: r.battersby@ed.ac.uk)

F   Veterinary Library, University of Edinburgh, Summerhall, Edinburgh EH9 1QH
☎0131 650 6175
Fax 0131 650 6593
Librarian Mrs M A R Kennett BA ALA (e-mail: a.kennett@ed.ac.uk)

G   Moray House Library (Education), University of Edinburgh, Dalhousie Land, St John
Street, Edinburgh EH8 8AQ
☎0131 651 6193
Fax 0131 557 3458
Librarian Mrs D Colledge BA ALA (e-mail: dennyc@mhie.ac.uk)

ESSEX UNIVERSITY

The Albert Sloman Library, Essex University, Wivenhoe Park, Colchester, Essex
CO4 3SQ
☎(01206) 873188
Fax (01206) 872289
Librarian R Butler MSc

UNIVERSITY OF EXETER

University Library, University of Exeter, Stocker Road, Exeter EX4 4PT
☎(01392) 263873 (enquiries), (01392) 263869 (administration)
Fax (01392) 263871
e-mail: library@exeter.ac.uk
Librarian A T Paterson MA ALAI

Departmental libraries
A   Exeter Cathedral Library, University of Exeter, Bishop's Palace, The Close, Exeter
     ☎(01392) 72894/424887
     Librarian P W Thomas MA DipLib
B   Devon and Exeter Institution Library, University of Exeter, 7 The Close, Exeter
     EX1 1EZ
     ☎(01392) 51017
     Librarian M Midgley BA MA DipLib
C   Law Library, University of Exeter, Amory Building, Rennes Drive, Exeter
     ☎(01392) 263356
     Librarian P V G Kershaw BA MA
D   Library, University of Exeter, School of Education, St Luke's, Exeter EX1 2LU
     ☎(01392) 264785
     Librarian M R Myhill MA ALA
E   Library, University of Exeter, Camborne School of Mines, Redruth, Cornwall
     TR15 3SE
     ☎(01209) 714866
     Fax (01209) 714322
     Librarian Ms J Foote BSc DipLib ALA

FALMOUTH COLLEGE OF ARTS

Library and Information Services, Falmouth College of Arts, Woodlane, Falmouth, Cornwall
TR11 4RA
☎(01326) 213815
Fax (01326) 211205
e-mail: library@falmouth.ac.uk
Head of Library and Information Services R C Towe BA PGDipLib (e-mail:
rogert@falmouth.ac.uk)
Information Services Librarian (Learner Support) Ms S J Rowe BA(Hons) PGDipLib
(e-mail: susan@falmouth.ac.uk)
Acquisitions, Cataloguing and Circulation Librarian S Gibson BA (e-mail:
stepheng@falmouth.ac.uk)
Information Services Librarian (Media Services) Ms R Ball BA(Hons) PGDipLib (e-mail:
rebeccab@falmouth.ac.uk)
Library IT Officer S Pellow BA(Hons) PGCE (e-mail: steve@falmouth.ac.uk)

UNIVERSITY OF GLAMORGAN

Learning Resources Centre, University of Glamorgan, Pontypridd CF37 1DL
☎(01443) 482625 (enquiries)

Fax (01443) 482629
e-mail: lrc@glam.ac.uk
url: http://www.glam.ac.uk/lrc/home.htm
Head of Learning Resources Centre J Atkinson BSc MPhil DipLib ALA
Deputy Head of Learning Resources Centre S Morgan BA Med MBA FLA

GLASGOW CALEDONIAN UNIVERSITY

A   City Campus, Glasgow Caledonian University, Caledonian Library and Information
     Centre, Cowcaddens Road, Glasgow G4 0BA
     ☎0141 331 3867 (enquiries), 0141 331 3859 (administration)
     Fax 0141 331 3968
     e-mail: library@gcal.ac.uk
     Acting Chief Librarian Mrs F Smith MA ALA (0141 331 3860)
     Depute Librarian P Blount (0141 331 3863)
B   Park Campus, Glasgow Caledonian University, 1 Park Drive, Glasgow G3 6LP
     ☎0141 337 4102
     Site Librarian Ms E McKee MA

GLASGOW SCHOOL OF ART

Library, Glasgow School of Art, 167 Renfrew Street, Glasgow G3 6RQ
☎0141 353 4551
Fax 0141 353 4670
url: http://www.gsa.ac.uk/library/
Head of Information Services J McKay MA DipLib ALA (e-mail: j.mckay@gsa.ac.uk)

GLASGOW UNIVERSITY

University Library, Glasgow University, Hillhead Street, Glasgow G12 8QE
☎0141 330 6704/5 (enquiries), 0141 330 5634 (administration)
Fax 0141 330 4952
e-mail: library@lib.gla.ac.uk
url: http://www.lib.gla.ac.uk/library/
Director of Library Services A C Wale BA ALA

Site/departmental libraries
A   Adam Smith Library, Glasgow University, Adam Smith Building, Bute Gardens,
     Glasgow G12 8RT
     ☎0141 330 5648
     e-mail: library@lib.gla.ac.uk
     Librarian J J K Ross (e-mail: jjr1q@udcf.gla.ac.uk)
B   Chemistry Branch, Glasgow University, Joseph Black Building, Glasgow
     G12 8QQ
     ☎0141 330 5502
     e-mail: library@lib.gla.ac.uk
     Librarian Mrs D Currie
C   James Ireland Memorial Library, Glasgow University, Dental School and Hospital,
     Sauchiehall Street, Glasgow G2 3JZ
     ☎0141 330 5502
     e-mail: library@lib.gla.ac.uk
     Librarian Ms B Rankin
D   James Herriot Library, Glasgow University, Veterinary School, Garscube Estate,
     Bearsden, Glasgow G61 1QH
     ☎0141 330 5708
     e-mail: vetlib@lib.gla.ac.uk

Librarian Mrs M Findlay
E   Modern Languages Library, Glasgow University, Modern Languages Building,
     Glasgow G12 8QL
     ☎0141 330 4234
     e-mail: library@lib.gla.ac.uk
     Librarian Mrs I Kennedy

UNIVERSITY OF GREENWICH

Library Administrative Office, University of Greenwich, Woolwich Campus, Riverside House,
Beresford Street, London SE18 6BU
☎020 8331 8192 (administration)
Fax 020 8331 9084
url: http://www.gre.ac.uk/directory/library
University Librarian D A Heathcote MA ALA (e-mail: d.heathcote@greenwich.ac.uk)
Deputy University Librarian P G Oliver BA ALA (020 8331 9095, e-mail:
p.oliver@greenwich.ac.uk)
Head of Information Services Ms A Murphy BA DipLib (020 8331 8196, e-mail:
a.e.murphy@greenwich.ac.uk)

Campus libraries
A   Avery Hill Campus Library, University of Greenwich, Bexley Road, London SE9 2PQ
     ☎020 8331 8484
     Fax 020 8331 9645
     Campus Librarian D Mitchell BSc ALA (e-mail: d.mitchell@greenwich.ac.uk)
B   Dartford Campus Library, University of Greenwich, Oakfield Lane, Dartford, Kent
     DA1 2SZ
     ☎020 8331 8585
     Fax 020 8331 9275
     Campus Librarian Ms R M Moon BA DipLib ALA (e-mail:
     r.m.moon@greenwich.ac.uk)
C   Kings Hill Learning Centre, University of Greenwich, Kings Hill, West Malling, Kent
     ME19 6DU
     ☎020 8331 9201
     Fax 020 8331 5042
     Learning Resources Manager Mrs J Cunningham DipAD (e-mail:
     j.y.cunningham@greenwich.ac.uk)
D   Dreadnought Library, University of Greenwich, Maritime Greenwich Campus,
     Greenwich, London SE10 9JH
     ☎020 8331 8000
     Campus Librarian Vacant
E   Medway Campus Learning Centre, University of Greenwich, Nelson Building,
     Chatham Maritime, Kent ME4 4TB
     ☎020 8331 9617
     Fax 020 8331 9837
     Campus Librarian/Librarian of NRI T Cullen BSc MSc ALA MIBiol MIInfSc (e-mail:
     t.cullen@greenwich.ac.uk)
F   Woolwich Campus/Learning Centre, University of Greenwich, Riverside House,
     Beresford Street, London SE18 6BU
     ☎020 8331 8160
     Fax 020 8331 8195
     Campus Librarian Ms V Malone BA DipLib (e-mail: v.g.malone@greenwich.ac.uk)

Library and Information Services Group, Natural Resources Institute, University of Greenwich,

Central Avenue, Chatham Maritime, Chatham, Kent ME4 4TB
☎(01634) 883410 (enquiries), (01634) 880088 (administration)
Fax (01634) 880066/77
e-mail: enquiries.library@nri.org
url: http://www.nri.org
Head of Library and Information Services Group T Cullen MSc ALA MIBiol MIInfSc

COLLEGE OF GUIDANCE STUDIES
Library, College of Guidance Studies, College Road, Hextable, Swanley, Kent BR8 7RN
☎(01322) 664407 ext 125
Fax (01322) 613265
Librarian Ms A Ford BA DipLib ALA (e-mail: andrea.ford@cogs.ac.uk)

HARPER ADAMS UNIVERSITY COLLEGE
Library, Harper Adams University College, Edgmond, Newport, Shropshire TF10 8NB
☎(01952) 820280
Librarian Ms K Greaves

HERIOT-WATT UNIVERSITY
University Library, Heriot-Watt University, Edinburgh EH14 4AS
☎0131 451 3571
Fax 0131 451 3164
e-mail: library@hw.ac.uk
url: http://www.hw.ac.uk/libwww
Librarian M Breaks BA DipLib

UNIVERSITY OF HERTFORDSHIRE
Learning and Information Services, University of Hertfordshire, College Lane, Hatfield,
Hertfordshire AL10 9AB
☎(01707) 284678 (enquiries), (01707) 284653 (administration)
Fax (01707) 284666
e-mail: lisadmin@herts.ac.uk
url: http://www.herts.ac.uk/lis
Director of Learning and Information Services Ms D Martin MA DipLib ALA CertEd

Learning resources centres
A   Hatfield Campus Learning Resources Centre, University of Hertfordshire, College
       Lane, Hatfield, Hertfordshire AL10 9AB
       ☎(01707) 284678
       Campus LIS Manager Mrs C Parr CertEd ALA
B   Hertford Campus Learning Resources Centre, University of Hertfordshire, Balls Park,
       Mangrove Road, Hertford, Herts SG13 8AR
       ☎(01707) 284678
       Campus LIS Manager Dr A J Wroot PhD
C   St Albans Campus Learning Resources Centre, University of Hertfordshire, 6 Hatfield
       Road, St Albans, Herts AL1 3RS
       ☎(01707) 284678
       Campus LIS Manager Ms K Thompson BSc DipLib
D   Watford Campus Learning Resources Centre, University of Hertfordshire, Aldenham,
       Watford, Herts WD2 8AT
       ☎(01707) 284678
       Campus LIS Manager Ms J Arthur MA MBA

UNIVERSITY OF HUDDERSFIELD

University Library, University of Huddersfield, Queensgate, Huddersfield, West Yorkshire HD1 3DH
☎(01484) 472040 (enquiries), (01484) 472039 (administration)
Fax (01484) 517987
e-mail: ills@hud.ac.uk
url: http://www.hud.ac.uk
Director of Library Services P Sykes BA DipLib ALA
Assistant Director of Library Services Ms S White BA DipLib ALA

UNIVERSITY OF HULL

The Brynmor Jones Library, Academic Services: Libraries, University of Hull, Cottingham Road, Hull HU6 7RX
☎(01482) 466581
Fax (01482) 466205
e-mail: libhelp@acs.hull.ac.uk
url: http://www.hull.ac.uk/lib/
Director of Academic Services and Librarian R G Heseltine BA DPhil DipLib ALA
Head of Library Services Ms B Towler BSc DipLib ALA

Site library
Health Library, University of Hull, East Riding Centre, Beverley Road, Willerby, Hull HU10 6NS
☎(01482) 466679
Fax (01482) 466680
Team Leader Mrs M Ullfors

ISLE OF MAN COLLEGE

Library, Isle of Man College, Homefield Road, Douglas, Isle of Man IM2 6RB
☎(01624) 648207
Fax (01624) 663675
e-mail: libiomc@enterprise.net
Senior Librarian Miss C I Graham BA ALA MSc
College Librarian T Kenyon BA ALA

KEELE UNIVERSITY

Department of Information Services, Keele University, Keele, Staffordshire ST5 5BG
☎(01782) 583535 (enquiries), (01782) 583232 (office)
Fax (01782) 711553
url: http://www.keele.ac.uk/depts/li/lihome.html
Director of Information Services A Foster BA ALA FIInfSc (e-mail: a.j.foster@keele.ac.uk)
Assistant Director M J Phillips MA ALA (e-mail: m.j.phillips@keele.ac.uk)

Departmental library
Nursing and Midwifery Library, Keele University, City General Hospital, Newcastle Road, Stoke-on-Trent, Staffordshire ST4 6QG
☎(01782) 552949
Fax (01782) 712941
Librarian D Bird BA MA MA (e-mail: d.bird@keele.ac.uk)

KENT INSTITUTE OF ART AND DESIGN

Library, Kent Institute of Art and Design, Oakwood Park, Maidstone, Kent ME16 8AG

☎(01622) 757286
Fax (01622) 692003
e-mail: librarymaid@kiad.ac.uk
Head of Library and Learning Resources Ms V Crane BA ALA (e-mail: vcrane@kiad.ac.uk)
Librarian, Maidstone Ms F Cooke BA ALA PGCE (e-mail: fcooke@kiad.ac.uk)

Campus libraries
A   Library, Kent Institute of Art and Design, Canterbury Campus, New Dover Road,
     Canterbury, Kent CT1 3AN
     ☎(01227) 769371
     Fax (01227) 451320
     e-mail: librarycant@kiad.ac.uk
     Librarian, Canterbury Mrs K Godfrey MA(Ed) ALA (e-mail: kgodfrey@kiad.ac.uk)
B   Library, Kent Institute of Art and Design, Rochester Campus, Design Fort Pitt,
     Rochester, Kent ME1 1DZ
     ☎(01634) 830022
     Fax (01634) 829461
     e-mail: libraryroch@kiad.ac.uk
     Librarian, Rochester Mrs P Sowry BA ALA (e-mail: psowry@kiad.ac.uk)

UNIVERSITY OF KENT AT CANTERBURY
Templeman Library, University of Kent at Canterbury, Canterbury, Kent CT2 7NU
☎(01227) 823570 (enquiries), 823565 (administration)
Fax (01227) 823984
e-mail: library@ukc.ac.uk
url: http://www.ukc.ac.uk/
Librarian M M Coutts MA(Glas) MA(Sheff) ALA

KING ALFRED'S COLLEGE, WINCHESTER
Library, King Alfred's College, Winchester, Sparkford Road, Winchester, Hants SO22 4NR
☎(01962) 827306
Fax (01962) 827443
url: http://www.lrc.wkac.ac.uk
Librarian D Farley BA(Hons) ALA (01962 827229; e-mail: d.farley@wkac.ac.uk)
Deputy Librarian Ms E Fletcher BA(Hons) MA (01962 827374; e-mail:
e.a.fletcher@wkac.ac.uk)
School Resources Librarian Ms S Bunn BA ALA (e-mail: s.bunn@wkac.ac.uk)

KINGSTON UNIVERSITY
Department of Library and Media Services, Kingston University, Penrhyn Road, Kingston-
upon-Thames, Surrey KT1 2EE
☎020 8547 7101 (enquiries), 020 8547 7105 (administration)
Fax 020 8547 7111
e-mail: library@kingston.ac.uk
url: http://www.kingston.ac.uk/library_media/
Head of Library and Media Services N P Pollard BA ALA

Site libraries
A   University Library, Kingston University, Kingston Hill, Kingston-upon-Thames, Surrey
     KT2 7LB
     ☎020 8547 7384
     Fax 020 8547 7312
     Librarian i/c Ms S O Robertson ALA (e-mail: s.robertson@kingston.ac.uk)

B   University Library, Kingston University, Knights Park, Kingston-upon-Thames, Surrey KT1 2QJ
☎020 8547 8035 (tel/fax)
Librarian i/c A Kent MA DipLib (e-mail: a.kent@kingston.ac.uk)

C   University Library, Kingston University, Penrhyn Road, Kingston-upon-Thames, Surrey KT1 2EE
☎020 8547 7101
Fax 020 8547 7111
Librarian i/c R James MA MPhil ALA (e-mail: r.james@kingston.ac.uk)

D   University Library, Kingston University, Roehampton Vale, London SW15 3DW
☎020 8547 7803
Fax 020 8547 7800
Librarian i/c R James MA MPhil ALA

UNIVERSITY OF LANCASTER

University Library, University of Lancaster, Bailrigg, Lancaster LA1 4YH
☎(01524) 592517 (enquiries), (01524) 592537 (administration)
Fax (01524) 63806
url: http://www.libweb.lancs.ac.uk
University Librarian Ms J M Whiteside MA ALA (e-mail: j.whiteside@lancaster.ac.uk)

LEEDS METROPOLITAN UNIVERSITY

Learning and Information Services, Leeds Metropolitan University, Calverley Street, Leeds LS1 3HE
☎0113 283 7467 or 283 5968
Fax 0113 283 3123
url: http://www/lmu.ac.uk/lis/
Head of Learning Support Services P Payne BA ALA MIInfSc (0113 283 5966; e-mail: p.payne@lmu.ac.uk)
Electronic Services Development Manager Ms J Driver (0113 283 2600 ext 4733; e-mail: j.driver@lmu.ac.uk)

Campus libraries

A   City Campus Learning Centre, Leeds Metropolitan University, Calverley Street, Leeds LS1 3HE
☎0113 283 3106 (counter), 0113 283 5968 (enquiries)
Fax 0113 283 3123
Learning Centre Manager Ms M Message BA ALA (0113 283 2600 ext 3975; e-mail: m.message@lmu.ac.uk)

B   Beckett Park Learning Centre, Leeds Metropolitan University, Beckett Park, Leeds LS6 3QS
☎0113 283 3164 (counter), 0113 283 7467 (enquiries)
Fax 0113 283 3211
Learning Centre Manager Ms N Thompson MA(Lib) (0113 283 7468; e-mail: n.thompson@lmu.ac.uk)

C   Harrogate College Learning Resource Centre, Leeds Metropolitan University, Hornbeam Park, Harrogate HG2 8QT
☎(01423) 878216/878213
Learning Resources Manager A Sargeant (01423 878282; e-mail: a.sargeant@lmu.ac.uk)

UNIVERSITY OF LEEDS

University Library, University of Leeds, Leeds LS2 9JT

☎0113 233 5513 (general enquiries), 0113 233 5501 (administration)
e-mail: library@library.leeds.ac.uk
url: http://www.leeds.ac.uk/library/library.html
Chief Librarian/Pro-Vice Chancellor Mrs L Brindley BA MA FLA FIInstIS FRSA (0113 233 5501)
Director of Strategic Development Ms J Wilkinson BA DipLib DMS FLA (0113 233 5580)

UNIVERSITY OF LEICESTER

University Library, University of Leicester, PO Box 248, University Road, Leicester LE1 9QD
☎0116 252 2042 (general enquiries), 0116 252 2031 (Librarian's secretary)
Fax 0116 252 2066
e-mail: library@leicester.ac.uk
url: http://www.le.ac.uk/library/
Librarian Dr T Hobbs MA PhD DipLib ALA

Site libraries
A   Education Library, University of Leicester, 21 University Road, Leicester LE1 7RF
      ☎0116 252 3738
      Fax 0116 252 5798
      Librarian i/c R W Kirk BA ALA
B   Clinical Sciences Library, University of Leicester, Clinical Sciences Building, Leicester
      Royal Infirmary, PO Box 65, Leicester LE2 7LX
      ☎0116 252 3104
      Fax 0116 252 3107
      Librarian i/c Ms L Jones MA DipLib ALA

UNIVERSITY OF LINCOLNSHIRE AND HUMBERSIDE

Learning Support, University of Lincolnshire and Humberside, Cottingham Road, Hull HU6 7RT
☎(01482) 440550 ext 3130 (enquiries & administration)
Fax (01482) 463529
e-mail: janicesmith@humber.ac.uk
Director of Learning Support M Foster BSc PhD CMath CPhy

LIVERPOOL HOPE UNIVERSITY COLLEGE

Sheppard–Worlock Library, Liverpool Hope University College, PO Box 95, Hope Park, Liverpool L16 9JD
☎0151 291 2000 (enquiries), 0151 291 2001 (administration)
Fax 0151 291 2037
Director of Learning Resources P F Capewell MLS ALA (0151 291 2013; e-mail: capewep@livhope.ac.uk)
Acting Library Manager Ms S Murray BA ALA (0151 291 2002; e-mail: murrays@hope.ac.uk)
Academic Services Librarians Mrs A Duckworth BA ALA (0151 291 2008; e-mail: duckwoa@hope.ac.uk); Mrs R Keane MA BA BPhil DipLib ALA (0151 291 2008; e-mail: keaner@hope.ac.uk) (job-share)
Acting Technical Services Manager Mrs C Hughes BA(Hons) ALA (0151 291 2016; e-mail: hughesc@hope.ac.uk)

LIVERPOOL INSTITUTE FOR PERFORMING ARTS

Learning Resources Centre, Liverpool Institute for Performing Arts, Mount Street, Liverpool L1 9HF

☎0151 330 3111
Fax 0151 330 3110
url: http://www.lipa.ac.uk
Head of Learning Support K O'Donoghue (0151 330 3250; e-mail:
k.odonoghue@lipa.ac.uk)

LIVERPOOL JOHN MOORES UNIVERSITY

Learning and Information Services, Liverpool John Moores University, 10 Rodney Street,
Liverpool L1 2TE
☎0151 231 3544
Fax 0151 231 3113
Head of Learning and Information Services Ms M Melling BA PGDipLib MLib ALA (0151
231 3682; e-mail: m.melling@livjm.ac.uk)

Site libraries

A   Aldham Robarts Learning Resource Centre, Liverpool John Moores University, Mount
Pleasant, Liverpool L3 5UZ
☎0151 231 3634/3701
Fax 0151 707 1307
Learning Resource Centre Manager K R Graham BA PGDipLib (0151 231 3436)

B   I M Marsh Library, Liverpool John Moores University, Barkhill Road, Liverpool
L17 6BD
☎0151 231 5216
Learning Resource Centre Manager Mrs B J Badger BA DipLib ALA , Mrs C Tootill
BA ALA

C   Avril Robarts Learning Resource Centre, Liverpool John Moores University, Tithebarn
Street, Liverpool
☎0151 231 4022/4246
Fax 0151 231 4479
Learning Resource Centre Manager G K L Chan MSc BSc ALA (0151 231 4015)

UNIVERSITY OF LIVERPOOL

University Library, University of Liverpool, Liverpool L69 3DA
☎0151 794 2679 (enquiries), 0151 794 2674 (administration)
Fax 0151 794 2681/5417
e-mail: library@liverpool.ac.uk
url: http://www.liv.ac.uk/library/libhomep.html
University Librarian Ms F M Thomson MA BLitt (e-mail: thomson@liverpool.ac.uk)

Site libraries

A   Sydney Jones Library (Humanities, Social Sciences, Special Collections and
Archives), University of Liverpool, Chatham Street, Liverpool L69 3DA
☎0151 794 2679
Fax 0151 794 2681
e-mail: ql10@liv.ac.uk
Reader Services Librarian Ms C E Kay BA MA DipLib

B   Harold Cohen Library (Science, Medicine, Engineering, Veterinary and Dental
Science), University of Liverpool, Ashton Street, Liverpool L69 3DA
☎0151 794 5411
Fax 0151 794 5417
e-mail: ql11@liv.ac.uk
Reader Services Librarian Miss D V Goodier BA DipLib

C   Law Library, University of Liverpool, Chatham Street, Liverpool L69 3DA

☎0151 794 2832
e-mail: qlis07@liv.ac.uk
Law Librarian Mrs W Spalton BA DipLib ALA

D   Education Library, University of Liverpool, 19 Abercromby Square, Liverpool L69 3DA
☎0151 794 2574
e-mail: ql05@liv.ac.uk
Assistant Subject Services Librarian M Kay BA MA

E   Continuing Education Library, University of Liverpool, 126 Mount Pleasant, Liverpool
L69 3DA
☎0151 794 3285
Assistant Subject Services Librarian Vacant

LONDON GUILDHALL UNIVERSITY

Library, London Guildhall University, Calcutta House, Old Castle Street, London E1 7NT
☎020 7320 1173 (administration)
Fax 020 7320 1177
url: http://www.lgu.ac.uk/as/
Director of Academic Services Miss M E Castens BSc MA ALA DMS (e-mail:
castens@lgu.ac.uk)
Head of Information Services and Learning Resources Ms A Constable BA DipLib ALA
(e-mail: constabl@lgu.ac.uk (general messages)
Head of Information Systems Ms J M Willers BA MA MSc ALA (e-mail: willers@lgu.ac.uk)

Site/departmental libraries

A   Calcutta House Library, London Guildhall University, Old Castle Street, London
E1 7NT
☎020 7320 1185
Fax 020 7320 1182
Learning Resources Manager

B   Commercial Road Library, London Guildhall University, 41 Commercial Road, London
E1 1LA
☎020 7320 1187
Fax 020 7320 1865
Learning Resources Manager

C   The Fawcett Library, London Guildhall University, Calcutta House, Old Castle Street,
London E1 7NT
☎020 7320 1189
Fax 020 7320 1188
Reference Librarian

D   Moorgate Library, London Guildhall University, 84 Moorgate, London EC2M 6SQ
☎020 7320 1567
Fax 020 7320 1565
Learning Resources Manager

THE LONDON INSTITUTE

Library, The London Institute, 65 Davies Street, London W1Y 2DA
☎020 7514 6000
Director of Library and Learning Resources Ms M J Auckland BSc MSc ALA (020 7514
8071; e-mail: m.auckland@linst.ac.uk)

Camberwell College of Arts

Library, Camberwell College of Arts, The London Institute, 43-45 Peckham Road, London
SE5 8UF

☎020 7514 6349
Fax 020 7514 6324
e-mail: pr-lib@linst.ac.uk
Acting Head of Learning Resources Ms R Creamer MSc ALA

Central St Martins College of Art and Design

Library, Central St Martins College of Art and Design, The London Institute, Southampton Row, London WC1B 4AP
☎020 7514 6349
Fax 020 7514 6324
e-mail: sr-lib@linst.ac.uk
Library Manager Ms E Powis MA

Site library
A Library, Central St Martins College of Art and Design, The London Institute, 107 Charing Cross Road, London WC2H 0DU
☎020 7514 7190
Fax 020 7514 7189
e-mail: cx-lib@linst.ac.uk
Site Librarian Ms A Huxstep BA(Hons) MA DipLib

London College of Fashion

Library, London College of Fashion, The London Institute, 20 John Princes Street, Oxford Circus, London W1M 0BJ
☎020 7514 7455/7543
Fax 020 7514 7580
e-mail: oc-lib@linst.ac.uk
Library Manager Ms D Mansbridge BA MA ALA

Chelsea College of Art and Design

Library, Chelsea College of Art and Design, The London Institute, Manresa Road, London SW3 6LS
☎020 7514 7773
Fax 020 7514 7785
e-mail: mr-lib@linst.ac.uk
Librarian Dr S Bury MA MA PhD DipLib FLA
Library Manager Ms E Ward BA MA ALA

Site libraries
A Chelsea College of Art and Design, Library, The London Institute, Hugon Road, London SW6 3ES
☎020 7514 7091
e-mail: hr-lib@linst.ac.uk
B Chelsea College of Art and Design, Library, The London Institute, Lime Grove, London W12 8EA
☎020 7514 7833
e-mail: lg-lib@linst.ac.uk

London College of Printing

Dept of Learning Resources, London College of Printing, The London Institute, Elephant and Castle, London SE1 6SB
☎020 7514 6527 (enquiries), 020 7514 6581 (administration)

Fax 020 7514 6597
e-mail: ec-lib@linst.ac.uk
Head of Learning Resources Ms E Davison BA ALA

Site library
A   Department of Learning Resources, London College of Printing, The London Institute,
     Backhill, London EC1R 5EN
     ☎020 7514 6882
     Fax 020 7514 6867
     e-mail: bh-lib@linst.ac.uk

UNIVERSITY OF LONDON
University Library, University of London, Senate House, Malet Street, London WC1E 7HU
☎020 7862 8500 (enquiries), 020 7862 8415 (administration)
Fax 020 7862 8480
e-mail: ull@ull.ac.uk
url: http://www.ull.ac.uk/ull/
University Librarian Mrs E-J Robinson BSc ALA FRSA (020 7862 8411; e-mail:
erobinson@ull.ac.uk)
Senior Sub-Librarian, User and External Services P McLaughlin MA ALA (020 7862
8413; e-mail: pmclaughlin@ull.ac.uk)
Sub-Librarian, Administration and Resources Vacant
Sub-Librarian, Information Strategy S Clews MA DipLib (020 7862 8452; e-mail:
sclews@ull.ac.uk)
Head of Historic Collections Services Dr J Walworth (020 7862 8471; e-mail:
jwalworth@ull.ac.uk)
(Includes libraries of the Institute of United States Studies, the Centre for English Studies and
the Institute of Romance Studies)

Depository Library, University of London, Spring Rise, Egham, Surrey TW20 9PP
☎(01784) 434560 (tel/fax)
Depository Librarian T West BA ALA (e-mail: twest@ull.ac.uk/dpmail@ull.ac.uk)

UNIVERSITY OF LONDON
(College, Institute and Departmental)
Each College listed below is an independent self-governing institution funded, where
applicable, by HEFCE, and awarding degrees of the University of London, of which each is a
member.

Birkbeck College
Library, Birkbeck College, Malet Street, London WC1E 7HX
☎020 7631 6063/4; 020 7631 6239 (administration & enquiries)
Fax 020 7631 6066
e-mail: libhelp@lib.bbk.ac.uk
url: http://www.bbk.ac.uk/Departments/Library/
Librarian Ms P Dolphin MA DipLib ALA (020 7631 6250; e-mail: p.dolphin@bbk.ac.uk)
Deputy Librarian N Bevan MSc DipLib ALA (020 7631 6366; e-mail: n.bevan@bbk.ac.uk)

Site libraries
A   Gresse Street Library, Birkbeck College, Gresse Street, London W1P 2LL
     ☎020 7631 6492/3
B   Faculty of Continuing Education Library, Birkbeck College, 39 Gordon Square,
     London WC1H 0PD
     ☎020 7631 6167
     (Postal address: 26 Russell Square, London WC1B 5DQ)

Fax 020 7631 6163
Librarian Ms E Charles MSc ALA

Centre for English Studies

See University of London Library, Senate House

Courtauld Institute of Art

Library, Courtauld Institute of Art, Somerset House, Strand, London WC2R 0RN
☎020 7848 2707 (enquiries), 020 7848 2645 (administration)
Fax 020 7848 2887
e-mail: booklib@courtauld.ac.uk
Librarian Dr S M Price BSc MA MSc PhD MIInfSc (020 7848 2705)

Eastman Dental Institute for Oral Health Care Sciences

Information Centre, Eastman Dental Institute for Oral Health Care Sciences, 256 Grays Inn
Road, London WC1X 8LD
☎020 7915 1045/1262
Fax 020 7915 1147
e-mail: ic@eastman.ucl.ac.uk
url: http://www.library.eastman.ucl.ac.uk
Librarian M Hunt BSc DipInfSci MIInfSci DipSciCom
Library Assistants Mrs S Jacobs (e-mail: s.jacobs@eastman.ucl.ac.uk), J Evans BSc Mlib

Goldsmiths College

Information Services Department, Goldsmiths College, New Cross, London SE14 6NW
☎020 7919 7150 (enquiries), 020 7919 7161 (administration)
Fax 020 7919 7165
e-mail: library@gold.ac.uk
url: http://www.gold.ac.uk/libweb/home.html
Director of Information Services Ms J G Pateman BSc

Guy's, King's and St Thomas' Schools of Medicine, Dentistry and Biomedical Sciences

Guy's, King's and St Thomas' Schools of Medicine, Dentistry and Biomedical Sciences,
Denmark Hill Campus, Weston Education Centre, Bessemer Road, London SE5 9PJ
☎020 7848 5541/5542 (enquiries), 020 7848 5554
Fax 020 7848 5550
url: http://www.kcl.ac.uk/depsta/iss/md_lib/welcome.html
Librarian Ms C G Hogg BA ALA MIInfSc
Assistant Librarians Ms A Tobin BA AALA, G Horrocks BA MSc

Campus libraries
Guy's Campus
A   Wills Library, Guy's, King's and St Thomas' Schools of Medicine, Dentistry and
     Biomedical Sciences, Hodgkin Building, Guy's Campus, London SE1 9RT
     ☎020 7955 4348
     Fax 020 7357 0458
B   F S Warner Library and Information Centre, Guy's, King's and St Thomas' Schools of
     Medicine, Dentistry and Biomedical Sciences, Floor 18, Guy's Tower, Guy's Hospital,
     London SE1 9RT
     ☎020 7955 4238
     Fax 020 7955 4103

St Thomas' Campus

A Medical Library, Guy's, King's and St Thomas' Schools of Medicine, Dentistry and Biomedical Sciences, Sherrington Building, St Thomas' Hospital, Lambeth Palace Road, London SE1 7EH
 ☎020 7928 9292 ext 2367
 Fax 020 7401 3932
 e-mail: library-web@umds.ac.uk
 url: http://www.kcl.ac.uk/medlib/
 Director of Information and Library Services, Guy's and St Thomas' Campuses
 Dr F Grainger BSc DipInfSc MIInfSc
 Deputy Librarian A Baster MA

B Calnan Library, Institute of Dermatology, Guy's, King's and St Thomas' Schools of Medicine, Dentistry and Biomedical Sciences, Block 7, St Thomas' Hospital, Lambeth Palace Road, London SE1 7EH
 ☎020 7928 9292 ext 1313
 Fax 020 7928 1428

Heythrop College

Library, Heythrop College, Kensington Square, London W8 5HQ
☎020 7795 4250 (enquiries), 020 7795 4252 (administration)
Fax 020 7795 4253
url: http://www.heythrop.ac.uk/library.html
Librarian M J Walsh MA STL
Deputy Librarian M Morgan (e-mail: m.morgan@heythrop.ac.uk)

Imperial College of Science, Technology and Medicine

Central Library, Imperial College of Science, Technology and Medicine, South Kensington, London SW7 2AZ
☎020 7594 8820 (enquiries), 020 7594 8816 (administration)
Fax 020 7584 3763
e-mail: library@ic.ac.uk
url: http://www.lib.ic.ac.uk
Director of Library and Audio-Visual Services Mrs M Czigány BA DipLib (020 7594 8880; e-mail: m.czigany@ic.ac.uk)
Deputy Librarian Ms L Curtis BA DipLib ALA (020 7594 8814)
IT Manager/Technical Services Sub-Librarian Mrs E J Bull BA DipInf ALA (e-mail: e.bull@ic.ac.uk)
Reader Services Sub-Librarian R Halls MA DipLib (020 7594 8823; e-mail: r.halls@ic.ac.uk)
Collections and Information Resources Sub-Librarian Ms J Yeadon BSc MSc ALA (020 7594 8840; e-mail: j.yeadon@ic.ac.uk)

Departmental libraries

A Aeronautics Library, Imperial College of Science, Technology and Medicine, London SW7 2BY
 ☎020 7594 5069
 Librarian Ms S Clarke BA (e-mail: sue.clarke@ic.ac.uk)

B Chemical Engineering and Chemical Technology Library, Imperial College of Science, Technology and Medicine, London SW7 2BY
 ☎020 7594 5598
 Librarian Ms E Corbett BA DipLib ALA (e-mail: e.corbett@ic.ac.uk)

C Chemistry Library, Imperial College of Science, Technology and Medicine, London SW7 2AY

☎020 7594 5736
Librarian Ms S Irwin MSc ALA (e-mail: s.irwin@ic.ac.uk)
D   Civil Engineering Library, Imperial College of Science, Technology and Medicine, London SW7 2BU
☎020 7594 6007
Librarian Mrs K Crooks BA DipEd DipLib (e-mail: k.crooks@ic.ac.uk)
E   Electrical and Electronic Engineering Library, Imperial College of Science, Technology and Medicine, London SW7 2BT
☎020 7594 6182
Librarian Mrs E Haigh BA DipInfSci ALA (e-mail: e.haigh@ic.ac.uk)
F   Materials Library, Imperial College of Science, Technology and Medicine, London SW7 2BP
☎020 7594 6751
Librarian Mrs S Inada-Kim BA BSc DipLib(Japan) (e-mail: s.inada-kim@ic.ac.uk)
G   Mathematics Library, Imperial College of Science, Technology and Medicine, London SW7 2BZ
☎020 7594 8542
Librarian A Clark BA DipLib (e-mail: a.clark@ic.ac.uk)
H   Mechanical Engineering Library, Imperial College of Science, Technology and Medicine, London SW7 2BX
☎020 7594 7166
Librarian Ms A R Sage BA DipLib ALA (e-mail: a.sage@ic.ac.uk)
I   Physics Library, Imperial College of Science, Technology and Medicine, London SW7 2BZ
☎020 7594 7871
Librarian Ms P Hatch (e-mail: p.hatch@ic.ac.uk)
J   The Huxley School of Environment, Imperial College of Science, Technology and Medicine, Earth Sciences and Engineering: Earth Resources Engineering, London SW7 2BP
☎020 7594 7323
Librarian Ms R Browning BA MA (e-mail: r.browning@ic.ac.uk)
K   The Huxley School of Environment, Imperial College of Science, Technology and Medicine, Earth Sciences and Engineering: Geology, London SW7 2BP
☎020 7594 6501
Librarian Ms L Barker BSc FGS (e-mail: l.barker@ic.ac.uk)
L   The Huxley School of Environment, Imperial College of Science, Technology and Medicine, Earth Sciences and Engineering: Environmental Technology, 48 Prince's Gardens, London SW7 2PE
☎020 7594 9307
Librarian Ms F Parker BA DipInsMan (e-mail: f.parker@ic.ac.uk)

Medical libraries
M   Library, Charing Cross Campus, Imperial College of Science, Technology and Medicine, Imperial College School of Medicine, The Reynolds Building, St Dunstan's Road, London W6 8RP
☎020 8846 7152
Fax 020 8846 7565
e-mail: librarycx@ic.ac.uk
Librarian Ms S Howard BA MSc ALA (e-mail: s.howard@ic.ac.uk)
N   The Library, Chelsea and Westminster Hospital, Imperial College of Science, Technology and Medicine, Imperial College School of Medicine, 369 Fulham Road, London SW10 9NH

      ☎020 8746 8107
      Fax 020 8746 8215
      Acting Librarian P Morrell BA ALA

O   Wellcome Library, Hammersmith Campus, Imperial College of Science, Technology
      and Medicine, Imperial College School of Medicine, Du Cane Road, London
      W12 0NN
      ☎020 8383 3246
      Fax 020 8383 2195
      e-mail: enquiry@rpms.ac.uk
      Librarian Ms E Davis BSc ALA (e-mail: e.davis@rpms.ac.uk)

P   Library, National Heart and Lung Institute, Imperial College of Science, Technology
      and Medicine, Royal Brompton Campus, Imperial College School of Medicine, Dove
      House Street, London SW3 6LY
      ☎020 7352 8121 ext 3098
      Fax 020 7376 3442
      Librarian Miss R Shipton BA DipLib ALA (e-mail: r.shipton@ic.ac.uk)

Q   Library, St Mary's Campus, Imperial College of Science, Technology and Medicine,
      Imperial College School of Medicine, Norfolk Place, London W2 1PG
      ☎020 7594 3692
      Fax 020 7724 7349
      Librarian N Palmer BA ALA (e-mail: n.palmer@ic.ac.uk)

Institute of Advanced Legal Studies

Library, Institute of Advanced Legal Studies, University of London School of Advanced Study,
17 Russell Square, London WC1B 5DR
☎020 7637 1731 (enquiries & administration)
Fax 020 7436 8824
e-mail: ials@sas.ac.uk
url: http://www.sas.ac.uk/ials
Librarian J R Winterton BA LLB ALA
Deputy Librarian Miss J Jones BA MA ALA
Systems Manager Mrs M Birch BA DipLib ALA

Institute of Cancer Research

Library, Institute of Cancer Research, 237 Fulham Road, London SW3 6JB
☎020 7352 5946/8133 ext 5120
Fax 020 7352 6283
e-mail: fullib@icr.ac.uk
Librarian Miss G M Davies BA ALA
Assistant Librarian Miss N Wolland NZLSC

Site library
Library, Institute of Cancer Research, University of London, 15 Cotswold Road, Belmont,
Sutton, Surrey SM2 5NG
☎020 8643 8901 ext 4230, 4430
Fax 020 8661 1823
e-mail: sutlib@icr.ac.uk
Assistant Librarian Mrs S Sugden ALA

Institute of Classical Studies

Institute of Classical Studies Library and Joint Library of the Hellenic and Roman Societies,
Institute of Classical Studies, Senate House, Malet Street, London WC1E 7HU

☎020 7862 8709
Fax 020 7862 8724
url: http://www.sas.ac.uk/icls/
Librarian C H Annis MA ALA (e-mail: ch.annis@sas.ac.uk)

Institute of Commonwealth Studies

Library, Institute of Commonwealth Studies, University of London, School of Advanced Study,
28 Russell Square, London WC1B 5DS
☎020 7862 8844 (switchboard)
Fax 020 7862 8820
e-mail: icommlib@sas.ac.uk
url: http://www.ihr.sas.ac.uk/ics/
Information Resources Manager and Archivist D Ward BA MA GradDipUCL (020 7862
8840; e-mail: dward@sas.ac.uk)
Deputy Information Resources Manager Ms J Evans BA MA (020 7862 8833; e-mail:
jevans@sas.ac.uk)

Institute of Education

Information Services, Institute of Education, 20 Bedford Way, London WC1H 0AL
☎020 7612 6080 (enquiries)
Fax 020 7612 6093
e-mail: lib.enquiries@ioe.ac.uk
url: http://www.ioe.ac.uk/library
Head of Information Services and Librarian Ms A Peters (020 7612 6052)

Institute of Germanic Studies

Library, Institute of Germanic Studies, University of London, 29 Russell Square, London
WC1B 5DP
☎020 7580 2711 (administration), 020 7580 3480 (enquiries)
Fax 020 7436 3497
e-mail: igslib@sas.ac.uk
url: http://www.sas.ac.uk/igs
Librarian W Abbey BA

Institute of Historical Research

Library, Institute of Historical Research, University of London, Senate House, Malet Street,
London WC1E 7HU
☎020 7636 0272
Fax 020 7862 8811
e-mail: ihrlib@sas.ac.uk
Librarian R Lyons BA DipLib

Institute of Latin American Studies

Library, Institute of Latin American Studies, School of Advanced Study, 31 Tavistock Square,
London WC1H 9HA
☎020 7862 8501
Fax 020 7862 8971
e-mail: ilas.lib@sas.ac.uk
url: http://www.sas.ac.uk/ilas/
Librarian A Biggins BSc ALA (e-mail: abiggins@sas.ac.uk)
Senior Assistant Librarian Miss V Cooper BA DipArch (e-mail: vcooper@sas.ac.uk)

Institute of Ophthalmology

Library, Institute of Ophthalmology, Bath Street, London EC1V 9EL
☎020 7608 6814
e-mail: ophthlib@ucl.ac.uk
Librarian Miss D Heatlie BA (020 7608 6815; e-mail: d.heatlie@ucl.ac.uk)

Institute of Psychiatry

Library, Institute of Psychiatry, King's College London, De Crespigny Park, London SE5 8AF
☎020 7919 3204
Fax 020 7703 4515
e-mail: spyllib@kcl.ac.uk
Librarian M Guha BA ALA
Deputy Librarian Ms C Martin BA ALA

Institute of Romance Studies

See University of London, Senate House

Institute of United States Studies

See University of London, Senate House

King's College London

King's College London Library, Strand, London WC2R 2LS
☎020 7848 2424 (enquiries), 020 7848 2139/2140 (administration)
Fax 020 7848 1777
e-mail: library@kcl.ac.uk
Director of Information Services and Systems A F MacDougall MA PhD ALA (020 7848 2737)
Director of Library Services Ms A Bell BA MA ALA

London Business School

Library, London Business School, Sussex Place, Regent's Park, London NW1 4SA
☎020 7262 5050
Fax 020 7706 1897
e-mail: libuser@lbs.ac.uk LA-NET 79:LLA2027
url: http://www.lbs.ac.uk/library/index.htm
Director of Information Systems R Altendorff
Head of Library Ms H Edwards BA ALA

LBS Information Service, London Business School, Sussex Place, Regent's Park, London NW1 4SA
☎020 7723 3404
Fax 020 7706 1897
Manager Ms S Watt DipLib MIInfSc

London School of Economics

British Library of Political and Economic Science, London School of Economics, 25 Southampton Buildings, London WC2A 1PH
☎020 7955 7229 (enquiries), 020 7955 7218 (administration)
Fax 020 7955 7454
e-mail: library.information.desk@lse.ac.uk
url: http://www.lse.ac.uk/blpes

Librarian and Director of Information Services Ms J M Sykes MA MLitt DipLib ALA (020 7955 7218; e-mail: j.sykes@lse.ac.uk)
Deputy Librarian Ms M P Wade BA DipLib ALA (020 7955 7224; e-mail: m.wade@lse.ac.uk)
Sub-Librarian, Information Services and Collection Development B Wynne BA DLIS ALA (020 7955 7217; e-mail: b.wynne@lse.ac.uk)
Archivist Ms S Donnelly BA DipArchiveAdmin (020 7955 7223; e-mail: document@lse.ac.uk)
IT Support Manager T Green DipCompStud (020 7955 6140; e-mail: t.green@lse.ac.uk)
The British Library of Political and Economic Science will remain at the above address until the Summer of 2001, when they expect to move back to their permanent premises at 10 Portugal Street (currently under redevelopment)

London School of Hygiene and Tropical Medicine
Library, London School of Hygiene and Tropical Medicine, Keppel Street, London WC1E 7HT
☎020 7927 2276 (enquiries), 020 7927 2283 (administration)
Fax 020 7927 2273
e-mail: library@lshtm.ac.uk
url: http://www.lshtm.ac.uk/as/library/libintro.htm
Librarian and Director of Information Services R B Furner BA MSc MIInfSc

London School of Jewish Studies (formerly Jews' College)
Library, London School of Jewish Studies, Schaller House, 44A Albert Road, London NW4 2SJ
☎020 8203 6427
Fax 020 8203 6420
e-mail: jewscoll@clus1.ulcc.ac.uk
Head Librarian E Kahn JL
Assistant Librarian A Prys BA MPhil DipLib ALA
Consultant A A E E Ettinghausen ALA

Queen Mary and Westfield College
Library, Queen Mary and Westfield College, Mile End Road, London E1 4NS
☎020 7775 3300 (enquiries), 020 7775 3302 (administration)
Fax 020 8981 0028
e-mail: library@qmw.ac.uk
url: http://www.library.qmw.ac.uk/
Director of Academic Information Services B Murphy BA ALA (020 7975 5004; e-mail: b.murphy@qmw.ac.uk)
Sub-Librarian (Services) Ms H Thomas BSc ALA (020 7775 3311; e-mail: h.thomas@qmw.ac.uk)
Sub-Librarian (Resources) N Entwistle BA MA ALA (020 7775 3304; e-mail: n.w.entwistle@qmw.ac.uk)
Medical Librarian P Hockney BSc ALA MIInfSci (020 7295 7114; e-mail: p.s.hockney@mds.qmw.ac.uk)

Site libraries
A   Whitechapel Library, Queen Mary and Westfield College, St Bartholomew's and The Royal London School of Medicine and Dentistry, Turner Street, London E1 2AD
☎020 7295 7115
Fax 020 7295 7113
e-mail: library@mds.qmw.ac.uk
Site Librarian Ms J Thomas BSc DipLib (020 7295 7116; e-mail: j.h.thomas@mds.qmw.ac.uk)

B   West Smithfield Library, Queen Mary and Westfield College, St Bartholomew's and
     The Royal London School of Medicine and Dentistry, West Smithfield, London
     EC1A 7BA
     ☎020 7601 7837
     Fax 020 7606 2137
     Site Librarian Ms C Cheney BA MSc ALA (020 7601 7849; e-mail:
     c.r.cheney@mds.qmw.ac.uk)
C   Charterhouse Square Library, Queen Mary and Westfield College, St Bartholomew's
     and The Royal London School of Medicine and Dentistry, Charterhouse Square,
     London EC1M 6BY
     ☎020 7982 6019
     Fax 020 7490 2851
     Site Librarian Ms F Moussavi BA MA DipLib (e-mail: f.moussavi@mds.qmw.ac.uk)

Royal Free and University College School of Medicine

Medical Library, Royal Free and University College School of Medicine of University College
London, Rowland Hill Street, London NW3 2PF
☎020 7794 0500 ext 3202
Fax 020 7794 3534
e-mail: ucylbet@ucl.ac.uk
Librarian Ms B Anagnostelis BSc(Hons) MSc DipLib

Royal Holloway

Library, Royal Holloway, Egham, Surrey TW20 0EX
☎(01784) 443823 (enquiries), 443334 (administration)
Fax (01784) 477670
url: http://www.rhbnc.ac.uk (College); http://www.lb.rhbnc.ac.uk (Library)
Librarian and Deputy Director of Information Services Ms S E Gerrard BA DipLib ALA
(01784 443330; e-mail: s.gerrard@rhbnc.ac.uk)
Deputy Librarian Miss J Sherlock BA DipLib (01784 443120; e-mail:
j.sherlock@rhbnc.ac.uk)
Academic Services Manager D Ward BA DipLib (01784 443123; e-mail:
d.ward@rhbnc.ac.uk)
Services Manager (Operations) Ms M Hiscoe BSc DipLib (01784 444066; e-mail:
m.hiscoe@rhbnc.ac.uk)

Music Library, Royal Holloway, Egham, Surrey TW20 0EX
☎(01784) 443560
Fax (01784) 477670
e-mail: library@rhbnc.ac.uk
Music Librarian Dr C Grogan BMus PhD DipLIS (01784 443759; e-mail:
c.grogan@rhbnc.ac.uk)

Royal Veterinary College

Library, Royal Veterinary College, Royal College Street, London NW1 0TU
☎020 7468 5164
Fax 020 7468 5162
Deputy College Librarian D Walker BSc(Hons) DipLIS ALA (e-mail: dwalker@rvc.ac.uk)

Campus library

Hawkshead Campus Library, Royal Veterinary College, University of London, Hawkshead
House, Hawkshead Lane, North Mimms, Hatfield, Herts AL9 7TA

☎(01707) 666214 (tel/fax)
College Librarian S Jackson MA ALA (e-mail: sjackson@rvc.ac.uk)

St George's Hospital Medical School

St George's Library, St George's Hospital Medical School, Hunter Wing, Cranmer Terrace, London SW17 0RE
☎020 8725 5466 (direct line)
Fax 020 8767 4696
Librarian and Director of Information Services Mrs S Gove BSc DipLib FLS FZS (e-mail: s.gove@sghms.ac.uk)

School of Oriental and African Studies

Library, School of Oriental and African Studies, Thornhaugh Street, Russell Square, London WC1H 0XG
☎020 7323 6109 (enquiries), 020 7323 6081 (library office)
Fax 020 7636 2834
url: http://www.libenquiry@soas.ac.uk
Acting Librarian W Batchelor BComm(Econ) DipLib (e-mail: w.b@soas.ac.uk)
Deputy Librarian (Central Information and Document Supply Services) W Batchelor BComm(Econ) DipLib (020 7323 6002; e-mail: wb@soas.ac.uk)
Deputy Librarian (Specialist Information Services and Collection Development) Miss H Cordell BA DipLib ALA MA MSc (020 7323 6220; e-mail: hc@soas.ac.uk)

School of Pharmacy

Library, School of Pharmacy, 29-39 Brunswick Square, London WC1N 1AX
☎020 7753 5833
Fax 020 7753 5947
e-mail: library@ulsop.ac.uk
Librarian Mrs L Lisgarten BA ALA MIInfSc

School of Slavonic and East European Studies

Library, School of Slavonic and East European Studies, University of London, Senate House, Malet Street, London WC1E 7HU
☎020 7862 8523
e-mail: ssees-library@ssees.ac.uk
url: http://www.ssees.ac.uk/library.htm
Librarian and Director of Information Services Ms L Pitman BA DipLib

University College London

University College Library, University College London, Gower Street, London WC1E 6BT
☎020 7380 7700 (enquiries), 020 7380 7051 (administration)
Fax 020 7380 7373
e-mail: library@ucl.ac.uk
url: http://www.ucl.ac.uk/library/
Director of Library Services P Ayris MA PhD ALA
Senior Sub-Librarian Mrs J Percival (020 7380 7791; e-mail: j.percival@ucl.ac.uk)
Sub-Librarian, Information Systems Mrs J Cropper MSc DipLib (020 7380 7373; e-mail: j.cropper@ucl.ac.uk)
Sub-Librarian, Reader Services Mrs J Edwards BSc MA ALA (e-mail: j.a.edwards@ucl.ac.uk)
Sub-Librarian, Bibliographic Services Ms D Mercer MSc DipLib (020 7504 2625; e-mail: d.mercer@ucl.ac.uk)

Sectional libraries

A   Institute of Archaeology Library, University College London, 31-34 Gordon Square, London WC1H 0PY
☎020 7380 7485
Librarian i/c R T Kirby MA

B   Boldero Library, University College London, Middlesex Hospital, Mortimer Street, London W1P 7PN
☎020 7380 9454
Librarian i/c Mrs P A Campbell BA DipInfSci

C   Clinical Sciences Library, University College London, Faculty of Clinical Sciences, University Street, London WC1E 6JJ
☎020 7209 6079
Librarian i/c G R Peacock BA DipLib

D   Environmental Studies Library, University College London, Faculty of the Built Environment, Wates House, 22 Gordon Street, London WC1H 0QB
☎020 7387 7050
Librarian i/c Ms S McGivern BA DipInf

E   Institute of Laryngology and Otology Library, University College London, Royal National Throat, Nose and Ear Hospital, Gray's Inn Road, London WC1X 8EE
☎020 7915 1445
Librarian i/c P Pearson BTh MTh PhD MA

F   Rockefeller Medical Library, University College London, Institute of Neurology, The National Hospital, Queen Square, London WC1N 3BG
☎020 7829 8709
Fax 020 7278 5069
e-mail: library@ion.ucl.ac.uk
url: http://www.ion.ucl.ac.uk/~admin/library.html
Librarian Mrs L J Shepherd BA (e-mail: shepherd@ion.ucl.ac.uk)
Assistant Librarian Ms S D Duerden MSc ALA (e-mail: sduerden@ion.ucl.ac.uk)

G   Institute of Orthopaedics Library, University College London, Royal National Orthopaedic Hospital, Brockley Hill, Stanmore, Middlesex HA7 4LP
☎020 8954 2300
Fax 020 8954 1213
Librarian i/c Ms B Adams BA MSc

H   Royal National Institute for Deaf People Library, University College London, Royal National Throat, Nose and Ear Hospital, Gray's Inn Road, London WC1X 8EE
☎020 7915 1553
Fax 020 7915 1443
Librarian i/c Ms M Plackett

I   Human Communication Library, University College London, Chandler House, 2 Wakefield Street, London WC1N 1PG
☎020 7837 0113
Fax 020 7713 0861
Librarian i/c Ms A Douglas

J   Institute of Child Health Library, University College London, 30 Guilford Street, London WC1N 1EE
☎020 7242 9789
Librarian i/c J Clarke

Warburg Institute

Library, Warburg Institute, Woburn Square, London WC1H 0AB
☎020 7862 8935 (reading room)

Fax 020 7862 8939
e-mail: warburg@sas.ac.uk
url: http://www.sas.ac.uk/warburg/
telnet (for library): lib.sas.ac.uk
Librarian W F Ryan MA DPhil FSA

Wye College
Library, Wye College, Wye, Ashford, Kent TN25 5AH
☎(01233) 812401 ext 515 (library enquiries)
Fax (01233) 813074
Librarian Mrs E M Lucas JP BSc ALA (e-mail: m.lucas@wye.ac.uk)

LOUGHBOROUGH UNIVERSITY
Pilkington Library, Loughborough University, Loughborough, Leics LE11 3TU
☎(01509) 222360 (enquiries), (01509) 222340 (administration)
Fax (01509) 223993
e-mail: library@lboro.ac.uk
url: http://info@lboro.ac.uk/library/index/html
University Librarian Mrs M D Morley BA DipLib ALA

Site library
Fairbairn Library, Loughborough University, Radmoor Road, Loughborough, Leics LE11 3BS
☎(01509) 239717
Fax (01509) 223993
Senior Library Assistant Ms M Brown (01509 239267)

UNIVERSITY OF LUTON
Learning Resources Centre, University of Luton, Park Square, Luton, Beds LU1 3JU
☎(01582) 34111 ext 2016 (enquiries), (01582) 489312 (administration)
Fax (01582) 489325
e-mail: lynda.boston@luton.ac.uk (admin)
Director of Learning Resources T Stone

Site libraries
A   Putteridge Bury Resource Centre, University of Luton, Hitchin Road, Luton, Beds LU2 8LE
     ☎(01582) 489079
     Fax (01582) 482689
     Faculty Information Officer (Management) Mrs A Stewart (e-mail: audrey.stewart@luton.ac.uk)
B   Nursing Library, University of Luton, School of Community and Mental Health, Britannia Road, Bedford, Beds MK40 2NU
     ☎(01234) 355122 ext 2707
     Health Studies Librarian (Beds) Mrs A Rowlands
C   Nursing Library, School of Acute Care/Midwifery, University of Luton, Luton and Dunstable Hospital, Dunstable Road, Luton, Beds LU4 0DT
     ☎(01582) 497296
     Health Studies Librarian (Beds) Mrs A Rowlands
D   Nursing Library, University of Luton, Lovelock Jones Nurse Education Centre, Barracks Road, High Wycombe, Bucks HP11 1QN
     ☎(01494) 425137/320
     Health Studies Librarian (Bucks) Mrs A Rowlands
E   Nursing Library, University of Luton, Nuffield Research Centre, Stoke Mandeville

Hospital, Mandeville Road, Aylesbury, Bucks HP21 8AL
☎(01296) 315901
Health Studies Librarian (Bucks) Mrs A Rowlands

MANCHESTER BUSINESS SCHOOL

Library and Information Service, Manchester Business School, Booth Street West,
Manchester M15 6PB
☎0161 275 6507 (enquiries), 0161 275 6500 (administration)
Fax 0161 275 6505
url: http://www.mbs.ac.uk/lis
Librarian and Information Services Manager B Clifford BA MA ALA FIInfSc (e-mail:
b.clifford@fs2.mbs.ac.uk)

MANCHESTER METROPOLITAN UNIVERSITY

Library, Manchester Metropolitan University, All Saints, Manchester M15 6BH
☎0161 247 3096
Fax 0161 247 6349
url: http://www.mmu.ac.uk/services/library/lib2.htm
Chief Librarian Professor C G S Harris BA MA MLS BPhil PhD FLA FIInfSc (0161 247 6100;
e-mail: c.harris@mmu.ac.uk)
Joint Deputy Librarians Mrs G R Barry BA MSc ALA (Head of Reader Services) (0161 247
6101, e-mail: g.r.barry@mmu.ac.uk), Mrs L Elliott MA FLA (Head of Technical Services)
(0161 247 6102; e-mail: l.elliott@mmu.ac.uk)
Faculty Librarian (Crewe & Alsager) Dr M Robinson BA DipLib (0161 247 5138; e-mail:
m.g.robinson@mmu.ac.uk)

Site libraries
A   Alsager Library, Manchester Metropolitan University, Hassall Road, Alsager, Stoke-
      on-Trent, Staffs ST7 2HL
      ☎0161 247 5356
      Site Manager Ms M Pickstone BSc DipLib ALA (0161 247 5355; e-mail:
      m.pickstone@mmu.ac.uk)
B   Aytoun Library, Manchester Metropolitan University, Aytoun Street, Manchester
      M1 3GH
      ☎0161 247 3093
      Site Librarian Mrs K Morrison BA ALA (0161 247 3091; e-mail:
      k.morrison@mmu.ac.uk)
C   Crewe Library, Manchester Metropolitan University, Crewe Green Road, Crewe,
      Cheshire CW1 1DU
      ☎0161 247 5002
      Site Manager Mrs F Hughes BA MLib ALA (0161 247 5012; e-mail:
      f.hughes@mmu.ac.uk)
D   Didsbury Library, Manchester Metropolitan University, 799 Wilmslow Road,
      Manchester M20 8RR
      ☎0161 247 6126
      Site Librarian Dr P Cohen BA MSc ALA (0161 247 6120; e-mail:
      p.cohen@mmu.ac.uk)
E   Elizabeth Gaskell Library, Manchester Metropolitan University, Hathersage Road,
      Manchester M13 0JA
      ☎0161 247 6134
      Site Librarian Ms A Mackenzie BA ALA (0161 247 6561; e-mail:
      a.mackenzie@mmu.ac.uk)
F   Hollings Library, Manchester Metropolitan University, Old Hall Lane, Manchester

M14 6HR
☎0161 247 6119
Site Librarian Ms C Williams BA MA ALA (0161 247 6118; e-mail:
c.williams@mmu.ac.uk)

UNIVERSITY OF MANCHESTER

The John Rylands University Library of Manchester, University of Manchester, Main Library,
Oxford Road, Manchester M13 9PP
☎0161 275 3738 (enquiries), 0161 275 3760 (administration)
Fax 0161 273 7488
url: http://rylibweb.man.ac.uk/
Director and University Librarian C J Hunt BA MLItt ALA FSA

Books and Special Collections Library, John Rylands University Library, University of
Manchester, 150 Deansgate, Manchester M3 3EH
☎0161 834 5343/6765
Fax 0161 834 5574
Librarian As above
See also UMIST

MIDDLESEX UNIVERSITY

Library Services, Middlesex University, Level 4 Bounds Green Road, London N11 2NQ
☎020 8362 5234
Fax 020 8362 5163
url: http://www.mdx.ac.uk/ilrs/lib/libinfo.htm
Head of ILRS and University Librarian W A J Marsterson MA ALA (020 8362 5234; e-mail:
w.marsterson@mdx.ac.uk)

Campus libraries
A   Bibliographical Services, Middlesex University, Bounds Green Road, London
N11 2NQ
☎020 8362 5254 (direct)
e-mail: libbg1@mdx.ac.uk
Bibliographical Services Librarian Mrs E M Barton BSc ALA
B   Library, Middlesex University at Bounds Green, Middlesex University, Bounds Green
Road, London N11 2NQ
☎020 8362 5240 (direct)
e-mail: libbg1@mdx.ac.uk
Campus Librarian Ms S Fellows BA ALA
C   Library, Middlesex University at Cat Hill, Middlesex University, Barnet, Herts EN4 8HT
☎020 8362 5042 (direct)
e-mail: libch1@mdx.ac.uk
Campus Librarian M M Wagstaff MA ALA
D   Library, Middlesex University at Enfield, Middlesex University, Queensway, Enfield,
Middlesex EN3 4SF
☎020 8362 5334 (direct)
e-mail: liben1@mdx.ac.uk
Campus Librarian Ms K McGowan MA ALA
E   Library, Middlesex University at Hendon, Middlesex University, The Burroughs,
London NW4 4BT
☎020 8362 5852 (direct)
e-mail: libhe1@mdx.ac.uk
Campus Librarian Ms P Hollis BA ALA

F Library, Middlesex University at Ivy House, Middlesex University, North End Road, London NW11 7HU
☎020 8362 5000 ext 4105
e-mail: libih1@mdx.ac.uk
Librarian i/c C Brough BA ALA

G Library, Middlesex University at Quicksilver Place, Middlesex University, Western Road, London N22 6XH
☎020 8362 5000 ext 2139
e-mail: libqp1@mdx.ac.uk
Assistant Librarian Ms M Brownlie BA

H Library, Middlesex University at Tottenham, Middlesex University, White Hart Lane, London N17 8HR
☎020 8362 5165
e-mail: libtm1@mdx.ac.uk
Campus Librarian Vacant

I Library, Middlesex University at Trent Park, Middlesex University, Bramley Road, London N14 4XS
☎020 8362 5646 (direct)
e-mail: libtp1@mdx.ac.uk
Campus Librarian L Greenfield BA ALA

J Health Campus Library, Middlesex University, Chase Farm Education Centre, Chase Farm Hospital, The Ridgeway, Enfield, Middlesex EN2 8JL
☎020 8366 9112
e-mail: libcf1@mdx.ac.uk
Faculty Librarian Ms D Hall BA ALA

K Health Campus Library, Middlesex University, Royal Free Education Centre, Royal Free Hospital, Pond Street, London NW3 2XA
☎020 7830 2788
e-mail: librf1@mdx.ac.uk
Site Librarian Ms S Hill BA

L Library, Middlesex University, London College of Dance, 10 Linden Road, Bedford MK40 2DA
☎(01234) 213331
Librarian i/c Ms D Bennett BA ALA

(The Health Campus libraries are also served by multidisciplinary libraries at: David Ferriman Library, North Middlesex Hospital, Sterling Way, London N18 1QX (020 8887 2223; e-mail: libnm1@mdx.ac.uk, libnm2@mdx.ac.uk) and The Archway Healthcare Library, Holborn Union Building, The Archway Campus, Highgate Hill, London N19 3UA (020 7288 3567; e-mail: libwh1@mdx.ac.uk, libwh2@mdx.ac.uk)

NAPIER UNIVERSITY
Main libraries
Sighthill Library, Napier University, Sighthill, Edinburgh EH11 4BN
☎0131 455 3426 (enquiries), 0131 455 3301 (administration)
Fax 0131 455 3428
url: http://www.napier.ac.uk/
Director of Learning Information Services C Pinder BA MLib DipLib ALA
Head, Acquisitions, Record Management and Supply Division G S Forbes BA MA MBA ALA (0131 455 3558)
Joint Head, Campus Library Services Division J White MA DipLib ALA (0131 455 3508)
Head, Information Strategy and IT Development G Dunsire BSc ALA (0131 455 3427)

Merchiston Library, Napier University, 10 Colinton Road, Edinburgh EH10 5DT
☎0131 455 2582 (enquiries), 0131 455 2693 (administration)
Fax 0131 455 2377
url: http://www.napier.ac.uk/
Head, Information and Advisory Services Division M Jones BA DipLib ALA
Head, Research Management and Start-up Division Dr D Cumming BSc DipLib MLib
PhD FGS MIInfSc (0131 455 2367; Fax: 0131 455 2368)

Comely Bank Library, Napier University, 13 Crewe Road South, Edinburgh EH4 2LD
☎0131 343 7918 (enquiries), 0131 343 7917 (administration)
Fax 0131 343 7958
url: http://www.napier.ac.uk/

Craiglockhart Library, Napier University, 219 Colinton Road, Edinburgh EH14 1DJ
☎0131 455 4383 (enquiries), 0131 455 4298 (administration)
Fax 0131 455 4328
url: http://www.napier.ac.uk/
Associate Librarian M Lobban MA DipLib DipEdTech ALA

Campus libraries
A Sighthill Library, Napier University, Sighthill, Edinburgh EH11 4BN
☎0131 455 3426
Fax 0131 455 3428
Campus Library Manager B Breaks
B Craighouse Library, Napier University, Craighouse Road, Edinburgh EH10 5LG
☎0131 455 6020
Fax 0131 455 6022
Campus Library Manager T Lavelle
C Merchiston Library, Napier University, 10 Colinton Road, Edinburgh EH10 5DT
☎0131 455 2582
Fax 0131 455 2377
Campus Library Manager C Gregson
D Melrose Library, Napier University, Education Centre, Borders General Hospital,
Melrose TD6 9BD
☎(01896) 661632
Fax (01896) 823869
Campus Library Manager J MacLaine
E Canaan Lane Library, Napier University, 74 Canaan Lane, Edinburgh EH10 4TB
☎0131 536 5616
Fax 0131 536 5608
Campus Library Manager M Gill
F Livingston Library, Napier University, Education Centre, St John's Hospital, Howden
Road West, Livingston EH54 6PP
☎(01506) 422831
Fax (01506) 422833
Campus Library Manager M Porter
G Comely Bank Library, Napier University, 13 Crewe Road South, Edinburgh EH4 2LD
☎0131 343 7919
Fax 0131 343 7958
Campus Library Manager H Steele
H Craiglockhart Library, Napier University, 219 Colinton Road, Edinburgh EH14 1DJ
☎0131 455 4383
Fax 0131 455 4328
Campus Library Manager C Walker

UNIVERSITY OF NEWCASTLE UPON TYNE

Robinson Library, University of Newcastle upon Tyne, Newcastle upon Tyne NE2 4HQ
☎0191 222 7662 (enquiries), 0191 222 7674 (administration)
Fax 0191 222 6235
e-mail: library@newcastle.ac.uk
url: http://www.ncl.ac.uk/library/
Librarian T W Graham MA PhD DipLib ALA

Divisional libraries
A   The Walton Library (Medical and Dental), University of Newcastle upon Tyne, The
    Medical School, Framlington Place, Newcastle upon Tyne NE2 4HH
    ☎0191 222 7550
    Librarian Mrs H MacFarlane BA DipLib ALA
B   Law Library, University of Newcastle upon Tyne, Faculty of Law, 22-24 Windsor
    Terrace, Newcastle upon Tyne NE1 7RU
    ☎0191 222 7944
    Librarian Mrs L Appiah BA ALA

NEWMAN COLLEGE OF HIGHER EDUCATION

Library, Newman College of Higher Education, Genners Lane, Bartley Green, Birmingham
B32 3NT
☎0121 476 1181 ext 208
Fax 0121 476 1196
e-mail: library@newman.ac.uk
url: http://www.newman.ac.uk/nw3/library
Librarian Mrs C Rock BA MA ALA (ext 298; e-mail: c.rock@newman.ac.uk)
Senior Assistant Librarian Miss A Huggan BA MA

NORTH EAST WALES INSTITUTE OF HIGHER EDUCATION

Information and Student Services, North East Wales Institute of Higher Education, Plas Coch,
Mold Road, Wrexham LL11 2AW
☎(01978) 293250
Fax (01978) 293254
url: http;//www.newi.ac.uk
Head of Information and Student Services A T Hughes (e-mail: a.hughes@newi.ac.uk)

UNIVERSITY OF NORTH LONDON

Learning Centre, University of North London, 236-250 Holloway Road, London N7 6PP
☎020 7753 2371 (enquiries), 020 7753 5409 (administration)
Fax 020 7753 7037
e-mail: 75liblc@unl.ac.uk (Learning Centre Reception)
url: http://www.unl.ac.uk/iss/lcguide.html
Director of Information Systems and Services R Williams BA ALA DipLib GradIPM

Section libraries
A   Academic Information Services Team, University of North London, 236-250 Holloway
    Road, London N7 6PP
    ☎020 7753 5409 ext 2101
    Fax 020 7753 7037
    e-mail: 75liblc@unl.ac.uk (Learning Centre reception)
    Team Manager Ms S Davy BA ALA

B   Circulation and Customer Services Team, University of North London, 236-250 Holloway Road, London N7 6PP
☎020 7753 5409 ext 2089
Fax 020 7753 7037
e-mail: 75liblc@unl.ac.uk (Learning Centre reception)
Team Manager Ms E Hansen MA ALA MLib

C   Learning Materials Team, University of North London, 236-250 Holloway Road, London N7 6PP
☎020 7753 5409 ext 2450
Fax 020 7753 7037
e-mail: 75liblc@unl.ac.uk (Learning Centre reception)
Team Manager Ms J Howell BSc DipLib

D   Ladbroke House Team, University of North London, Ladbroke House, 62-66 Highbury Grove, London N5 2AD
☎020 7753 5149 ext 5148
Fax 020 7753 5100
e-mail: 75liblh@unl.ac.uk
Team Manager Ms A Aungle BA ALA DipLib

E   European Documentation Centre, University of North London, 236-250 Holloway Road, London N7 6PP
☎020 7753 5142
Fax 020 7753 7037
Manager D Griffiths BA(Hons) DipLib (e-mail: d.griffiths@unl.ac.uk)

F   Trades Union Congress Library Collections, University of North London, 236-250 Holloway Road, London N7 6PP
☎020 7753 3184
Fax 020 7753 3191
Librarian Ms C Coates MA ALA (e-mail: c.coates@unl.ac.uk)

UNIVERSITY COLLEGE NORTHAMPTON

Rockingham Library, University College Northampton, Park Campus, Boughton Green Road, Northampton NN2 7AL
☎(01604) 735500 ext 2477 (enquiries), ext 2046 (administration)
Fax (01604) 718819
url: http://www.northampton.ac.uk
Chief Librarian Ms H J Johnson BA ALA (e-mail: hilary.johnson@northampton.ac.uk)
Deputy Librarian A Martin BSc MA ALA (ext 2047; e-mail: andrew.martin@northampton.ac.uk)

Campus Library
Avenue Library, Maidwell Building, St George's Avenue, Northampton NN2 6JD
☎(01604) 735500 ext 3900
Fax (01604) 719618
Other details: as above

NORTHERN COLLEGE

Aberdeen Campus
Library, Northern College, Aberdeen Campus, Hilton Place, Aberdeen AB24 4FA
☎(01224 283571)
Fax (01224) 283655/283900
Principal Librarian Vacant
Senior Librarians Miss J Jolly ALA, L McMorran MA ALA

Dundee Campus
Library, Northern College, Dundee Campus, Gardyne Road, Dundee DD5 1NY

☎(01382) 464267
Fax (01382) 464255
Campus Library Manager J McCaffery BA DipLib ALA

NORTHERN SCHOOL OF CONTEMPORARY DANCE

Library, Northern School of Contemporary Dance, 98 Chapeltown Road, Leeds
LS7 4BH
☎0113 219 3020
Fax 0113 219 3030
Librarian Miss S King BA(Hons) (e-mail: samk@nscd.ac.uk)
Assistant Librarian Miss H Cox (e-mail: hesterc@nscd.ac.uk)

UNIVERSITY OF NORTHUMBRIA AT NEWCASTLE

City Campus Library, University of Northumbria at Newcastle, Ellison Place, Newcastle upon
Tyne NE1 8ST
☎0191 227 4125 (enquiries), 0191 227 4143 (administration)
Fax 0191 227 4563
Director of Information Services I R Winkworth BA DipLib MPhil ALA (e-mail:
ian.winkworth@unn.ac.uk)

Site libraries
A   Coach Lane Library, University of Northumbria at Newcastle, Coach Lane, Newcastle
upon Tyne NE7 7XA
☎0191 227 4138 (enquiries)
Librarian i/c J G Walton BSc FETC MA ALA
B   Carlisle Campus Library, University of Northumbria at Newcastle, 4-5 Paternoster
Row, Carlisle, Cumbria CA3 8TT
☎0191 227 4838
Fax 0191 227 4820
Librarian i/c D Roberts BA ALA
C   Longhirst Campus Library, University of Northumbria at Newcastle, Longhirst Hall,
Longhirst, Morpeth, Northumberland NE61 3LL
☎(01670) 791348
Librarian i/c J Storey BA ALA

NORWICH SCHOOL OF ART AND DESIGN

Library, Norwich School of Art and Design, St George Street, Norwich NR3 1BB
☎(01603) 610561 (enquiries), ext 3072 (administration)
Fax (01603) 615728
url: http://www.nsad.ac.uk
Coordinator of Learning Resources T Giles BA ALA (e-mail: tim.g@nsad.ac.uk)
Assistant Librarians Ms K Guiver MA ALA (e-mail: kitty.g@nsad.ac.uk), Ms J MacLachlan
BA(Hons) DipLIS

NOTTINGHAM TRENT UNIVERSITY

The Boots Library, Library and Information Services, Nottingham Trent University, Goldsmith
Street, Nottingham NG1 4FZ
☎0115 941 8418 ext 2175 (enquiries), 0115 948 6446 (administration)
Fax 0115 848 2286
Director of Library and Information Services Ms E Lines BSc ALA (e-mail:
liz.lines@ntu.ac.uk)

Site library
Clifton Campus Library, Nottingham Trent University, Clifton Lane, Nottingham NG11 8NS
☎0115 941 8418 ext 3246
Fax 0115 948 6304
Information Team Manager Mrs C Coates BA ALA

UNIVERSITY OF NOTTINGHAM

Hallward Library, University of Nottingham, University Park, Nottingham NG7 2RD
☎0115 951 4555
Fax 0115 951 4558
url: http://www.nottingham.ac.uk/library/
Director of Library Services R E Oldroyd BA FLA (0115 951 4547)
Systems, Networked Information and Technical Services Librarian R J Chamberlain BA DipLib ALA (0115 951 4553)

Component libraries
A   Hallward Library (Arts, Social Sciences, Education), University of Nottingham, University Park, Nottingham NG7 2RD
    ☎0115 951 4555
    Fax 0115 951 4588
    Librarian M G R Smith BA MA ALA (0115 951 4617)
B   Hallward Library (Department of Manuscripts and Special Collections), University of Nottingham, University Park, Nottingham NG7 2RD
    ☎0115 951 4565
    Fax 0115 951 4588
    Keeper D B Johnston BA PhD DipLib (0115 951 4563)
C   Law Library, University of Nottingham, Trent Building, University Park, Nottingham NG7 2RD
    ☎0115 951 4568
    Fax 0115 951 4583
    Librarian Mrs P A Williams BA
D   George Green Library of Science and Engineering, University of Nottingham, University Park, Nottingham NG7 2RD
    ☎0115 951 4570
    Fax 0115 951 4578
    Librarian Mrs M J E Noble BLib (0115 951 4572)
E   Greenfield Medical Library, University of Nottingham, Queen's Medical Centre, Nottingham NG7 2UH
    ☎0115 970 9445
    Fax 0115 970 9449
    Medical Librarian A J Coggins BA ALA
F   James Cameron Gifford Library of Agricultural and Food Sciences, University of Nottingham, Sutton Bonington Campus, Sutton Bonington, nr Loughborough, Leics LE12 5RD
    ☎0115 951 6390
    Fax 0115 951 6389
    Librarian Mrs E A Dodds MA PGCE DipLib (0115 951 6388)
G   New Campus LRC (Education, Business School, Computer Science), University of Nottingham, Wollaton Road, Nottingham NG8 1FF
    ☎0115 846 6700
    Fax 0115 846 6705
    Librarian P G Haywood BA DipLib (0115 951 4579)

OPEN UNIVERSITY

Library, Open University, Walton Hall, Milton Keynes MK7 6AA
☎(01908) 653138
Fax (01908) 653571
e-mail: oulibrary@open.ac.uk
Director of Library Services Mrs N Whitsed MSc FLA (01908 653254; e-mail:
n.whitsed@open.ac.uk)
Collections and Facilities Manager R Stubbs BA DMS (01908 653252; e-mail:
g.r.stubbs@open.ac.uk)
Information Services Manager Ms A Davies BSc MSc (01908 652057; e-mail:
ann.davies@open.ac.uk)
IT Development Manager Ms E Simpson BA (01908 655703; e-mail:
e.simpson@open.ac.uk)
Interactive Open Learning Centre Manager R van der Zwan MA (01908 653530; e-mail:
r.m.vanderzwan@open.ac.uk)

ORCHARD LEARNING RESOURCES CENTRE

Orchard Learning Resources Centre, Hamilton Drive, Weoley Park Road, Selly Oak,
Birmingham B29 6QW
☎0121 415 2255
e-mail: olrc@sellyoak.ac.uk
url: http://www.sellyoak.ac.uk/colleges.htm
Director G Harris BSocSc MPhil FLA MIInfSc MIMgt (0121 415 2339)

Selly Oak Colleges
Orchard Learning Resources Centre, Hamilton Drive, Weoley Park Road, Selly Oak,
Birmingham B29 6QW
☎0121 415 2255
e-mail: olrc@sellyoak.ac.uk
url: http://www.sellyoak.ac.uk/colleges.htm
Director G Harris BSocSc MPhil FLA MIInfSc MIMgt (0121 415 2339; e-mail:
g.harris@sellyoak.ac.uk)
Services Manager and Deputy Director Mrs M Nielsen BA MA ALA (0121 415 2287;
e-mail: m.nielsen@sellyoak.ac.uk)

Westhill College of Higher Education
Details as Selly Oak Colleges above

OXFORD BROOKES UNIVERSITY

Library, Oxford Brookes University, Gipsy Lane Campus, Headington, Oxford OX3 0BP
☎(01865) 483156 (enquiries), (01865) 483130 (administration)
Fax (01865) 483998
e-mail: library@brookes.ac.uk
Head of Learning Resources and University Librarian Dr H M Workman PhD ALA MIInfSc
Deputy Librarians Ms J Haines BLib DipM ALA, A Robbins BA MSc ALA

Site libraries
A   Wheatley Library, Oxford Brookes University, Wheatley Campus, Wheatley, Oxford
     OX9 1HX
     ☎(01865) 485869
     Fax (01865) 485750
     Deputy Librarian Ms C M Jeffrey BSc DipLib DMS ALA
B   Dorset House Library, Oxford Brookes University, Dorset House, 58 London Road,

Headington, Oxford OX3 7PE
☎(01865) 485261
Site Librarian Ms S Croft DipCOT

UNIVERSITY OF OXFORD

Bodleian Library, University of Oxford, Broad Street, Oxford OX1 3BG
☎(01865) 277000 (enquiries), (01865) 277170 (administration)
Fax (01865) 277182
e-mail: enquiries@bodley.ox.ac.uk
url: http://www.bodley.ox.ac.uk/
Director of University Library Services and Bodley's Librarian R P Carr BA MA FRSA
Deputy to the Director of University Library Services and to Bodley's Librarian J P Tuck MA ALA

Dependent libraries

A   Bodleian Law Library, St Cross Building, Manor Road, Oxford
OX1 3UR
☎(01865) 271463
Fax (01865) 271475
e-mail: law.library@bodley.ox.ac.uk
Librarian Miss B M Tearle LLB ALA
B   Hooke Library, Parks Road, Oxford OX1 3QP
☎(01865) 272812
e-mail: hooke.library@bodley.ox.ac.uk
Hooke Librarian Ms J K L Ralph MSc ALA
C   Indian Institute Library, Bodleian Library, Broad Street, Oxford
OX1 3BG
☎(01865) 277082
Fax (01865) 277182
e-mail: indian.institute@bodley.ox.ac.uk
Librarian Dr G A Evison MA DPhil Mphil
D   Bodleian Japanese Library at the Nissan Institute, 27 Winchester
Road, Oxford OX2 6NA
☎(01865) 284506
Fax (01865) 284500
e-mail: japanese@bodley.ox.ac.uk
Librarian Mrs I K Tytler MA
E   Library, Oriental Institute, Pusey Lane, Oxford OX1 2LE
☎(01865) 278202
Fax (01865) 278190
e-mail: library@orinst.ox.ac.uk
Librarian A D Hyder MA
F   Philosophy Library, 10 Merton Street, Oxford OX1 4JJ
☎(01865) 276927
Fax (01865) 276932
e-mail: philosophy.library@bodley.ox.ac.uk
Librarian Dr H A Wait MA Dphil
G   Radcliffe Science Library, Parks Road, Oxford OX1 3QP
☎(01865) 272800
Fax (01865) 272821
e-mail: rsl.enquiries@bodley.ox.ac.uk
Keeper of Scientific Books P Leggate MA DPhil
H   Rhodes House Library, South Parks Road, Oxford OX1 3RG

☎(01865) 270909
Fax (01865) 270912
e-mail: rhodes.house.library@bodley.ox.ac.uk
Librarian J R Pinfold MA

UNIVERSITY OF OXFORD
(College, Institute and Departmental)

All Souls College
Codrington Library, All Souls College, Oxford OX1 4AL
☎(01865) 279318
Fax (01865) 279299
e-mail: codrington.library@all-souls.ox.ac.uk
Librarian in Charge Dr N Aubertin-Potter BA PhD ALA

Ashmolean
Ashmolean Library, Oxford OX1 2PH
☎(01865) 278087
Fax (01865) 278098
Librarian B McGregor MA MPhil
(Access to the Library is limited to members of Oxford University)

Balliol College
Library, Balliol College, Oxford OX1 3BJ
☎(01865) 277709
Fax (01865) 277803
e-mail: library@balliol.oxford.ac.uk
Librarian Dr P A Bulloch ALA FSA
Assistant Librarian A Tadiello

Brasenose College
Library, Brasenose College, Oxford OX1 4AJ
☎(01865) 277827
Fax (01865) 277831
Fellow Librarian J W Davies
Assistant Librarians R H Laver, Mrs S Glen FCSD DipLib ALA

Campion Hall
Library, Campion Hall, Brewer Street, Oxford OX1 1QS
☎(01865) 286104
Librarian Dr N Tanner BTh MA DPhil FRHistSoc
Assistant Librarian L Weeks MA

Christ Church
Library, Christ Church, Oxford OX1 1DP
☎(01865) 276169
e-mail: library@christ-church.ox.ac.uk
url: http://www.chch.ox.ac.uk/library/
Assistant Librarians M E Phillips MA MA, Mrs J E McMullin MA ALA

Corpus Christi College
Library, Corpus Christi College, Merton Street, Oxford OX1 4JF

☎(01865) 276744
Fax (01865) 276767
url: http://www.ccc.ox.ac.uk/library/library.htm
Librarian i/c Ms S Newton MA ALA (e-mail: sarah.newton@ccc.ox.ac.uk)
Assistant Librarian Miss R Margolis MA MA ALA (e-mail: rachel.margolis@ccc.ox.ac.uk)

Department of Educational Studies

Library, Department of Educational Studies, 15 Norham Gardens, Oxford OX2 6PY
☎(01865) 274028 (library), (01865) 274011 (Librarian)
Fax (01865) 274027 (department)
url: http://units.ox.ac.uk/departments/edstud/libwww.html
Librarian Ms J Reading MA ALA
Assistant Librarian Ms A-J Hemming MA ALA

Economics Department

Economics Library, Economics Department, St Cross Building, Manor Road, Oxford OX1 3UL
☎(01865) 271071 (Librarian), (01865) 271093 (library)
Fax (01865) 271072
url: http://www.economics.ox.ac.uk/ieslib/library.htm
Social Studies Librarian Ms M Robb BS MLS ALA

Exeter College

Library, Exeter College, Turl Street, Oxford OX1 3DP
☎(01865) 279600 (switchboard), (01865) 279657 (direct)
Fax (01865) 279630
e-mail: librarian@exeter.ox.ac.uk
Fellow Librarian Dr J R Maddicott DPhil FBA

Faculty of Music

Faculty of Music Library, St Aldate's, Oxford OX1 1DB
☎(01865) 276146 (librarian), (01865) 276148 (enquiries)
Fax (01865) 286260
url: http://www.music.ox.ac.uk/library/
Librarian D J Wagstaff (e-mail: john.wagstaff@music.ox.ac.uk)

Green College

Library, Green College (at the Radcliffe Observatory), Woodstock Road, Oxford OX2 6HG
☎(01865) 274788/274770
Fax (01865) 274796
Assistant Librarian Ms G C Edwards (e-mail: gill.edwards@green.ox.ac.uk)

Harris Manchester College

Library, Harris Manchester College, Mansfield Road, Oxford OX1 3TD
☎(01865) 271016 (enquiries), (01865) 271015 (administration)
Fax (01865) 271012
e-mail: librarian@hmc.ox.ac.uk
Librarian Mrs M A Sarosi BA HDipLib (e-mail: margaret.sarosi@hmc.ox.ac.uk)

Hertford College

Library, Hertford College, Catte Street, Oxford OX1 3BW
☎(01865) 279409
Fax (01865) 279466

Fellow Librarian Dr S R West FBA
Librarian Mrs S Griffin BA DipLib (e-mail: susan.griffin@hertford.ox.ac.uk)

International Development Centre

Library, International Development Centre, Queen Elizabeth House, 21 St Giles,
Oxford OX1 3LA
☎(01865) 273590
Fax (01865) 273607
e-mail: library@qeh.ox.ac.uk
url: http://www.qeh.ox.ac.uk/library/
Librarian and Information Services Manager Mrs S Allcock BSc
Deputy Librarian (Commonwealth Studies Subject Specialist) R J Townsend

Site library
Refugee Studies Programme Documentation Centre, International Development Centre,
Queen Elizabeth House, 21 St Giles, Oxford OX1 3LA
☎(01865) 270298
Fax (01865) 270721
e-mail: rspdoc@ermine.ox.ac.uk
url: http://www.bodley.ox.ac.uk/rsp/
Documentalist Ms S Rhodes BA DipLib MA

Jesus College

Library, Jesus College, Oxford OX1 3DW
☎(01865) 279704
Fax (01865) 279687 (attn. Librarian)
e-mail: library@jesus.ox.ac.uk
Fellow Librarian T J Horder MA PhD
College Librarian Miss S A Cobbold MA DipLib
Archivist Dr B Allen (01865 279761)
(The Fellows' Library is available to bona fide scholars only by prior appointment with the
College Librarian or Archivist)

Keble College

Library, Keble College, Oxford OX1 3PG
☎(01865) 272797
e-mail: library@keb.ox.ac.uk
Librarian Mrs M Szurko BA DipLib ALA

Lady Margaret Hall

Library, Lady Margaret Hall, Norham Gardens, Oxford OX2 6QA
☎(01865) 274361
Fax (01865) 270708
Librarian Miss R Staples BA (e-mail: roberta.staples@lmh.ox.ac.uk)
Archivist Mrs J Courtenay BA
(The library is for the use of members of college only, though bona fide researchers may be
allowed access to books by arrangement with the Librarian)

Linacre College

Library, Linacre College, St Cross Road, Oxford OX1 3JA
☎(01865) 271661
Fax (01865) 271668

e-mail: library@linacre.ox.ac.uk
Librarian G Barber
Assistant Librarian Mrs R Key

Lincoln College

Library, Lincoln College, Turl Street, Oxford OX1 3DR
☎(01865) 279831
e-mail: library@lincoln.ox.ac.uk
Librarian Mrs F Piddock BA DipLib

Magdalen College

Library, Magdalen College, Oxford OX1 4AU
☎(01865) 276045 (enquiries)
Fax (01865) 276094
e-mail: magdlib@ermine.ox.ac.uk
Fellow Librarian Dr C Y Ferdinand BA MA MA MA DPhil
Assistant Librarian Ms K S Speirs BA(Econ) BA MSt MLIS

Mansfield College

Library, Mansfield College, Mansfield Road, Oxford OX1 3TF
☎(01865) 270975
Fax (01865) 270970
Librarian Ms A Jenner (e-mail: alma.jenner@mansfield.ox.ac.uk)

Merton College

Library, Merton College, Oxford OX1 4JD
☎(01865) 276380
Fax (01865) 276361
e-mail: library@merton.oxford.ac.uk
Librarian Dr A S Bendall MA PhD ALA FSA
Assistant Librarian Mrs F Wilkes MA DipLib ALA

New College

Library, New College, Oxford OX1 3BN
☎(01865) 279580 (enquiries & administration)
Fax (01865) 279590
Librarian Miss S Cromey MA(Oxon) MA(Lond) DipLib ALA (e-mail:
sandra.cromey@new.ox.ac.uk)

Nuffield College

Library, Nuffield College, New Road, Oxford OX1 1NF
☎(01865) 278550
Fax (01865) 278621
url: http://www.nuff.ox.ac.uk/library
Librarian J Legg (e-mail: james.legg@nuf.ox.ac.uk)

Oriel College

Library, Oriel College, Oxford OX1 4EW
☎(01865) 276558
Librarian Ms M L E Mangels MA DipLib

Pembroke College
McGowin Library, Pembroke College, Oxford OX1 1DW
☎(01865) 276409
Fax (01865) 276418
Fellow Librarian Prof M R Godden MA DPhil
Deputy Librarian Mrs N Van Loo MA ALA (e-mail: naomi.vanloo@pmb.ox.ac.uk)

Plant Sciences and Oxford Forestry Institute
Library, Plant Sciences and Oxford Forestry Institute, Department of Plant Sciences, South
Parks Road, Oxford OX1 3RB
☎(01865) 275082
Fax (01865) 275074
e-mail: library@plant-sciences.oxford.ac.uk
url: http://www.plants.ox.ac.uk/library
Librarian R A Mills MA ALA

Queen's College
Library, Queen's College, Oxford OX1 4AW
☎(01865) 279130
Fax (01865) 790819
e-mail: queenlib@ermine.ox.ac.uk
Librarian J B Bengtson MA MPhil (01865 279213; e-mail:
jonathan.bengtson@queens.ox.ac.uk)
Assistant Librarian (Research) Miss H Powell
Assistant Librarian (Administration) Ms T M Shaw
Assistant Librarian (Cataloguing) Mrs V Vernier
Fellow Librarian Dr W J Blair

Regent's Park College
Library, Regent's Park College, Oxford OX1 2LB
☎(01865) 288120; (01865) 288142 (Angus Library direct line)
Fax (01865) 288121
url: http://www.rpc.ox.ac.uk/rpc/
Librarian/Archivist Mrs S J Mills MA ALA (e-mail: sue.mills@regents-park.ox.ac.uk)
(General College Library open to members of College only. The Angus Library, a research
library for Baptist history, incorporating the former libraries of the Baptist Union of Great Britain
and the Baptist Historical Society, and the archives of the Baptist Missionary Society on
deposit, available by appointment to bona fide researchers.)

St Anne's College
Library, St Anne's College, Woodstock Road, Oxford OX2 6HS
☎(01865) 274810
Fax (01865) 274899
Librarian Dr D F Smith MA DPhil ALA (e-mail: david.smith@st-annes.ox.ac.uk)

St Antony's College
Library, St Antony's College, Oxford OX2 6JF
☎(01865) 274480
Fax (01865) 310518
Librarian R Campbell

St Benet's Hall

Library, St Benet's Hall, 38 St Giles, Oxford OX1 3LN
☎(01865) 515006
Fax (01865) 513917
The Master

St Catherine's College

Library, St Catherine's College, Manor Road, Oxford OX1 3UJ
☎(01865) 271707
Librarian Dr A G Rosser MA PhD
Assistant Librarian Mrs S Collins

St Cross College

Library, St Cross College, Oxford OX1 3LZ
☎(01865) 273629/278481
e-mail: librarian@stx.ox.ac.uk
Librarian Mrs S L Allcock BSc

St Edmund Hall

Library, St Edmund Hall, Oxford OX1 4AR
☎(01865) 279000
Fax (01865) 279062
e-mail: library@seh.ox.ac.uk
url: http://www.lib.ox.ac.uk/guides/colleges/edm/edm.htm
Librarian Ms D Eaton BA MA
(The Library is for the use of members of St Edmund Hall only. Housed in 12th century church of historical interest. Visitors welcome but only by prior application to the Librarian; groups shown round only during vacations.)

St Hilda's College

Library, St Hilda's College, Oxford OX4 1DY
☎(01865) 276848/276849 (general enquiries)
Librarian Miss M Croghan MA ALA (e-mail: maria.croghan@st-hildas.ox.ac.uk)

St Hugh's College

Library, St Hugh's College, St Margaret's Road, Oxford OX2 6LE
☎(01865) 274900 (enquiries), (01865) 274938 (administration)
Fax (01865) 274912
e-mail: library@st-hughs.ox.ac.uk
Librarian Miss D C Quare BA MLitt ALA

St John's College

Library, St John's College, Oxford OX1 3JP
☎(01865) 277300 (main lodge), (01865) 277330/1 (direct to library)
Fax (01865) 277435 (College office), (01865) 277421 (main lodge)
e-mail: library@fyfield.sjc.ox.ac.uk
Principal Librarian Dr P M S Hacker
Assistant Librarians Miss A Williams, Mrs R Ogden

St Peter's College

Library, St Peter's College, New Inn Hall Street, Oxford OX1 2DL

☎(01865) 278882
Fax (01865) 278855
Librarian Mr A Ricketts MA(Oxon) DipLib (e-mail: alistair.ricketts@st-peters.ox.ac.uk)

Social Studies Faculty

Library, Social Studies Faculty, Social Studies Faculty Centre, George Street, Oxford OX1 2RL
☎(01865) 278710
Fax (01865) 278711
e-mail: library@socstud.ox.ac.uk
url: http://www.economics.ox.ac.uk/ieslib/library.htm
Social Studies Librarian Ms M Robb BS MLS ALA (e-mail:
margaret.robb@socstud.ox.ac.uk)

Somerville College

Library, Somerville College, Oxford OX2 6HD
☎(01865) 270694
Fax (01865) 270620
Librarian Miss P Adams BLitt MA DipLib (01865 270694; e-mail:
pauline.adams@somerville.ox.ac.uk)
Assistant Librarian Miss S Purver MA DipLIS (01865 270694; e-mail:
susan.purver@somerville.ox.ax.uk)

Taylor Institution

Library, Taylor Institution, St Giles, Oxford OX1 3NA
☎(01865) 278154
Fax (01865) 278165
e-mail: enquiries@taylib.ox.ac.uk
url: http://www.taylib.ox.ac.uk
Librarian Ms E A Chapman BA MA DipLib FLA

Templeton College

Information Centre and Library, Templeton College, Kennington, Oxford OX1 5NY
☎(01865) 422560
Fax (01865) 422501
e-mail: infocent@templeton.oxford.ac.uk
Information Centre and Library Manager Ms G Powell BA(Hons) DipLib ALA (e-mail:
gill.powell@templeton.oxford.ac.uk)

Trinity College

Library, Trinity College, Oxford OX1 3BH
☎(01865) 279863 (enquiries & administration)
Fax (01865) 279911
Librarian Mrs J Martin MA (e-mail: jan.martin@trinity.ox.ac.uk)

University College

Library, University College, Oxford OX1 4BH
☎(01865) 276621
Fax (01865) 276987
e-mail: library@university-college..ox.ac.uk
url: http://www.lib.ox.ac.uk/guides/colleges/uni.htm
Fellow Librarian Dr T W Child MA BPhil DPhil(Oxon)

Librarian Miss C M Ritchie MA(Aber) MA(Lond) ALA

Wadham College

Library, Wadham College, Oxford OX1 3PN
☎(01865) 277900
Fax (01865) 277937
e-mail: library@plato.wadham.ox.ac.uk
Librarian Ms S Bailey BA MA DipLib

Wolfson College

The Floersheimer Library, Wolfson College, Oxford OX2 6UD
☎(01865) 274076
e-mail: adrian.hale@wolfson.ox.ac.uk
url: http://www.wolfson.ox.ac.uk/library
Fellow Librarian Dr S R J Woodell
Librarian A Hale BA MA DipLIS
(Open to members of College and Common Room only)

Worcester College

Library, Worcester College, Oxford OX1 2HB
☎(01865) 278354
Fax (01865) 278387
Librarian Dr J Parker MA DPhil

UNIVERSITY OF PAISLEY

Library, University of Paisley, Paisley PA1 2BE
☎0141 848 3758 (enquiries), 0141 848 3751 (administration)
Fax 0141 887 0812
e-mail: library@paisley.ac.uk
url: http://www.paisley.ac.uk/welcome/lp.index.htm
Librarian S James BA FLA MIInfSc FRSA

Site libraries
A   Ayr Campus Library, University of Paisley, Beech Grove, Ayr KA8 0SR
☎(01292) 886000
Fax (01292) 886006
Librarian Ms A J Goodwin MA DipLib
B   Library, University of Paisley, Royal Alexandra Hospital, Corsebar Road, Paisley
PA2 9BN
☎0141 580 4757
Fax 0141 887 4962
Librarian Mrs v Murray MA(Hons) MSc

UNIVERSITY OF PLYMOUTH

Library, University of Plymouth, Drake Circus, Plymouth, Devon PL4 8AA
☎(01752) 232323 (enquiries); (01752) 232352 (administration)
Fax (01752) 232340
url: http://www.plym.ac.uk
Dean of Academic and Information Services I D Sidgreaves BA FLA DipLib DipEd (e-mail:
isidgreaves@plymouth.ac.uk)
Associate Dean of Academic and Information Services J Priestley BA DipLIS ALA
(e-mail: jpriestley@plymouth.ac.uk)

Head of Public Services Ms P Holland BA DipLib ALA (e-mail: pholland@plymouth.ac.uk)
Head of Learning and Research Support Services Ms J Gosling BSc DipLib ALA (e-mail: jgosling@plymouth.ac.uk)

Campus libraries
A   Library, University of Plymouth, Seale Hayne Campus, Newton Abbot, Devon
        TQ12 6NQ
        ☎(01626) 325828
        Fax (01626) 325836
        Academic and Information Services Coordinator Mrs A Blackman BA ALA
        (e-mail: ablackman@plymouth.ac.uk)
B   Library, University of Plymouth, Earl Richards Road North, Exeter, Devon EX2 6AS
        ☎(01392) 475049
        Fax (01392) 475053
        Academic and Information Services Coordinator Mrs J Cartwright BA ALA
        (e-mail: jcartwright@plymouth.ac.uk)
C   Library, University of Plymouth, Douglas Avenue, Exmouth, Devon EX8 2AT
        ☎(01395) 255332
        Fax (01395) 255337
        Academic and Information Services Coordinator Ms R Smith BA(Hons) DLIS ALA
        (e-mail: rsmith@plymouth.ac.uk)

UNIVERSITY OF PORTSMOUTH
Frewen Library, University of Portsmouth, Cambridge Road, Portsmouth, Hants PO1 2ST
☎023 9284 3228/9 (enquiries), 023 9284 3222 (administration)
Fax 023 9284 3233
e-mail: library@port.ac.uk
url: http://www.libr.port.ac.uk
University Librarian I Bonar BSc ALA

QUEEN MARGARET UNIVERSITY COLLEGE
Library, Queen Margaret University College, Clerwood Terrace, Edinburgh EH12 8TS
☎0131 317 3301
Fax 0131 339 7057
e-mail: b.smith@libmail.qmced.ac.uk
url: http://www.qmced.ac.uk/lb/lbmain.htm
Librarian Mrs P Aitken BA AALIA

Leith campus library
Library, Queen Margaret University College, Leith Campus, Duke Street, Edinburgh EH6 8HF
☎0131 317 3308
Fax 0131 317 3308
Librarian Miss V Cormie MSc ALA

QUEEN'S UNIVERSITY OF BELFAST
University Library, Queen's University of Belfast, Belfast BT7 1LS
☎028 9033 5020
Fax 028 9032 3340
url: http://www.qub.ac.uk/lib/
Chief Librarian N J Russell BA MPhil ALA (e-mail: n.russell@qub.ac.uk)

Site libraries
A   Agriculture Library, Agriculture and Food Science Centre, Queen's University of

Belfast, Newforge Lane, Belfast BT9 5PX
☎028 9025 5226
Fax 028 9025 5400
Agriculture Librarian E Traynor MA DipLibStud ALA (e-mail: e.traynor@qub.ac.uk)
B   Medical Library, Institute of Clinical Science, Queen's University of Belfast, Grosvenor Road, Belfast BT12 6BJ
☎028 9026 3154
Fax 028 9024 7068
Medical Librarian T A Lyttle BSc DipLibStud ALA (e-mail: t.lyttle@qub.ac.uk)
C   Science Library, Queen's University of Belfast, Chlorine Gardens, Belfast BT9 5EQ
☎028 9033 5441
Fax 028 9038 2636
Science Librarian Ms S Landy BA DipLibStud (e-mail: s.landy@qub.ac.uk)
D   Main Library, Queen's University of Belfast, Belfast BT7 1LS
☎028 9033 5023
Fax 028 9032 3340
Associate Librarian N B Butterwick BSc MSc MLS ALA (e-mail: n.butterwick@qub.ac.uk)

RAVENSBOURNE COLLEGE OF DESIGN AND COMMUNICATION

Library, Ravensbourne College of Design and Communication, Walden Road, Chislehurst, Kent BR7 5SN
☎020 8289 4900 ext 8117
Fax 020 8325 8320
Head of Library and Information Services Ms S Fowler BA ALA MA(Ed) (020 8289 4919; e-mail: s.fowler@rave.ac.uk)
Media Librarian P Rogers (e-mail: p.rogers@rave.ac.uk)
Information Services Officer Vacant

UNIVERSITY OF READING

University Library, University of Reading, Whiteknights, PO Box 223, Reading, Berks RG6 6AE
☎0118 931 8770 (enquiries), 0118 931 8773 (administration)
Fax 0118 931 6636
e-mail: library@reading.ac.uk
url: http://www.rdg.ac.uk
University Librarian Ms S M Corrall MA DipLib MBA FLA MIMgt FRSA (0118 931 8772; e-mail: s.m.corrall@reading.ac.uk)
Deputy Librarian Mrs J H Munro BSc MSc MIInfSc (0118 931 8774; e-mail: j.h.munro@reading.ac.uk)
Head of Collections D H Knott BA DipLib (0118 931 8787; e-mail: d.knott@reading.ac.uk)
Head of Systems Miss C A Ayres BSc DipInfSc ALA (0118 931 8781; e-mail: c.a.ayres@reading.ac.uk)
Support Services Manager I J P Burn BA (0118 931 8775; e-mail: i.j.burn@reading.ac.uk)

Site libraries
A   Bulmershe Library, University of Reading, Bulmershe Court, Earley, Reading, Berks RG6 1HY
☎0118 931 8652
Fax 0118 931 8651
Faculty Team Manager (Education and Community Studies) M G Connell MA MSc ALA (0118 987 5123 ext 4280; e-mail: g.connell@reading.ac.uk)

B Music Library, University of Reading, 35 Upper Redlands Road, Reading, Berks RG1 5JE
☎0118 931 8413
Fax 0118 931 8412
Liaison Librarian (Music) Dr A M Laurie MA BMus PhD ARCM (0118 931 8413; e-mail: a.m.laurie@reading.ac.uk)

COLLEGE OF RIPON AND YORK ST JOHN
Library, College of Ripon and York St John, Lord Mayor's Walk, York YO31 7EX
☎(01904) 616700
Fax (01904) 612512
e-mail: library@ucrysj.ac.uk
url: http://www.ucrysj.ac.uk/services/library/index.htm
College Librarian A Chalcraft BA MA ALA (01904 616701; e-mail: a.chalcraft@ucrysj.ac.uk)
Principal Assistant Librarian (IT) Ms H Westmancoat BA ALA (e-mail: h.westmancoat@ucrysj.ac.uk)
Senior Assistant Librarian (User Services York) Ms J Munks BA ALA (j.munks@ucrysj.ac.uk)
Senior Assistant Librarian (User Services Ripon) J Hagart BA ALA (01765 602691; j.hagart@ucrysj.ac.uk)
Senior Assistant Librarian (Acquisitions) B Jones BA (01765 602691; b.jones@ucrysj.ac.uk)

Campus library
Campus Library, College of Ripon and York St John, College Road, Ripon, North Yorkshire HG4 2QX
☎(01765) 602691
Senior Assistant Librarian J Hagart BA ALA
(see details above)

THE ROBERT GORDON UNIVERSITY
Garthdee Library, The Robert Gordon University, Garthdee Road, Aberdeen AB10 7QB
☎(01224) 263450
Fax (01224) 263460
e-mail: library@rgu.ac.uk
url: http://www.rgu.ac.uk/library/library.htm
Acting Chief Librarian Ms D M Devine MA ALA (e-mail: d.devine@rgu.ac.uk)
Acting Depute Librarian Ms S Copeland MA MPhil ALA MIInfSc (e-mail: s.copeland@rgu.ac.uk)
Acting Depute Librarian Ms J Brown MA ALA (e-mail: j.brown@rgu.ac.uk)
Acting Senior Librarian Miss M Buchan MA ALA (e-mail: m.buchan@rgu.ac.uk)

Site libraries
A Foresterhill Library, The Robert Gordon University, Westburn Road, Aberdeen AB9 2XS
☎(01224) 663123 ext 52544
Fax (01224) 685249
e-mail: library@rgu.ac.uk
url: http://www.rgu.ac.uk/library/library.htm
Site Librarian Mrs J Simpson MA DipILS (e-mail: j.simpson@rgu.ac.uk)
B Kepplestone Library, The Robert Gordon University, Queen's Road, Aberdeen AB15 4PH
☎(01224) 263070

Fax (01224) 263010
e-mail: library@rgu.ac.uk
url: http://www.rgu.ac.uk/library/library.htm
Site Librarian Mrs J Simpson MA DipILS (e-mail: j.simpson@rgu.ac.uk)

C   St Andrew Street Library, The Robert Gordon University, St Andrew Street, Aberdeen AB25 1HG
☎(01224) 262888
Fax (01224) 262889
e-mail: library@rgu.ac.uk
url: http://www.rgu.ac.uk/library/library.htm
Site Librarian K Fraser BA DMS ALA (e-mail: k.fraser@rgu.ac.uk)

D   Woolmanhill Library, The Robert Gordon University, Woolmanhill, Aberdeen AB9 1GS
☎(01224) 663123 ext 55473
Fax (01224) 404025
e-mail: library@rgu.ac.uk
url: http://www.rgu.ac.uk/library/library.htm
Site Librarian K Fraser BA DMS ALA (01224 262888; e-mail: k.fraser@rgu.ac.uk)

ROEHAMPTON INSTITUTE

Roehampton Lane Learning Resources Centre, Roehampton Institute, Digby Stuart College, Roehampton Lane, London SW15 5SZ
☎020 8392 3700 (enquiries), 020 8392 3053 (administration)
Fax 020 8392 3259
e-mail: edesk@roehampton.ac.uk
url: http://www.roehampton.ac.uk/is/is_home.html
Director of Information Services Ms S Clegg BA MBA ALA (020 8392 3051; e-mail: s.clegg@roehampton.ac.uk)
Assistant Director (Information Resources) P Scarsbrook BA MA (020 8392 3052)
Assistant Director (Academic Services) Vacant
Assistant Director (Communications and IT) J Hill (020 8392 3446; e-mail: j.hill@roehampton.ac.uk)

Whitelands Learning Resources Centre, Roehampton Institute, West Hill, London SW15 3SN
☎020 8392 3554
Fax 020 8392 3559
Faculty Information Officer Ms A Peace BA MA (020 8392 3551; e-mail: a.peace@roehampton.ac.uk)

ROSE BRUFORD COLLEGE

Library, Rose Bruford College, Lamorbey Park, Sidcup, Kent DA15 9DF
☎020 8308 2626 (enquiries), 020 8300 3024 (administration)
Fax 020 8308 0524
College Librarian J Collis BA ALA ARCM (e-mail: john@bruford.ac.uk)
Assistant Librarian Ms E Skedgell BA

Site library
Library, Rose Bruford College, Creek Road, Deptford, London SE8 3BZ
☎020 8300 3024
Fax 020 8692 0134
Site Librarian Mrs J Nelson

ROYAL ACADEMY OF MUSIC

Library, Royal Academy of Music, Marylebone Road, London NW1 5HT

☎020 7873 7323 (enquiries & administration)
Fax 020 7873 7322
e-mail: library@ram.ac.uk
url: http://www.ram.ac.uk
Acting Librarian Ms K Adamson BA MA DipLib

ROYAL COLLEGE OF ART

College Library, Royal College of Art, Kensington Gore, London SW7 2EU
☎020 7590 4224 (enquiries)
Fax 020 7590 4500
e-mail: info@rca.ac.uk
url: http://www.rca.ac.uk
Head of Information Services Ms A George ALA (e-mail: amg@rca.ac.uk)

ROYAL COLLEGE OF MUSIC

Library, Royal College of Music, Prince Consort Road, London SW7 2BS
☎020 7589 3643
Fax 020 7589 7740
url: http://www.rcm.ac.uk
Chief Librarian Ms P Thompson BA (020 7591 4323; e-mail: pthompson@rcm.ac.uk)
Reference Librarian Dr P Horton (020 7591 4324; e-mail: phorton@rcm.ac.uk)

ROYAL COLLEGE OF NURSING OF THE UNITED KINGDOM

Library, Royal College of Nursing of the United Kingdom, 20 Cavendish Square, London
W1M 0AB
☎020 7647 3610/3613
Fax 020 7647 3420
e-mail: rcn.library@rcn.org.uk
url: http://www.rcn.org.uk
Head of Library and Information Services J Lord BA(Hons) DipLib ALA
(Access for non-members is by appointment)

ROYAL NORTHERN COLLEGE OF MUSIC

Library, Royal Northern College of Music, 124 Oxford Road, Manchester M13 9RD
☎0161 907 5243
Fax 0161 273 7611
e-mail: library@rncm.ac.uk
url: http://www.rncm.ac.uk/library/
Librarian Dr R Williamson PhD MA BMus
Senior Assistant Librarians Ms A E Smart BA MA ALA, G Thomason MusB MusM ARCM
LTCL

ROYAL SCOTTISH ACADEMY OF MUSIC AND DRAMA

Library, Royal Scottish Academy of Music and Drama, 100 Renfrew Street, Glasgow G2 3DB
☎0141 332 4101
Fax 0141 332 5924
Chief Librarian Vacant

RUSKIN COLLEGE

College Library, Ruskin College, Walton Street, Oxford
☎(01865 554331
Fax (01865) 554372
e-mail: library@ruskin.ac.uk
Librarian D Horsfield MA
(Admission by appointment only)

UNIVERSITY OF ST ANDREWS

University Library, University of St Andrews, North Street, St Andrews, Fife KY16 9TR
☎(01334) 462281 (enquiries & administration), (01334) 462280 (management)
Fax (01334) 462282
e-mail: library@st-and.ac.uk
url: http://www-library.st-and.ac.uk
Librarian Mr N F Dumbleton MA MA

COLLEGE OF ST MARK AND ST JOHN

Library, College of St Mark and St John, Derriford Road, Plymouth, Devon PL6 8BH
☎(01752) 761145 (enquiries), (01752) 636700 ext 4206 (administration)
Fax (01752) 636712
Head of Learning Resources F A Clements FLA (01752 636700 ext 4215; e-mail: clemef@marjon.ac.uk)
Librarian Mrs A Bidgood (ext 4200)

ST MARTIN'S COLLEGE

Harold Bridges Library, St Martin's College, St Martin's Services Ltd, Bowerham Road, Lancaster, Lancashire LA1 3JD
☎(01524) 384243
Fax (01524) 384588
e-mail: library@ucsm.ac.uk
url: http://www.ucsm.ac.uk
College Librarian D Brown BA MA ALA (01524 384238; e-mail: d.brown:@ucsm.ac.uk)

Site libraries
A   Ambleside Site Library, St Martin's College, Rydal Road, Ambleside, Cumbria LA22 9BB
       ☎(015394) 30274
       Fax (015394) 30371
       e-mail: library@ucsm.ac.uk
       Site Librarian Mrs J Henderson BA DipLib MLib ALA (01524 385244; e-mail: j.henderson@ucsm.ac.uk)
B   Library, St Martin's College, Clarence House, Fusehill Street, Carlisle, Cumbria CA1 2HG
       ☎(01228) 616262
       Fax (01228) 616263
       e-mail: library@ucsm.ac.uk
       Senior Information Officer Ms S Green BA ALA (01228 616219; e-mail: shirley.green@ucsm.ac.uk)

ST MARY'S, STRAWBERRY HILL

Information Resources Centre, St Mary's, Strawberry Hill, Waldegrave Road, Twickenham, Middlesex TW1 4SX

☎020 8240 4097 (enquiries), 020 8240 4301 (administration)
Fax 020 8240 4270
e-mail: enquiry@smuc.ac.uk)
Director of Information Resources, Services and Systems Dr M Davis BA DipLib ALA MIInfSc PhD (e-mail: davism@smuc.ac.uk)
Customer Services Manager Mrs S Bellingham BA DipLib MA (020 8240 4301: e-mail: bellings@smuc.ac.uk)
Systems Coordinator Miss C O'Sullivan BA ALA (020 8240 4303)

UNIVERSITY OF SALFORD
Academic Information Services, University of Salford, Clifford Whitworth Building, Salford, Lancs M5 4WT
☎0161 295 2444
Fax 0161 295 5666
e-mail: advisor@ais.salford.ac.uk
Director of Academic Information Services Prof M J Clark
Deputy Director Mrs M Duncan (0161 295 5180)
Associate Director D Lomas (0161 295 5388)

Campus libraries
A   Academic Information Services, University of Salford, Clifford Whitworth Building, Salford, Lancs M5 4WT
       ☎0161 295 5846
       Fax 0161 295 5888
       Campus Manager Mrs J Berry (0161 295 5037)
B   Academic Information Services, University of Salford, Allerton Campus, Frederick Road, Salford, Lancs M6 6PU
       ☎0161 295 2448
       Fax 0161 295 2437
       Campus Manager Ms L Doyle, Mrs L Leader (0161 295 2440)
C   Academic Information Service, University of Salford, Adelphi Campus, Peru Street, Salford, Lancs M3 6EQ
       ☎0161 295 6185
       Fax 0161 295 6189
       Campus Manager Ms G McGowan (0161 295 6187)
D   Academic Information Services, University of Salford, Eccles Campus, Peel House, Albert Street, Eccles, Lancs M30 0NJ
       ☎0161 295 2747
       Fax 0161 295 2796
E   Academic Information Services, University of Salford, Irwell Valley Campus, Blandford Road, Salford, Lancs M6 6BD
       ☎0161 295 2633
       Fax 0161 295 2631
F   Academic Information Services, University of Salford, Oldham Campus, Westhulme Avenue, Oldham, Lancs OL1 2PN
       ☎0161 627 8171 (tel/fax)

UNIVERSITY COLLEGE SCARBOROUGH
Library, University College Scarborough, Filey Road, Scarborough, North Yorkshire YO11 3AZ
☎(01723) 362392 ext 277 (enquiries), ext 254 (administration)
Fax (01723) 370815
Head of Learning Resources Ms S Franklin BA(Hons) (ext 254; e-mail:

sandraf@ucscarb.ac.uk)
Assistant Librarians Ms M Sarjantson BA(Hons) MA ALA (e-mail:
maggies@ucscarb.ac.uk), Ms F Smith BA(Hons) PGDipLib (e-mail: fionas@ucscarb.ac.uk)

SCOTTISH AGRICULTURAL COLLEGE

Library and Information Centre, Scottish Agricultural College, Edinburgh Campus, West Mains
Road, Edinburgh EH10 4RH
☎0131 535 4117 (enquiries), 0131 535 4116 (administration)
Fax 0131 535 4246
Senior Librarian Mrs M Mullay MA ALA (e-mail: m.mullay@ed.sac.ac.uk)

Campus libraries
A   Library, Scottish Agricultural College, Auchincruive Campus, Auchincruive, Ayr
KA6 5HW
☎(01292) 525208
Fax (01292) 525211
Senior Librarian Ms E P Muir MA PGDipLib ALA (e-mail: e.muir@au.sac.ac.uk)
B   SAC Library, Scottish Agricultural College, Ferguson Building, Craibstone Estate,
Aberdeen AB21 9YA
☎(01224) 272600
Fax (01224) 491989
url: http://www.abdn.ac.uk/
Librarian M Sommer BA ALA (e-mail: m.sommer@ab.sac.ac.uk)
C   Bush Agriculture Library and Information Centre, Scottish Agricultural College,
Edinburgh Campus, Bush Estate, Penicuik, Edinburgh EH26 0PH
☎0131 535 3006
Fax 0131 535 3070
Assistant Librarian Mrs M Lightbody BA ALA (e-mail: m.lightbody@ed.sac.ac.uk)

SELLY OAK COLLEGES *see* ORCHARD LEARNING RESOURCES CENTRE

SHEFFIELD HALLAM UNIVERSITY

Learning Centre, Sheffield Hallam University, City Campus, Pond Street, Sheffield S1 1WB
☎0114 225 2109 (enquiries), 0114 225 2103 (administration)
Fax 0114 225 3859
e-mail: learning.centre@shu.ac.uk
url: http://www.shu.ac.uk/services/lc/index.html
Director, Learning Centre, and University Librarian G Bulpitt MA ALA CertEd

Campus learning centres
A   Learning Centre, Sheffield Hallam University, City Campus, Sheffield S1 1WB
☎0114 225 2109
Fax 0114 225 3859
Head of Academic Services and Development Ms B M Fisher MLib ALA
B   Learning Centre, Sheffield Hallam University, Collegiate Crescent Campus, Sheffield
S10 2BP
☎0114 225 2473
Fax 0114 225 2476
Information Specialist K Moore BA DipLib ALA (0114 225 2475)
C   Learning Centre, Sheffield Hallam University, Psalter Lane Campus, Sheffield S11 8UZ
☎0114 225 2721
Fax 0114 225 2717
Information Specialist C Abson BA MA ALA (0114 225 2724)

UNIVERSITY OF SHEFFIELD

Main Library, University of Sheffield, Western Bank, Sheffield S10 2TN
☎0114 222 7200 (General enquiries); 0114 222 7224 (Library administration)
Fax 0114 273 9826
e-mail: library@sheffield.ac.uk
University Librarian M S-M Hannon MA DipLibStud DMS ALA FRSA (e-mail:
m.hannon@sheffield.ac.uk)
Deputy Librarian M J Lewis MA DipLib ALA (0114 222 7225; e-mail:
m.j.lewis@sheffield.ac.uk)
Sub-Librarian (User Services) D E Jones BA(Econ) MA ALA (0114 222 7226; e-mail:
d.e.jones@sheffield.ac.uk)
Sub-Librarian (Information Systems and Technical Services) Mrs K O'Donovan BA ALA
MIInfSci (0114 222 7227; e-mail: kath.odonovan@sheffield.ac.uk)

Major libraries
A   St George's Library (Engineering & Management), University of Sheffield, Mappin
       Street, Sheffield S1 4DT
       ☎0114 222 7300
       Fax 0114 279 6406
       e-mail: sgl@sheffield.ac.uk
       Sub-Librarian P H Stubley BSc DipLib (0114 222 7327; e-mail:
       p.stubley@sheffield.ac.uk)
B   Crookesmoor Library (Law), University of Sheffield, Crookesmoor Building, Conduit
       Road, Sheffield S10 1EW
       ☎0114 222 7341
       Fax 0114 275 4620
       e-mail: ckmlib@sheffield.ac.uk
       Assistant Librarian H J Thrift BMus MA ALA (0114 222 7348; e-mail:
       h.thrift@sheffield.ac.uk)
C   Health Sciences Library, University of Sheffield, Royal Hallamshire Hospital, Sheffield
       S10 2JF
       ☎0114 271 2030
       Fax 0114 278 0923
       e-mail: hsl.rhh@sheffield.ac.uk
       Sub-Librarian J van Loo BA DMS DipLib ALA (0114 271 3025; e-mail:
       j.vanloo@sheffield.ac.uk)

SOUTH BANK UNIVERSITY

Perry Library, South Bank University, 250 Southwark Bridge Road, London SE1 6NJ
☎020 7815 6607 (enquiries), 020 7815 6602 (administration)
Fax 020 7815 6699
url: http://www.sbu.ac.uk/lis
Head of Learning and Information Services J Akeroyd MPhil BSc ALA DipLibInfSc MIInfSc
(e-mail: akeroyJ@sbu.ac.uk)
Deputy Head C Miller BA ALA (e-mail: millerc@sbu.ac.uk)

Learning Resources Centre, 105-108 Borough Road, London SE1 0AA
☎020 7815 6670

Site libraries
A   Faculty of the Built Environment Library, South Bank University, Wandsworth Road,
       London SW8 2JZ
       ☎020 7815 8320

Learning Resources Manager P Noble ALA (e-mail: noblep@sbu.ac.uk)
B   Library, Redwood College, South Bank University, Harold Wood Hospital, Gubbins Lane, Romford, Essex RM3 0BE
☎020 7815 5982
Learning Resources Manager Ms L Jolly
C   Library, South Bank University, Whipps Cross Education Centre, Whipps Cross Hospital, Leytonstone, London E11 1NR
☎020 7815 4747
Learning Resources Officer Ms D Watmough

SOUTHAMPTON INSTITUTE

Mountbatten Library, Southampton Institute, Southampton SO14 0YN
☎023 8031 9681 (enquiries), 023 8031 9248 (administration)
Fax 023 8031 9672
Head of Library J Moore BA ALA (e-mail: john.moore@solent.ac.uk)
User Services Librarian R Burrell MSc(Econ) ALA (023 8031 9342; e-mail: robert.burrell@solent.ac.uk)
Technical Services Librarian C MacArthur BA MSc ALA (023 8031 9686; e-mail: chris.macarthur@solent.ac.uk)

Site library

Warsash Library, Southampton Institute, Newtown Road, Warsash, Southampton SO31 9ZL
☎(01489) 556269
Site Librarian Mrs H Dixon BA DipLib

UNIVERSITY OF SOUTHAMPTON

Hartley Library, University of Southampton, Highfield, Southampton SO17 1BJ
☎023 8059 2180 (enquiries), 023 8059 2677 (administration)
Fax 023 8059 5451
e-mail: library@soton.ac.uk
url: http://www.soton.ac.uk/~library/
University Librarian B Naylor MA ALA FRSA
Deputy Librarian M Brown MA PhD DipLib ALA (023 8059 2371; e-mail: mlb@soton.ac.uk)
Head of User Services C C Parker BSc MPhil FIInfSc (023 8059 2378; e-mail: ccp@soton.ac.uk)
Head of Collection Management Services R L Wake MA MA ALA (023 8059 3453; e-mail: rlw1@soton.ac.uk)
Head of Archives and Special Collections C M Woolgar BA PhD DipArchAdmin FRHistS (023 8059 2721; e-mail: cmw@soton.ac.uk)

Site libraries

A   Biomedical Sciences Library, University of Southampton, Bassett Crescent East, Southampton SO16 7PX
☎023 8059 4215
Fax 023 8059 3251
e-mail: b.s.library@soton.ac.uk
url: http://www.soton.ac.uk/~library/biomedical
Site Librarian Miss A M Norman BA DipLib ALA
B   Health Services Library, University of Southampton, Mailpoint 883, Southampton General Hospital, Southampton SO16 6YD
☎023 8079 6541
Fax 023 8079 8939
e-mail: hslib@soton.ac.uk

url: http://www.soton.ac.uk/~library/health
Head of Health Care Services Division Ms C A Fowler MA BSc(Hons) ALA MIInfSc
C   National Oceanographic Library, Southampton Oceanography Centre, University of
     Southampton, Waterfront Campus, European Way, Southampton SO14 3ZH
     ☎023 8059 6111 (Marine Information and Advisory Service), 023 8059 6116
     (General)
     Fax 023 8059 6115
     url: http://www.soc.soton.ac.uk/LIB/libindex.html
     Head of Information Services Mrs P Simpson BA ALA MIInfSc (e-mail:
     pauline.simpson@soc.soton.ac.uk)
D   New College Library, University of Southampton, The Avenue, Southampton
     SO17 1BG
     ☎023 8021 6220
     Fax 023 8023 0944
     url: http://www.soton.ac.uk/~library/new
     Head of Library and Information Services Mrs E Upson BA ALA (e-mail:
     eu@soton.ac.uk)
E   Winchester School of Art Library, University of Southampton, West Side, Park
     Avenue, Winchester, Hants SO23 8DL
     ☎023 8059 6900
     Fax 023 8059 6901
     url: http://www.soton.ac.uk/~library/wsa
     Head of Library and Information Services Ms L A Newington BA(Hons) PGDip ALA
     (e-mail: l.a.newington@soton.ac.uk)

SPURGEON'S COLLEGE

Library, Spurgeon's College, 189 South Norwood Hill, London SE25 6DJ
☎020 8653 0850
Fax 020 8771 0959
e-mail: enquiries@spurgeons.ac.uk
Librarian Mrs J C Powles BA ALA (e-mail: j.powles@spurgeons.ac.uk)

STAFFORDSHIRE UNIVERSITY

Library and Information Service, Staffordshire University, PO Box 664, College Road, Stoke-
on-Trent, Staffs ST4 2XS
☎(01782) 294443
Fax (01782) 744035
e-mail: library@staffs.ac.uk
url: http://www.staffs.ac.uk
University Librarian Ms E A Hart BA DipLib FLA MIInfSc
Deputy University Librarian G Borrows BA DipLib ALA

Site libraries
A   Thompson Library, Staffordshire University, PO Box 664, College Road, Stoke-on-
     Trent, Staffs ST4 2XS
     ☎(01782) 294817
     Fax (01782) 744035
B   Law Library, Staffordshire University, Leek Road, Stoke-on-Trent, Staffs ST4 2DF
     ☎(01782) 294307
     Fax (01782) 294306
     Site Librarian A J Pope BA LLB DipLib ALA
C   Nelson Library, Staffordshire University, PO Box 368, Beaconside, Stafford ST18 0YU
     ☎(01785) 353236

Fax (01785) 251058
Site Librarian S Taylor MA DMS ALA
D   Health Library, Staffordshire University, School of Health, Royal Shrewsbury Hospital
(North), Mytton Oak Road, Shrewsbury, Salop SY3 8XQ
☎(01743) 261440
Fax (01743) 261061
Site Librarian S ApThomas BA

UNIVERSITY OF STIRLING

University Library, University of Stirling, Stirling FK9 4LA
☎(01786) 467235 (enquiries), (01786) 467227 (administration)
Fax (01786) 466866
e-mail: library@stirling.ac.uk
url: http://www.stir.ac.uk/infoserv/library/
Director of Information Services P Kemp MA PhD

Campus library
Highland Health Sciences Library, University of Stirling, Highland Campus, Inverness IV2 3UJ
☎(01463) 705269
Librarian Mrs A Gillespie BA DipLibStud ALA

UNIVERSITY OF STRATHCLYDE

Andersonian Library, University of Strathclyde, Curran Building, 101 St James' Road,
Glasgow G4 0NS
☎0141 548 3701 (enquiries), ext 4621 (administration)
Fax 0141 552 3304
e-mail: library@strath.ac.uk
url: http://www.lib.strath.ac.ukj/home
Librarian and Director of Information Strategy D Law MA DipLib ALA FLA FIInfSci FKC
FRSE (0141 548 4619; e-mail: d.law@strath.ac.uk)

Constituent libraries
A   Business Information Centre, University of Strathclyde, Sir William Duncan Building,
130 Rottenrow, Glasgow G4 0GE
☎0141 552 3701 ext 746125
B   Fleck (Chemistry) Library, University of Strathclyde, Thomas Graham Building, 295
Cathedral Street, Glasgow G1 1XL
☎0141 552 3701 ext 2880
C   Law Library, University of Strathclyde, Stenhouse Building, 173 Cathedral Street,
Glasgow G4 0RQ
☎0141 552 3701 ext 3293
D   Jordanhill Library, University of Strathclyde, 76 Southbrae Drive, Glasgow G13 1PP
☎0141 950 3000
Fax 0141 950 3150
e-mail: jordanhill.library@strath.ac.uk

UNIVERSITY OF SUNDERLAND

Information Services, University of Sunderland, Chester Road, Sunderland SR1 3SD
☎0191 515 2900 (enquiries), 0191 515 2230 (administration)
Fax 0191 515 3914
Director of Information Services A McDonald BSc ALA (0191 515 2905; e-mail:
andrew.mcdonald@sunderland.ac.uk)
Assistant Directors Mrs V Edwards BA MA ALA (0191 515 3904; e-mail:

vilas.edwards@sunderland.ac.uk), Mrs L Hall BA ALA (0191 515 3059; e-mail:
lorraine.hall@sunderland.ac.uk)

Site libraries
A   Ashburne Library, University of Sunderland, Tyne and Wear SR2 7EG
        ☎0191 515 2119
        Fax 0191 515 3166
        Site Librarian Mrs E Astandoust BA ALA (0191 515 2120; e-mail:
        elizabeth.astandoust@sunderland.ac.uk)
B   Hutton Library, University of Sunderland, Chester Road, Sunderland SR1 3SD
        ☎0191 515 2644
        Fax 0191 515 2422
        Site Librarian Mrs E Wilkinson BSc MSc (0191 515 2637; e-mail:
        eileen.wilkinson@sunderland.ac.uk)
C   St Peter's Library, University of Sunderland, Prospect Building, St Peter's Riverside
        Campus, St Peter's Way, Sunderland SR6 0DD
        ☎0191 515 3059
        Fax 0191 515 3061
        Site Librarian Mrs L Hall BA ALA (0191 515 3060; e-mail:
        lorraine.hall@sunderland.ac.uk)
D   Chester Road Library, University of Sunderland, Chester Road, Sunderland SR1 3SD
        ☎0191 515 2900
        Fax 0191 515 2904
        Site Librarian Ms J Archer BA (0191 515 3272; e-mail:
        julie.archer@sunderland.ac.uk)

SURREY INSTITUTE OF ART AND DESIGN
Library, Surrey Institute of Art and Design, Falkner Road, The Hart, Farnham, Surrey
GU9 7DS
☎(01252) 722441
Fax (01252) 892725
Librarian Ms L Hayes BA DipLib ALA

Site library
Library, Surrey Institute of Art and Design, Epsom Campus, Ashley Road, Epsom, Surrey
KT18 5BE
☎(01372) 202458
Fax (01372) 747050
Site Librarian Ms J Seabourne BA(Hons) DipLib

UNIVERSITY OF SURREY
George Edwards Library, University of Surrey, Guildford, Surrey GU2 5XH
☎(01483) 259000 ext 3325 (enquiries), (01483) 259232 (administration)
Fax (01483) 259500
e-mail: library@surrey.ac.uk
url: http://www.surrey.ac.uk/library/library.html
Director of Information Services and Librarian T J A Crawshaw BEng DLIS
Head of Library and Media Services M P Burch BA MLib
Head of Research and Learning Support Systems Dr E J Lyon BSc PhD

UNIVERSITY OF SUSSEX
University Library, University of Sussex, Falmer, Brighton, Sussex BN1 9QL
☎(01273) 678163 (enquiries), (01273) 678158 (administration)

Fax (01273) 678441
e-mail: library@sussex.ac.uk
url: http://www.sussex.ac.uk/usis/library.html
University Librarian A N Peasgood BA ALA (e-mail: a.n.peasgood@sussex.ac.uk)

British Library for Development Studies, Institute of Development Studies, University of
Sussex, Falmer, Brighton, Sussex BN1 9RE
☎(01273) 678263 (enquiries), 606261 (administration)
Fax (01273) 621202
e-mail: blds@sussex.ac.uk
url: http://www/ids.ac.uk
Gopher: gopher://gopher.ids.ac.uk
ftp: ftp://ftp.ids.ac.uk
Telnet: telnet://info.ids.ac.uk
Head of Information Provision Services M G Bloom

Library, SPRU – Science and Technology Policy Research, University of Sussex, Mantell
Building, Falmer, Brighton, Sussex BN1 9RF
☎(01273) 678178 (enquiries), (01273) 678066 (administration)
Fax (01273) 685865
Librarian Ms B Merchant BSc MIInfSc ALA
Information Officer Ms M Winder BA MSc MIInfSc (e-mail: m.e.winder@sussex.ac.uk
url: http://www.sussex.ac.uk/spru/)

SWANSEA INSTITUTE OF HIGHER EDUCATION

Art and Education Library, Swansea Institute of Higher Education, Townhill Road, Swansea
SA2 0UT
☎(01792) 481000 ext 2293
Fax (01792) 298017
Head of Library and Learning Support Services A Lamb (e-mail: tlamb@mp.sihe.ac.uk)

Site libraries
A   Business Library, Swansea Institute of Higher Education, Mountpleasant, Swansea
    SA1 6ED
    ☎(01792) 481000 ext 4221
B   Engineering Library, Swansea Institute of Higher Education, Mountpleasant, Swansea
    SA1 6ED
    ☎(01792) 481000 ext 4141
    Site Librarian Ms A Harvey LLB

UNIVERSITY OF TEESSIDE

Library and Information Services, University of Teesside, Middlesbrough TS1 3BA
☎(01642) 342100 (enquiries), (01642) 342103 (administration)
Fax (01642) 342190
url: http://www.tees.ac.uk/lis/
Director of Library & Information Services I C Butchart MSc BA(Hons) ALA PGCertEd
(e-mail: ian.butchart@tees.ac.uk)

THAMES VALLEY UNIVERSITY

University Centre for Complementary Learning (UCCL), Thames Valley University, St Mary's
Road, Ealing, London W5 5RF
☎020 8231 2248 (enquiries), 020 8231 2246 (administration)
Fax 020 8231 2631
e-mail: lrc@tvu.ac.uk

url: http://www.tvu.ac.uk/
Director of the University Centre for Complementary Learning Prof A Irving PhD ALA MLS ALA DipAdultEd
Head of Learning Resources J Wolstenholme (020 8231 2678; fax 020 8231 2631; e-mail: john.wolstenholme@tvu.ac.uk)

Learning resource centres
A   St Mary's Road LRC, Thames Valley University, Ealing, London W5 5RF
     ☎020 8231 2248
     Fax 020 8231 2631
     e-mail: lrc.ealing:tvu.ac.uk
     LRC Manager P Hassell
B   Westel House Health Sciences LRC, Thames Valley University, Westel House, 32 Uxbridge Road, Ealing, London W5 2BS
     ☎020 8280 5043
     Fax 020 8280 5045
     e-mail: lrc.westel@tvu.ac.uk
     LRC Manager B Evans
C   Paul Hamlyn LRC, Thames Valley University, Wellington Street, Slough, Berks SL1 1YG
     ☎(01753) 697536
     Fax (01753) 697538
     e-mail: lrc.hamlyn@tvu.ac.uk
     LRC Manager Ms L Chan
D   Royal Berkshire Hospital LRC, Thames Valley University, Royal Berkshire Hospital, London Road, Reading, Berks RG1 5AN
     ☎0118 987 7661
     Fax 0118 986 8675
     e-mail: lrc.reading@tvu.ac.uk
     LRC Coordinator F Oliver-Tasker
E   Wexham Park LRC, Thames Valley University, Wolfson Institute of Health Sciences, Wexham Park Hospital, Slough, Berks SL2 4HL
     ☎(01753) 634343
     Fax (01753) 634344
     e-mail: lrc.wexham@tvu.ac.uk
     LRC Coordinator F Oliver-Tasker

TRINITY AND ALL SAINTS COLLEGE
Library, Trinity and All Saints College, Brownberrie Lane, Horsforth, Leeds LS18 5HD
☎0113 283 7244
Fax 0113 283 7200
Director of Information Support Services J Matthews BA(Hons) MSc ALA (e-mail: j.matthews@tasc.ac.uk)
Senior Librarian Ms E Murphy BSocSci ALA (e-mail: e.murphy@tasc.ac.uk)

TRINITY COLLEGE
Library, Trinity College, College Road, Carmarthen, Carmarthenshire SA31 3EP
☎(01267) 676780
Fax (01267) 676766
url: http://www.trinity-cm.ac.uk/pages/library.htm
Librarian Ms E Le Bourdon (e-mail: e.lebourdon@trinity-cm.ac.uk)

TRINITY COLLEGE OF MUSIC
Library, Trinity College of Music, 10–11 Bulstrode Place, London W1M 5FW

☎020 7487 9656
Fax 020 7486 6018
e-mail: library@tcm.ac.uk
Chief Librarian Ms K Sloss

UNIVERSITY OF ULSTER AT COLERAINE

Library, University of Ulster at Coleraine, Cromore Road, Co Londonderry, N Ireland
BT52 1SA
☎028 7032 4345
Fax 028 7032 4928
Director of Educational Services N S Macartney MA BA DipLib CertEd (e-mail:
n.macartney@ulst.ac.uk)

Library, University of Ulster, Shore Road, Jordanstown, Newtownabbey, Co Antrim, N Ireland
BT37 0QB
☎028 9036 6370
Fax 028 9036 6849
Coordinator of Library Services Mrs D C Shorley BA ALA (028 9036 6370; e-mail:
dc.shorley@ulst.ac.uk)

Campus libraries
A Library, Faculty of Art and Design, University of Ulster at Belfast, York Street, Belfast,
   N Ireland BT15 1ED
   ☎028 9026 7269
   Fax 028 9026 7278
   Belfast Campus Contact Mrs O Fitzpatrick (e-mail: o.fitzpatrick@ulst.ac.uk)
B Library, University of Ulster at Coleraine, Cromore Road, Co Londonderry, N Ireland
   BT52 1SA
   ☎028 7032 4345
   Fax 028 7032 4928
   Coleraine Campus Contact Mrs E E Urquhart (e-mail: ee.urquhart@ulst.ac.uk)
C Library, University of Ulster at Jordanstown, Shore Road, Jordanstown,
   Newtownabbey, Co Antrim, N Ireland BT37 0QB
   ☎028 9036 6370
   Fax 028 9036 6849
   Jordanstown Campus Contact L S Drake (e-mail: ls.drake@ulst.ac.uk)
D Library, University of Ulster at Magee, Northland Road, Londonderry, N Ireland
   BT48 7JL
   ☎028 7137 5264
   Fax 028 7137 5626
   Magee Campus Contact P D Teskey (e-mail: pd.teskey@ulst.ac.uk)

UMIST

Library and Information Service, UMIST, PO Box 88, Manchester M60 1QD
☎0161 200 4924 (enquiries), 0161 200 4921 (Librarian's secretary)
Fax 0161 200 4941
url: http://www/umist.ac.uk/UMIST_Library
University Librarian M P Day BSc MSc (e-mail: m.day@umist.ac.uk)

UNIVERSITY OF WALES ABERYSTWYTH

Hugh Owen Library, University of Wales Aberystwyth, Penglais, Aberystwyth, Dyfed
SY23 3DZ
☎(01970) 622399 (enquiries), (01970) 622391 (administration)
Fax (01970) 622404

e-mail: library@aber.ac.uk
url: http://www.inf.aber.ac.uk
Director of Information Services M Hopkins BA PhD ALA

Site/departmental libraries

A   Education Library, University of Wales Aberystwyth, Old College, King Street,
         Aberystwyth, Dyfed SY23 2AX
         ☎(01970) 622130
         Fax (01970) 622122
         Librarian i/c E P Davies BA DipLib

B   Thomas Parry Library, University of Wales Aberystwyth, Llanbadarn Fawr,
         Aberystwyth, Dyfed SY23 3AS
         ☎(01970) 622412 (enquiries), (01970) 622417 (administration)
         Fax (01970) 622190
         e-mail: parrylib@aber.ac.uk
         Librarian i/c A J Clark BSocSci DipLib ALA MIInfSc

C   Law Library, University of Wales Aberystwyth, The Hugh Owen Building, Penglais,
         Aberystwyth, Dyfed SY23 3DZ
         ☎(01970) 622401
         e-mail: as Hugh Owen Library
         Librarian i/c Mrs L Stevenson LLB DipLib ALA

D   Physical Sciences Library (Mathematics, Computer Sciences and Physics), University
         of Wales Aberystwyth, Penglais, Aberystwyth, Dyfed SY23 3BZ
         ☎(01970) 622407
         e-mail: as Hugh Owen Library
         Librarian i/c Mrs T Meredith

UNIVERSITY OF WALES BANGOR

Main Library, University of Wales Bangor, Information Services, College Road, Bangor,
Gwynedd LL57 2DG
☎(01248) 382980 (enquiries), (01248) 382963 (administration)
Fax (01248) 382979/383826 (administration)
e-mail: general mail: libstaff@bangor.ac.uk; interlibrary loans: ill@bangor.ac.uk
Director of Information Services P R Brady (e-mail: p.r.brady@bangor.ac.uk)

Information Services, Deiniol Building, University of Wales Bangor, Deiniol Road, Bangor,
Gwynedd LL57 2UN
☎(01248) 382982
Science Librarians S Harling, P Rolfe

Site libraries

A   Health Studies Library, University of Wales Bangor, Archimedes Centre, Technology
         Park, Wrexham LL13 7YP
         ☎(01978) 316368/9/70
         Fax (01978) 311154
         e-mail: iss059@bangor.ac.uk
         Librarian Mrs G Haylock BA DipLib

B   Health Studies Library, University of Wales Bangor, Fron Heulog, Holyhead Road,
         Bangor, Gwynedd LL57 2EF
         ☎(01248) 383173
         e-mail: iss070@bangor.ac.uk
         Librarian Ms M Poulton BA DipLib ALA

C   Normal Site Library, University of Wales Bangor, Holyhead Road, Bangor,

Gwynedd LL57 2PX

☎(01248) 383087

e-mail: iss186@bangor.ac.uk

Librarian Ms B Wyn Jones

D   Music Library, University of Wales Bangor, College Road, Bangor, Gwynedd

☎(01248) 382187

e-mail: iss063@bangor.ac.uk

Librarian Miss E Bird BA MA ALA

UNIVERSITY OF WALES COLLEGE OF MEDICINE

Department of Information Services, Sir Herbert Duthie Library, University of Wales College of Medicine, Heath Park, Cardiff CF14 4XN

☎029 2074 2875 (enquiries), 029 2074 2874 (administration)

Fax 029 2074 3651

e-mail: duthielib@cf.ac.uk

url: http://www.uwcm.ac.uk/uwcm/lib/

Director of Information Services Prof J M Lancaster MPhil ALA

Deputy Director of Information Services (Library) S J Pritchard BA ALA

Site libraries

A   Dental Library, University of Wales College of Medicine, Heath Park, Cardiff CF14 4XY

☎029 2074 2523

Fax 029 2074 3834

e-mail: dentlib@cf.ac.uk

Librarian Miss J Stevens BA ALA

B   Cochrane Library, University of Wales College of Medicine, Llandough Hospital, Penarth, South Glamorgan CF6 1XX

☎029 2071 1711

e-mail: cochranelib@cf.ac.uk

Librarian Ms R Soper BA DipLib ALA

C   The Violet Hughes Library, University of Wales College of Medicine, Velindre Hospital, Whitchurch, Cardiff CF14 7XL

☎029 2061 5888

e-mail: vhvlib@cf.ac.uk

Librarian Mrs B M Coles BSc MSc

D   Library, School of Nursing and Healthcare Studies, University of Wales College of Medicine, Ty Dewi Sant, Heath Park, Cardiff CF14 4XN

☎029 2074 2387

Fax 029 2074 7763

e-mail: healthlib@cf.ac.uk

Librarian Ms M Gorman BA

E   Library, School of Nursing Studies, University of Wales College of Medicine, Grounds of St Cadoc's Hospital, Caerleon, Newport NP6 1XR

☎(01633) 430346 ext 222

Fax (01633) 430717

e-mail: caerleonlib@cf.ac.uk

Librarian Ms M Gorman BA

F   Library, Postgraduate Medical Centre, University of Wales College of Medicine, Whitchurch Hospital, Whitchurch, Cardiff CF14 7XB

☎029 2069 3919 ext 6382

Fax 020 2052 0170

e-mail: whitlib@cf.ac.uk

Librarian Mrs H Kitcher BA MSc

UNIVERSITY OF WALES COLLEGE, NEWPORT

Library and Learning Resources, University of Wales College, Newport, Caerleon Campus,
PO Box 179, Newport, South Wales NP18 1YG
☎(01633) 432108
Fax (01633) 432105
url: http://www.newport.ac.uk
Head of Library and Learning Resources Ms J Peters BA MLS ALA (e-mail:
jmpeters@newport.ac.uk)

UNIVERSITY OF WALES INSTITUTE, CARDIFF

Library Division, University of Wales Institute, Cardiff, Llandaff Campus, Western Avenue,
Cardiff CF5 2YB
☎029 2041 6244
Fax 029 2041 6908
url: http://www.uwic.ac.uk
Head of Library Division P Riley BA(Hons) (029 2041 6240; e-mail: priley@uwic.ac.uk)

UNIVERSITY OF WALES LAMPETER

The Library, University of Wales Lampeter, Lampeter, Ceredigion SA48 7ED
☎(01570) 424772 (enquiries/Librarian)
Fax (01570) 423875
e-mail: library@lampeter.ac.uk
url: http://www.lamp.ac.uk/library
Systems Librarian Ms M Perrett MA DipLib (e-mail: m.perrett@lamp.ac.uk)
Library Administrator Ms J Bracher (e-mail: j.bracher@lamp.ac.uk)

UNIVERSITY OF WALES SWANSEA

Library and Information Centre, University of Wales Swansea, Singleton Park, Swansea
SA2 8PP
☎(01792) 295697 (enquiries), (01792) 295175 (administration)
Fax (01792) 295851
e-mail: library@swansea.ac.uk
url: http://www.swan.ac.uk/lis/index.htm
Director of Library and Information Services C West MA BA ALA

Branch libraries
A   Natural Sciences Library, University of Wales Swansea, Singleton Park, Swansea
       SA2 8PP
       ☎(01792) 295024
       e-mail: nslmail@swansea.ac.uk
       Branch Librarian Mrs C J Hindley BSc MSc ALA
B   Education Library, University of Wales Swansea, Hendrefoelan House, Gower Road,
       Swansea SA2 7NB
       ☎(01792) 518659
       e-mail: edmail@swansea.ac.uk
       Branch Librarian Ms M M Rogerson BA DipLib PGCE(FE)
C   South Wales Miners' Library, University of Wales Swansea, Hendrefoelan House,
       Gower Road, Swansea SA2 7NB
       ☎(01792) 518603
       e-mail: miners@swansea.ac.uk
       Branch Librarian Ms S F Williams BSc ALA
D   Nursing Library, University of Wales Swansea, Morriston Hospital, Morriston,
       Swansea SA6 6NL

☎(01792) 703767
e-mail: s.m.storey@swansea.ac.uk
Health Science Librarian Ms R Davies BLib PGCE

UNIVERSITY OF WARWICK

Library, University of Warwick, Gibbet Hill Road, Coventry, Warwickshire CV4 7AL
☎(01203) 523033
Fax (01203) 524211
e-mail: library@warwick.ac.uk
url: http://www.warwick.ac.uk/services/library/library.html
Chief Librarian J A Henshall MA PhD
Deputy Librarian C Fyfe BA MA

UNIVERSITY OF THE WEST OF ENGLAND, BRISTOL

Library Services, University of the West of England, Bristol, Frenchay Campus, Coldharbour
Lane, Bristol BS16 1QY
☎0117 965 6261 ext 2576 (enquiries), ext 2404 (administration)
Fax 0117 976 3846
url: http://www.uwe.ac.uk/library/
Head of Library Services M J Heery BA MA FLA MIInfSc FRSA (e-mail:
mike.heery@uwe.ac.uk)

WESTHILL COLLEGE OF HIGHER EDUCATION see ORCHARD LEARNING RESOURCES CENTRE

WESTMINSTER COLLEGE

Library, Westminster College, North Hinksey, Oxford OX2 9AT
☎(01865) 247644
Fax (01865) 253382
e-mail: lr@ox-we.ac.uk
Head of Learning and Information Services Vacant

UNIVERSITY OF WESTMINSTER

Information Resource Services, University of Westminster, 115 New Cavendish Street,
London W1M 8JS
☎020 7911 5095 (enquiries), 020 7911 5000 (administration)
Fax 020 7911 5093
url: http://www.wmin.ac.uk/
Acting Director of Information Resource Services Miss S Enright BA DipLib ALA (e-mail:
s.enright@westminster.ac.uk)

Campus libraries
A   Cavendish Campus Library, University of Westminster, 115 New Cavendish Street,
London W1M 8JS
☎020 7911 5000 ext 3613
Fax 020 7911 5871
Library Manager Ms D Herman BSc MSc (e-mail: d.herman@wmin.ac.uk)
B   IRS Centre, Harrow Campus, University of Westminster, Watford Road, Northwick
Park, Harrow, Middlesex HA1 3TP
☎020 7911 5000 ext 4664
Fax 020 7911 5952
Deputy IRS Centre Manager Ms J N Dye BA ALA (e-mail: j.n.dye@wmin.ac.uk)

C Marylebone Campus Library, University of Westminster, 35 Marylebone Road, London NW1 5LS
☎020 7911 5000 ext 3212
Fax 020 7911 5058
Library Manager Ms J Harrington BA MLib ALA (e-mail: j.harrington@wmin.ac.uk)

D Little Titchfield Street Library, University of Westminster, Regent Campus, 4-12 Little Titchfield Street, London W1P 7FH
☎020 7911 5000 ext 2537
Fax 020 7911 5846
Library Manager Ms E Salter BA DipLib MLib (e-mail: e.salter@wmin.ac.uk)

E Euston Centre Library, University of Westminster, Regent Campus, 9-18 Euston Centre, London NW1 3ET
☎020 7911 5000 ext 4347
Fax 020 7911 5893
Library Manager Ms B Singh BA DipLib ALA (e-mail: b.singh@wmin.ac.uk)

F University Archives, University of Westminster, Regent Campus, 4-12 Little Titchfield Street, London W1P 7FH
☎020 7911 5000 ext 2524
Fax 020 7911 5846
Archivist Ms B Weeden MA MSc DipArchAdmin (e-mail: b.c.weeden@wmin.ac.uk)

WIMBLEDON SCHOOL OF ART

Library, Wimbledon School of Art, Merton Hall Road, London SW19 3QA
☎020 8408 5000 (enquiries), 020 8408 5028 (administration)
Fax 020 8408 5050
Head of Learning Resources Miss P Harrison BA(Hons) ALA DipHA (e-mail: p.harrison@wimbledon.ac.uk)
Deputy Head of Learning Resources J Dunne PGDE (020 8408 5081; e-mail: j.dunne@wimbledon.ac.uk)
Assistant Librarian P Crollie BA(Hons) (020 8408 5027; e-mail: p.crollie@wimbledon.ac.uk)

UNIVERSITY OF WOLVERHAMPTON

Harrison Learning Centre, University of Wolverhampton, St Peter's Square, Wolverhampton, West Midlands WV1 1RH
☎(01902) 322300 (enquiries), (01902) 322302 (administration)
Fax (01902) 322668
e-mail: lib@wlv.ac.uk
Director of Learning Centres Ms M Heaney BA DipLib MIInfSc FRSA
Assistant Director of Learning Centres (Resources) Ms F Mill MA DipLib
Assistant Director of Learning Centres (Operations) C Evans ALA MLS

Nursing and Midwifery site libraries
Learning Centre Manager (Nursing and Midwifery) Mrs P Collins BA(Hons)

A Compton Learning Centre, University of Wolverhampton, Compton Road West, Wolverhampton, West Midlands WV3 9DX
☎(01902) 323642
Fax (01902) 323702
Learning Centre Manager O Pritchard BA(Hons) MA ALA AIMgt

B Dudley Learning Centre, University of Wolverhampton, Castle View, Dudley, West Midlands DY1 3HR
☎(01902) 323560
Fax (01902) 323354
Learning Centre Manager Mrs D Davies BA(Hons) ALA

C Harrison Learning Centre, University of Wolverhampton, St Peter's Square,

Wolverhampton, West Midlands WV1 1RH
☎(01902) 322300
Fax (01902) 322194
Learning Centre Manager Mrs I Ordidge BSc PGDipLib

D   Telford Learning Centre, University of Wolverhampton, Priorslee Hall, Priorslee, Telford, Shropshire TF2 9NT
☎(01902) 323983
Fax (01902) 323985
Learning Centre Manager D W Clare BA ALA

E   Walsall Learning Centre, University of Wolverhampton, Gorway, Walsall, West Midlands WS1 3BD
☎(01902) 323275
Fax (01902) 323079
Learning Centre Manager Mrs G Hughes BLib ALA

Site libraries

F   Burton Learning Centre, University of Wolverhampton, Burton Nurse Education Centre, Belvedere Road, Burton upon Trent, Staffs DE13 0RB
☎(01283) 566333 ext 2217/2237
Fax (01283) 515978
Site Librarian Ms E Watson BA(Hons) PGDipLib ALA

G   Manor Learning Centre, University of Wolverhampton, Education and Training Centre, Manor Hospital, Moat Road, Walsall, West Midlands WS2 9PS
☎(01922) 721172 ext 7181
Fax (01922) 649008
Acting Site Librarian Miss L Thompson BA(Hons)

H   New Cross Learning Centre, University of Wolverhampton, Education Centre, New Cross Hospital, Wolverhampton, West Midlands WV10 0QP
☎(01902) 307999 ext 2049
Fax (01902) 306072
Acting Site Librarian Mrs V Hyde

I   Russells Hall Learning Centre, University of Wolverhampton, Esk House, Russells Hall Hospital, Dudley, West Midlands DY1 2HQ
☎(01384) 456111 ext 2594
Fax (01384) 237543
Site Librarian Mrs G Williamson BA(Hons) ALA

UNIVERSITY COLLEGE WORCESTER

Library, University College Worcester, Henwick Grove, Worcester WR2 6AJ
☎(01905) 855414
Fax (01905) 855132
Head of Library Services Ms A Hannaford BA(Hons) DipLib (e-mail: a.hannaford@worc.ac.uk)
Customer Services Manager Ms G Walford (e-mail: g.walford@worc.ac.uk)

WRITTLE COLLEGE

Library, Writtle College, Chelmsford, Essex CM1 3RR
☎(01245) 424200
Fax (01245) 420456
Head of Learning Information Services R M Hewings BSc(Econ) DMS DipLib ALA (ext 26009; e-mail: rmh@writtle.ac.uk)
Faculty Librarian (Science) Ms J Lamb BA(Hons) DipLib ALA (ext 26008; e-mail: jl@writtle.ac.uk)

Faculty Librarian (Horticulture) Ms S Davey BA(Hons) (ext 26008; e-mail: sld@writtle.ac.uk)
Faculty Librarian (Agriculture, Mechanization and Business Management) Ms K Davis BA(Hons) DipIM ALA (ext 26008; e-mail: kld@writtle.ac.uk)

UNIVERSITY OF YORK

J B Morrell Library, University of York, Heslington, York YO10 5DD
☎(01904) 433865 (enquiries), (01904) 433863 (administration)
Fax (01904) 433866
url: http://www.york.ac.uk/services/library/
University Librarian Ms A E M Heaps BA MA DipLib ALA (e-mail: aemh1@york.ac.uk)

Branch/department libraries
A   King's Manor Library, University of York, The King's Manor, York YO1 7EP
       ☎(01904) 433969
       Fax (01904) 433949
       Librarian Ms P A Haywood BA MA (e-mail: ph16@york.ac.uk)
B   Library and Information Service, University of York, The Strayside Education Centre,
       Harrogate District Hospital, Lancaster Park Road, Harrogate HG2 7SX
       ☎(01423) 553104
       e-mail: library.harrogate@pulse.york.ac.uk
       Manager of Library and Information Service Ms G Senior BA (e-mail:
       g.senior@pulse.york.ac.uk)

Selected Government, National and Special Libraries in the United Kingdom

ADVOCATES LIBRARY

Advocates Library, Parliament House, Edinburgh EH1 1RF
☎0131 260 5683 (enquiries), 0131 260 5637 (Librarian)
Fax 0131 260 5663 (9am–5pm weekdays)
Librarian Mrs C A Smith MA DipLib ALA (e-mail: catherine.smith@advocates.org.uk)
General enquiries Mrs A Longson BSc DipLib (e-mail: andrea.longson@advocates.org.uk)
Open to members only. Non-members may access stock at the National Library of Scotland

AMBLESS CARES LIBRARY

Ambless Cares Library, Shalom House, Lower Celtic Park, Enniskillen, Co Fermanagh,
N Ireland BT74 6HP
☎028 6632 0320
Fax 028 6632 0320
Librarian J Wood

THE ARMITT TRUST

Armitt Library, The Armitt Trust, Rydal Road, Ambleside, Cumbria LA22 9BL
☎(015394) 31212
Fax (015394) 31313
e-mail: almc@armitt.com
url: http://www.armitt.com
Library Manager Mrs E Gabb BSc ALA MEd

ASLIB, THE ASSOCIATION FOR INFORMATION MANAGEMENT

Information Resource Centre, Aslib, The Association for Information Management, Staple
Hall, Stone House Court, London EC3A 7PB
☎020 7903 0000
Fax 020 7903 0011
url: http://www.aslib.co.uk
Information Resource Officer Miss A Benson (020 7903 0051; e-mail:
alison.benson@aslib.co.uk)
Library and Information Assistant P Liu (e-mail: patrick.liu@aslib.co.uk)

ASSOCIATION OF COMMONWEALTH UNIVERSITIES

Reference Library, Association of Commonwealth Universities, John Foster House,
36 Gordon Square, London WC1H 0PF
☎020 7387 8572
Fax 020 7387 2655
e-mail: info@acu.ac.uk
url: http://www.acu.ac.uk
Librarian N Mulhern

THE BABRAHAM INSTITUTE

Library, The Babraham Institute, Babraham, Cambridge CB2 4AT
☎(01223) 496214 (enquiries)
Fax (01223) 496020
e-mail: babraham.library@bbsrc.ac.uk
Librarian Miss J R Maddock BA DipLib ALA (01223 496235; e-mail:
jennifer.maddock@bbsrc.ac.uk)

BANK OF ENGLAND

Information Centre, Bank of England, Threadneedle Street, London EC2R 8AH
☎020 7601 4715 (enquiries), 020 7601 4668 (administration)
Fax 020 7601 4356
e-mail: library@bankofengland.co.uk
Information Centre Manager Ms P A Hope BA MA MSc DipLib ALA

BG PLC

Corporate Information Centre, BG plc, Building B/1, 100 Thames Valley Park Drive, Reading, Berkshire RG6 1PT
☎0118 929 2496 (enquiries and administration)
Fax 0118 929 2482
Information Centre Manager D Fairbairn (0118 929 2490)
Senior Information Officer P Cronin (0118 929 2496)
Data Coordinator D Freemantle (0118 929 2497)

BIRMINGHAM AND MIDLAND INSTITUTE

Library, Birmingham and Midland Institute, 9 Margaret Street, Birmingham B3 3BS
☎0121 236 3591
Fax 0121 212 4577
Librarian H W Woodward ALA
(Private members' library)

BISHOPSGATE INSTITUTE

Reference Library, Bishopsgate Institute, 230 Bishopsgate, London EC2M 4QH
☎020 7247 6198
Fax 020 7247 6318
Chief Librarian Ms A MacKay

BOOK TRUST

Children's Reference Library, Book Trust, Young Book Trust, Book House, 45 East Hill, London SW18 2QZ
☎020 8516 2977
Fax 020 8516 2978
e-mail: booktrust@dial.pipex.com
url: http://dialspace.dial.pipex.com/booktrust/
Children's Librarian E Zaghini ALA

BRITANNIA ROYAL NAVAL COLLEGE

College Library, Britannia Royal Naval College, Dartmouth, Devon TQ6 0HJ
☎(01803) 677279
Fax (01803) 677015
Librarian R J Kennell ALA
Assistant Librarian R Wardle BA(Hons) DipLib ALA
(Prior appointment necessary)

BRITISH ANTARCTIC SURVEY

Library, British Antarctic Survey, High Cross, Madingley Road, Cambridge CB3 0ET
☎(01223) 221617
Fax (01223) 362616
Librarian Ms C Phillips MA ALA (e-mail: c.phillips@bas.ac.uk)

BRITISH BROADCASTING CORPORATION

BBC Information and Archives, British Broadcasting Corporation, G067, Broadcasting House, Portland Place, London W1A 1AA

☎020 7557 2962

Head of Information and Archives P Fiander MSc

Customer Service Manager, Information and Archives G Strickland (e-mail: guy.strickland@bbc.co.uk)

Further sites at

Research Centre: B209 Television Centre, Wood Lane, London W12 7RJ

Research Centre: LG30 Bush House, Strand, London WC2B 4PH

BRITISH COUNCIL

Information Services Management, British Council, Bridgewater House, 58 Whitworth Street, Manchester M1 6BB

☎0161 957 7755 (enquiries), 0161 957 7170 (administration)

Fax 0161 957 7762 (enquiries), 0161 957 7168 (administration)

e-mail: firstname.surname@britcoun.org

Director S Roman (e-mail: stephan.roman@britcoun.org)

Deputy Directors C Edwards (e-mail: chris.edwards@britcoun.org); Ms S Buckwell (e-mail: sue.buckwell@britcoun.org)

Regional Information Coordinators

Middle East Libraries R Weyers (e-mail: richard.weyers@britcoun.org)

East and Central African Libraries Ms G Stoddard (e-mail: gaynor.stoddard@brit.coun.org)

South Asia Libraries Ms J Ugonna (e-mail: judy.ugonna@britcoun.org)

West African Libraries Ms B O'Connor (e-mail: brigid.oconnor@britcoun.org)

Central European Libraries D Skinner (e-mail: david.skinner@britcoun.org)

Americas Libraries R Drury (e-mail: russell.drury@britcoun.org)

Eastern and Southern European Libraries Ms L Noble (e-mail: liz.noble@britcoun.org)

East Asian and Australasian Libraries Ms G Morgan (e-mail: gwyneth.morgan@britcoun.org)

Southern African Libraries Ms P Middleton (e-mail: paula.middleton@britcoun.org)

British Council enquiries e-mail: general.enquiries@britcoun.org

(For details of British Council information services in 109 countries see url: http://www.britcoun.org)

Education Information Centre (London), British Council, 10 Spring Gardens, London SW1A 2BN

☎020 7389 4383

e-mail: education.enquiries@britcoun.org

Librarians Ms E Fryd, Ms U Aafjes-Sinnadurai (job-share)

BRITISH DENTAL ASSOCIATION

BDA Information Centre, British Dental Association, 64 Wimpole Street, London W1M 8AL

☎020 7935 0875

Fax 020 7935 6492

e-mail: infocentre@bda-dentistry.org.uk

url: http://www.bda-dentistry.org.uk

Librarian R Farbey BA DipLib ALA MIInfSc

BRITISH FILM INSTITUTE

National Library, British Film Institute, 21 Stephen Street, London W1P 2LN
☎020 7255 1444 (enquiries), ext 2264 (administration)
Fax 020 7436 2338
e-mail: library@bfi.org.uk
url: http://www.bfi.org.uk/
Head of BFI National Library R Templeton BA DipLib ALA FRSA
Deputy Head (User Services) D Sharp BA ALA
Deputy Head (Technical Services) S Pearson BA MLS CertEd ALA

BRITISH GEOLOGICAL SURVEY

Library and Information Services, British Geological Survey, Kingsley Dunham Centre,
Keyworth, Nottingham NG12 5GG
☎0115 936 3205 (enquiries), 0115 936 3472 (Chief Librarian)
Fax 0115 936 3200
e-mail: libuser@bgs.ac.uk
Chief Librarian G McKenna MA ALA (e-mail: g.mckenna@bgs.ac.uk)

Branch libraries

A   Library, British Geological Survey, Scottish Regional Office, Murchison House, West
     Mains Road, Edinburgh EH9 3LA
     ☎0131 667 1000, 0131 650 0322 (direct dial)
     Fax 0131 668 2683
     e-mail: librarymh@bgs.ac.uk
     Site Librarian R P McIntosh BSc DipLib
B   London Information Office, British Geological Survey, Natural History Museum,
     Exhibition Road, South Kensington, London SW7 2DE
     ☎020 7589 4090
     Fax 020 7584 8270
     Officer-in-Charge Miss S J Brackell (e-mail: s.brackell@bgs.ac.uk)

BRITISH HOROLOGICAL INSTITUTE

Library, British Horological Institute, Upton Hall, Newark, Notts NG23 5TE
☎(01636) 813795/6
Fax (01636) 812258
e-mail: clocks@bhi.co.uk
url: http://www.bhi.co.uk
Librarian Viscount A Midleton FBHI

BRITISH LIBRARY

Board Headquarters, British Library, 96 Euston Road, London NW1 2DB
☎020 7412 7332 (visitor enquiries), 020 7412 7000 (switchboard)
BT Gold 81:BL1202
Chairman Dr J Ashworth
Chief Executive B Lang (020 7412 7262)
Director General, Collections and Services D Bradbury
Deputy Chief Executive D Russon (Tel 01937 546131; Fax 01937 546246; e-mail:
david.russon@bl.uk)

A   Bibliographic Services and Document Supply, British Library, Boston Spa,
     Wetherby, West Yorkshire LS23 7BQ
     ☎(01937) 546000

BT Gold 81:BL1501
Director M Smith
Head of National Bibliographic Service R Smith
Head of Document Supply R Aspey
London Unit, 96 Euston Road, London NW1 2DB (020 7412 7077)

B Acquisitions Processing and Cataloguing, British Library, Boston Spa, Wetherby, West Yorkshire LS23 7BQ
☎(01937) 546000
Director S J Ede

C Information Systems, British Library, 96 Euston Road, London NW1 2DB and Boston Spa, Wetherby, West Yorkshire LS23 7BQ
☎020 7412 7228 and (01937) 546000
Director J R Mahoney

D Reader Services and Collection Development, British Library, 96 Euston Road, London NW1 2DB
☎020 7412 7676 (general enquiries, reader services and advance reservations)
Director M Crump
Head of Reader Services Ms P Chapman
Head of Modern Collections G Smith
Head of Early Printed Collections G Jefcoate (020 7412 7673)
Reader Admissions ☎020 7412 7677
(Advice on who may use the Library and how to apply for a pass)

E Library Information Sciences Service (LISS), British Library, 96 Euston Road, London NW1 2DB
☎020 7412 7676
Head C Burden

F Newspaper Library, British Library, Colindale Avenue, London NW9 5HE
☎020 7412 7353/4810
Head E King

G National Sound Archive, British Library, 96 Euston Road, London NW1 2DB
☎020 7412 7440
Head C Jewitt

H Collections and Preservation, British Library, 96 Euston Road, London NW1 2DB
☎020 7412 7552
Director Dr M Foot

I National Preservation Office, British Library, Great Russell Street, London WC1B 3DG
☎020 7412 7612
Director V Marshall

J Special Collections, British Library, 96 Euston Road, London NW1 2DB
☎020 7412 7513
Director Dr A Prochaska
Head of Manuscripts Ms A Payne
Philatelic Services ☎020 7412 7635
Head of Philatelic Services D Beech
Map Enquiries ☎020 7412 7702)
Head of Maps T Campbell
Music Enquiries ☎020 7412 7772
Head of Music H Cobbe
Head of Oriental and India Office Collections G Shaw (020 7412 7873)

K Science, Technology and Business Service, British Library, 96 Euston Road, London NW1 2DB
☎020 7412 7494/7496

L Public Affairs, British Library, 96 Euston Road, London NW1 2DB

☎020 7412 7111
Director Ms J Carr

Visitor Services (general enquiries for visitors 020 7412 7332)
(Public Affairs also includes exhibition services, education services, events
services, Publishing and Bookshop, and audiovisual services)

BRITISH MEDICAL ASSOCIATION
Library, British Medical Association, BMA House, Tavistock Square, London WC1H 9JP
☎020 7388 6625
Fax 020 7383 2544
e-mail: bma-library@bma.org.uk
url: http://www.bma.org.uk
Librarian T McSeán FLA
Deputy Librarian Ms J E Smith BA(Hons)

BRITISH MUSEUM
Ethnography Library (Museum of Mankind), British Museum, 6 Burlington Gardens, London
W1X 2EX
☎020 7323 8031
Fax 020 7323 8013 (British Museum)
Librarian i/c Ms S Mackie
(Although the Dept of Ethnography (Museum of Mankind) closed to the public in Dec 1997
in order to prepare for its move back to the main British Museum site, the library will remain
open until nearer the move. Not automatically open to the public; open to ticket holders or
by prior appointment only.)

BRITISH NATIONAL SPACE CENTRE
Information Unit, British National Space Centre, 151 Buckingham Palace Road, London
SW1W 9SS
☎020 7215 0901 (enquiries)
Fax 020 7215 0936
e-mail: information@bnsc-hq.ccmail.compuserve.com
url: http://www.bnsc.gov.uk
Librarian Ms K Seelhoff

BRITISH PSYCHOLOGICAL SOCIETY
c/o Psychology Library, British Psychological Society, University of London Library, Senate
House, Malet Street, London WC1E 7HU
☎020 7862 8451/8461
Fax 020 7862 8480
e-mail: ull@ull.ac.uk
url: http://www.ull.ac.uk
Psychology Librarian, University of London Library Mrs S E Tarrant BA ALA
(The BPS collection of periodicals is held at the Psychology Library and amalgamated with
the University of London Library collection of psychology periodicals. For details of services
etc see under University of London Library.)

BRITISH STANDARDS INSTITUTION
Library, British Standards Institution, 389 Chiswick High Road, London W4 4AL
☎020 8996 7004
Fax 020 8996 7005

e-mail: library@bsi.org.uk
url: http://www.bsi.org.uk
Library Manager Ms M Yates BSc DipLib (020 8996 7041)
(Reference only to non-members)

BRITISH STEEL PLC
Information and Library Services, British Steel plc, Swinden Technology Centre, Moorgate,
Rotherham, South Yorkshire S60 3AR
☎(01709) 820166
Fax (01709) 825464
e-mail: stc_library@technology.britishsteel.co.uk
Librarian Ms C E Rawson ALA

BRITISH UNIVERSITIES FILM & VIDEO COUNCIL
Information Service, British Universities Film & Video Council, 77 Wells Street, London
W1P 3RE
☎020 7393 1500
Fax 020 7393 1555
e-mail: bufvc@open.ac.uk
Head of Information Dr N Hiley

BTG INTERNATIONAL LTD
BTG International Ltd, 10 Fleet Place, London EC4M 7SB
☎020 7575 0000
Fax 020 7575 0010
url: http://www.btgplc.com
Information Executive Miss A Newman (020 7575 1549; e-mail:
anna.newman@btgplc.com)
Librarian Mrs E Woodruff (020 7575 1550; e-mail: elizabeth.woodruff@btgplc.com)

BUSINESS INFORMATION SOURCE
Business Information Source, Bridge House, 20 Bridge Street, Inverness IV1 1QR
☎(01463) 715400 (enquiries & administration)
Fax (01463) 715600
e-mail: bis.enquiries@bis.co.uk.com
url: http://www.bis.uk.com
General Manager C Davidson

CCLRC (COUNCIL FOR THE CENTRAL LABORATORY OF THE RESEARCH COUNCILS)
Chadwick Library, CCLRC (Council for the Central Laboratory of the Research Councils),
Daresbury Laboratory, Daresbury, Warrington, Cheshire WA4 4AD
☎(01925) 603397 (enquiries)
Fax (01925) 603195
e-mail: library@dl.ac.uk
url: http://www.clrc.ac.uk/Library/LIB
Librarian Mrs D Franks BSc ALA (01925 603189)

Library, CCLRC (Council for the Central Laboratory of the Research Councils), Rutherford
Appleton Laboratory, Chilton, Didcot, Oxon OX11 0QX
☎(01235) 445384 (general enquiries), (01235) 446668 (Librarian)
Fax (01235) 446403

e-mail: library@rl.ac.uk
url: http://www.clrc.ac.uk/Library/LIB
Senior Librarian Mrs S Lockley BSc MSc(Econ) ALA
Deputy Librarians Miss C M Ellis BA AKC DipLib ALA, Mrs K S Tomlinson BA MLS ALA
Assistant Librarian Mrs S Seddon

CENTRE FOR COASTAL AND MARINE SCIENCES

Library, Centre for Coastal and Marine Sciences, PO Box 3, Oban, Argyll PA34 4AD
☎(01631) 562244
Fax (01631) 565518
e-mail: ew@dml.ac.uk
url: http://www:nerc-oban.ac.uk/dml/index.html
Librarian Ms E Walton MA ALA

CENTRE FOR INFORMATION ON LANGUAGE TEACHING AND RESEARCH (CILT)

CILT Resources Library, Centre for Information on Language Teaching and Research
(CILT), 20 Bedfordbury, London WC2N 4LB
☎020 7379 5110
Fax 020 7379 5082
e-mail: library@cilt.org.uk
url: http://www.cilt.org.uk
Librarian J E Hawkins BA ALA

CENTRE FOR POLICY ON AGEING

Library, Centre for Policy on Ageing, 25-31 Ironmonger Row, London EC1V 3QP
☎020 7253 1787
Fax 020 7490 4206
e-mail: ageinfo@cpa.org.uk
url: http://www.cpa.org.uk
Deputy Director and Head of Information Ms G Crosby BA ALA (e-mail:
gcrosby@cpa.org.uk)
Librarians Ms R Hayes BA, Ms A Kassman-McKerrell BA
Assistant Librarian Ms K Jones BA ALA
Information Officer M Webber BA MSc

CHARTERED INSTITUTE OF BANKERS (CIB)

Library and Information Service, Chartered Institute of Bankers (CIB), 90 Bishopsgate,
London EC2N 4DQ
☎020 7444 7100
Fax 020 7444 7109
e-mail: library@cib.org.uk
url: http://www.cib.org.uk
Manager, Membership Research Miss S Vazquez BA(Hons) (020 7444 7125; e-mail:
svazquez@cib.org.uk)
Manager, Business Research Ms B Delaney BA(Hons) (020 7444 7123; e-mail:
bdelaney@cib.org.uk)

CHARTERED INSTITUTE OF MANAGEMENT ACCOUNTANTS

Technical Advisory Service, Chartered Institute of Management Accountants, 63 Portland

Place, London W1N 4AB
☎020 7917 9259 (enquiries), 020 7637 2311 (administration)
Fax 020 7323 0587
TAS Coordinator C de Vidas

CHARTERED INSURANCE INSTITUTE
Library, Chartered Insurance Institute, 20 Aldermanbury, London EC2V 7HY
☎020 7417 4415/4416
Fax 020 7972 0110
e-mail: library@cii.co.uk
url: http://www.cii.co.uk
Librarian R L Cunnew BA FLA

CHETHAM'S LIBRARY
Chetham's Library, Long Millgate, Manchester M3 1SB
☎0161 834 7961
Fax 0161 839 5797
e-mail: chetlib@dial.pipex.com
Chetham's Librarian M R Powell BD PhD

CHILD ACCIDENT PREVENTION TRUST
Resource Centre, Child Accident Prevention Trust, 4th Floor, Clerk's Court, 18-20
Farringdon Lane, London EC1R 3HA
☎020 7608 3828
Fax 020 7608 3674
e-mail: safe@capt.demon.co.uk
Information Officer Ms K Pordage

CIVIC TRUST
Library, Civic Trust, 17 Carlton House Terrace, London SW1Y 5AW
☎020 7930 0914
Fax 020 7321 0180
url: http://www.civictrust.org.uk
Librarian Miss S Hallam

CIVIL AVIATION AUTHORITY
Library and Information Centre, Civil Aviation Authority, Aviation House, South Area,
Gatwick Airport South, West Sussex RH6 0YR
☎(01293) 573725
Fax (01293) 573181
Manager S R Moore BA ALA (e-mail: stephen.moore@srg.caa.co.uk)

COMMISSION OF THE EUROPEAN COMMUNITIES
Press and Information Office, Commission of the European Communities, 8 Storey's Gate,
London SW1P 3AT
☎020 7973 1992
Fax 020 7973 1900/1910
BT Gold DGX004
Librarian Mrs M M Brenchley
(Enquiries may only be referred to this library via a recognized PIR (Public Information
Relay). For details of your nearest PIR centre please contact your local library)

COMMITTEE OF VICE-CHANCELLORS AND PRINCIPALS

Information Centre, Committee of Vice-Chancellors and Principals, Woburn House, 20 Tavistock Square, London WC1H 9HQ
☎020 7419 5429
Fax 020 7383 5766
e-mail: info@cvcp.ac.uk
url: http://www.cvcp.ac.uk
Web and Information Officer J Hood BA(Hons) DipLib MIInfSc ALA

COMMON SERVICES AGENCY

Information and Statistics Division, Common Services Agency, NHS in Scotland, Trinity Park House, South Trinity Road, Edinburgh EH5 3SQ
☎0131 551 8775
Fax 0131 551 1392
Health Information Scientist A H Jamieson MA DipLib ALA (e-mail: alanj@isdlib.demon.co.uk)

COMMONWEALTH INSTITUTE

Commonwealth Resource Centre, Commonwealth Institute, Kensington High Street, London W8 6NQ
☎020 7603 4535 ext 210
Fax 020 7603 2807
e-mail: info@commonwealth.org.uk
url: http://www.commonwealth.org.uk/
Head of Library and Information Services Mrs K Peters ALA

COMMONWEALTH SECRETARIAT

Library, Commonwealth Secretariat, Marlborough House, Pall Mall, London SW1Y 5HX
☎020 7747 6164/6165/6166/6167
Fax 020 7747 6168
Librarian D Blake BA DipLib MSc ALA

COMPETITION COMMISSION

Information Centre, Competition Commission, Room 567, 48 Carey Street, London WC2A 2JT
☎020 7324 1467
Fax 020 7324 1400
e-mail: info@competition-commission.gov.uk
url: http://www.competition-commission.gov.uk
Information Centre Manager Miss L J Fisher MA ALA
Press and Publicity Officer Miss L K Horwood BA(Hons) ALA
(Open to government libraries by appointment. Not open to the public, but deals with public telephone and written enquiries.)

CONFEDERATION OF BRITISH INDUSTRY

Information Centre, Confederation of British Industry, Centre Point, 103 New Oxford Street, London WC1A 1DU
☎020 7379 7400
Fax 020 7240 0988
url: http://www.cbi.org.uk
Librarian J A Hyde MIInfSc ALA (e-mail: jack.hyde@cbi.org.uk)

CONSERVATIVE RESEARCH DEPARTMENT

Library, Conservative Research Department, Conservative Central Office, 32 Smith Square,
London SW1P 3HH
☎020 7896 4203 (direct), 020 7222 9000 (main)
Fax 020 7233 2065
Head Librarian Ms E Watts
(Not open to the public)

COUNTRYSIDE AGENCY

Library, Countryside Agency, John Dower House, Crescent Place, Cheltenham,
Gloucestershire GL50 3RA
☎(01242) 521381
Fax (01242) 584270
url: http://www.countryside.gov.uk
Librarian Ms J Bacon MSc ALA
(The Countryside Agency was formed on 1 April 1999 when the Countryside Commission
merged with the national, advisory and countrywide functions of the Rural Development
Commission.)

COUNTRYSIDE COUNCIL FOR WALES (CYNGOR CEFN GWLAD CYMRU)

Library, Countryside Council for Wales (Cyngor Cefn Gwlad Cymru), Plas Penrhos, Ffordd
Penrhos, Bangor, Gwynedd LL57 2LQ
☎(01248) 385522
Fax (01248) 355782
e-mail: library@ccw.gov.uk
url: http://www.ccw.gov.uk
Librarian Ms D Lloyd BA ALA

CPRE (COUNCIL FOR THE PROTECTION OF RURAL ENGLAND)

Library and Records Unit, CPRE (Council for the Protection of Rural England), Warwick
House, 25 Buckingham Palace Road, London SW1W 0PP
☎020 7976 6433
Fax 020 7976 6373
e-mail: cpre@gn.apc.org
url: http://www.greenchannel.com/cpre
Head of Library and Records Ms H Morris BA ALA

DEFENCE EVALUATION AND RESEARCH AGENCY

Information Centre, Defence Evaluation and Research Agency, Winfrith Technology Centre,
Building A32, Dorchester, Dorset DT2 8DH
☎(01305) 202653
Fax (01305) 202601
Manager Mrs N Clyne BA DipLib ALA (e-mail: nicky.clyne@ukaea.org.uk)

DEPARTMENT FOR CULTURE, MEDIA AND SPORT

Information Centre, Department for Culture, Media and Sport, 2-4 Cockspur Street, London
SW1Y 5DH
☎020 7211 6200 (enquiries), 020 7211 6041 (administration)
Fax 020 7211 6032

e-mail: enquiries@culture.gov.uk
Manager Ms F Montgomery BEd DipLib ALA

DEPARTMENT FOR EDUCATION AND EMPLOYMENT

Library and Information Services Team (LIST), Department for Education and Employment, LG, Sanctuary Buildings, London SW1P 3BT
☎020 7925 5042 (enquiries), 020 7925 5555 (public enquiry unit)
Fax 020 7925 5085
e-mail: SB.library@dfee.gov.uk
Chief Librarian P Ryan BA MBA ALA (020 7925 5058; e-mail: patrick.ryan@dfee.gov.uk)
Systems Librarian Ms P Collins BA ALA (020 7925 5451; e-mail:
paula.collins@dfee.gov.uk)
Information Services Librarian J Quinn BA (020 7925 5798; e-mail:
john.quinn@dfee.gov.uk)
Finance and Serials Librarian R Walters BA DPhil ALA (020 7925 5049; e-mail:
richard.walters@dfee.gov.uk)
Departmental Records Officer C Crooks BA (020 7925 5879; e-mail:
collin.crooks@dfee.gov.uk)
Records Manager Miss J Kennedy BEd(Hons) MA ALA MIInfSc (020 7925 6058; e-mail:
jane.kennedy@dfee.gov.uk)

Site library
Library and Information Services Team (LIST), Department for Education and Employment, E3, Moorfoot, Sheffield S1 4PQ
☎0114 259 3338 (enquiries); 020 7925 5555 (public enquiry unit)
Fax 0114 259 3564
e-mail: moorfoot.library-enq@dfee.gov.uk
Deputy Librarian and Sheffield Site Librarian Ms J Reid MA MA(InfSc) ALA MIInfSc
(0114 259 3339; e-mail: julia.reid@dfee.gov.uk)

DEPARTMENT FOR INTERNATIONAL DEVELOPMENT

Library, Department for International Development, Abercrombie House, Eaglesham Road, East Kilbride, Glasgow G75 8EA
☎0845 300 4100 (public enquiries), (01355) 843599/843877/843165 (library enquiries)
Fax (01355) 843632
e-mail: enquiry@dfid.gov.uk
Senior Librarian Ms A Fraser MA ALA MLib

Library Information Point, Department for International Development, 94 Victoria Street, London SW1E 5JL
☎020 7917 0005/0574
Fax 020 7917 0523
e-mail: library@dfid.gov.uk
Librarian Ms J Chandler BLib

DEPARTMENT OF EDUCATION FOR NORTHERN IRELAND

Library, Department of Education for Northern Ireland, Rathgael House, Balloo Road, Bangor, Co Down BT19 7PR
☎028 9127 9598

Fax 028 9127 9248
Librarian Mrs A Nightingale

DEPARTMENT OF HEALTH

Library, Department of Health, Skipton House, 80 London Road, London SE1 6LH
☎020 7972 (+ extension), 020 7210 4580 (public enquiries)
Fax 020 7972 1609
url: http://www.open.gov.uk/doh/dhome.htm
Head, Library and Information Services Mrs P L Bower BA DipLib ALA (ext 5927)
Senior Librarians J Scott Cree MA ALA (Customer Services – London, ext 5928);
A Albrow (Customer Services – Leeds, 0113 254 5071)

Libraries
A   Library, Department of Health, Skipton House, 80 London Road, Elephant and
     Castle, London SE1 6LH
     ☎020 7972 6541 (enquiries)
     Fax 020 7972 5976
     Librarian Miss K George BA DipLib
B   Library, Department of Health, Quarry House, Quarry Hill, Leeds LS2 7UE
     ☎0113 254 5080/81
     Fax 0113 254 5084
     Librarian Miss K Hanson BA
C   Wellington House Library, Department of Health, 135-155 Waterloo Road, London
     SE1 8UG
     ☎020 7972 4204/06
     Fax 020 7972 4209
     Librarian Miss M Peffer BA DipLib

Agency libraries
A   Medical Devices Agency Library, Department of Health, Room 1001, Hannibal
     House, London SE1 6TQ
     ☎020 7972 8075
     Fax 020 7972 8079
     Librarian Mrs K L Morgan MSc
B   Medicines Control Agency Information Centre, Department of Health, Market
     Towers, 1 Nine Elms Lane, London SW8 5NQ
     ☎020 7273 0344
     Fax 020 7273 0353
     Head of Information Resources Miss J E Male MLib MIInfSc ALA
C   NHS Estates Library, Department of Health, 1 Trevelyan Square, Boar Lane, Leeds
     LS1 6AE
     ☎0113 254 7091/92
     Fax 0113 254 7299
     e-mail: nhse.library@dial.pipex.com
     Librarian Ms L Vickers BA

DEPARTMENT OF SOCIAL SECURITY

Information and Library Services, Department of Social Security, Room 114, The Adelphi,
1-11 John Adam Street, London WC2N 6HT
☎020 7712 2500
Fax 020 7962 8491
e-mail: library@ade004.dss.gov.uk
Head of Library Services G Monk BA(Hons)Lib ALA

Librarian Mrs H Dunn BA(Hons) ALA

Solicitors Library, Department of Social Security, 4th Floor, New Court, Carey Street, London WC2A 2LS
☎020 7412 1333
Fax 020 7412 1332
Librarian Ms M Harris

DEPARTMENT OF THE ENVIRONMENT FOR NORTHERN IRELAND
Library, Department of the Environment for Northern Ireland, Room 5-30, Clarence Court, 10-18 Adelaide Street, Belfast BT2 8GB
☎028 9054 1045/6
Fax 028 9054 1100
Librarian Vacant

DEPARTMENT OF THE ENVIRONMENT, TRANSPORT AND THE REGIONS (DETR)
Information Strategy and Library Services, Department of the Environment, Transport and the Regions (DETR), 2/H34 Ashdown House, 123 Victoria Street, London SW1E 6DE
☎020 7890 3333 (public information); 020 7890 3000 (switchboard)
e-mail: infman@detr.gov.uk
Information Strategy and Library Services Manager G Tate BA DipLib ALA (020 7890 6148)

Site libraries
A   Eland House Information Centre, Department of the Environment, Transport and the Regions (DETR), 1/P8 Eland House, London SW1E 5DU
☎020 7890 3199
Fax 020 7890 3189
B   Great Minster House Information Centre, Department of the Environment, Transport and the Regions (DETR), LG9 Great Minster House, London SW1P 4DR
☎020 7676 2002
Fax 020 7890 4716
C   Ashdown House Information Centre, Department of the Environment, Transport and the Regions (DETR), 2/H22 Ashdown House, 123 Victoria Street, London SW1E 6DE
☎020 7890 3039
Fax 020 7890 6098
D   Tollgate House Information Centre, Department of the Environment, Transport and the Regions (DETR), Room 112, Tollgate House, Houlton Street, Bristol BS2 9DJ
☎0117 987 8676/7
Fax 0117 987 8970

DEPARTMENT OF TRADE AND INDUSTRY
Administrative Headquarters and Support Services, Department of Trade and Industry, 1 Victoria Street, London SW1H 0ET
Assistant Director, Information Management and Process Engineering Mrs M A Bridge OBE MA ALA (020 7215 6542)
Head of Information and Library Service Mrs A S Raisin BA(Hons) DipLib MLib ALA (020 7215 6686; Fax 020 7215 5713)

Support Services Manager (job-share) M Byng BA(Hons) DipLib MA ALA, Ms R Zolynski BA(Hons) DipLib ALA (020 7215 6007 or 6697; Fax 020 7215 5713)
Systems Manager Ms J Garner BA(Hons) DipLib (020 7215 6618; Fax 020 7215 5713)
Information Centre Manager Miss A Cotterill BLib MA ALA (020 7215 5855; Fax 020 7215 5713)
(The DTI network also includes the libraries of the following organizations which will be found under their respective headings: British National Space Centre; Competition Commission; Office of Fair Trading; Office of Gas Supply (OFGAS); Office of Telecommunications (OFTEL); Office of Electricity Regulation (OFFER))

A   Information Centre, Department of Trade and Industry, 1 Victoria Street, London SW1H 0ET
        ☎020 7215 5006/7 (enquiries)
        Fax 020 7215 5665
        Customer Services Manager Ms D Rowland BLib MSc ALA (020 7215 6896)
        (Limited public access by appointment only)
B   Information Centre, Department of Trade and Industry, 151 Buckingham Palace Road, London SW1W 9SS
        ☎020 7215 1930/1
        Fax 020 7215 1932
        Customer Services Manager G Davies BA ALA
        (Open to Departmental Staff only)
C   Legal Library and Information Centre, Department of Trade and Industry, 10A Victoria Street, London SW1H 0NN
        ☎020 7215 3054
        Fax 020 7215 3535
        Librarian N A Hasker LLB ALA
        (Open to Departmental Staff only)

THE DEVELOPMENT GROUP

Library, The Development Group, Scottish Health Service Centre, Crewe Road South, Edinburgh EH4 2LF
☎0131 623 2535
Fax 0131 315 2369
e-mail: mdg@ednet.co.uk
Librarian Mrs A Bogle MA DipLib ALA

DEVON AND EXETER INSTITUTION

Library and Reading Rooms, Devon and Exeter Institution, 7 Cathedral Close, Exeter, Devon EX1 1EZ
☎(01392) 251017
e-mail: library@exeter.ac.uk
url: http://www.ex.ac.uk/~ijtilsed/lib/devonex.html
Librarian i/c Ms M Midgley MA MLib ALA

ELECTRICITY ASSOCIATION

Business Information Centre, Electricity Association, 30 Millbank, London SW1P 4RD
☎020 7963 5789
Fax 020 7963 5870
e-mail: enquiries@electricity.org.uk
url: http://www.electricity.org.uk
Manager, Business Information Centre Ms H J Abbott

ENGLISH FOLK DANCE AND SONG SOCIETY

Vaughan Williams Memorial Library, English Folk Dance and Song Society, Cecil Sharp House, 2 Regent's Park Road, London NW1 7AY

☎020 7485 2206

Fax 020 7284 0523

Librarian M H Taylor BA(Lib) ALA

Assistant Librarian: Dr E Bradtke

Indexer Ms M Hogan MA PhD

ENGLISH HERITAGE

Library, English Heritage, Room B1, Fortress House, 23 Savile Row, London W1X 1AB

☎020 7973 3031 (general enquiries)

Fax 020 7973 3001

url: http://www.english-heritage.org.uk

Librarian Ms C Phillpotts BA MA ALA (020 7973 3029; e-mail: cathy.philpotts@english-heritage.org.uk)

Assistant Librarian C Brodie BA DipLib

(Prior appointment necessary)

ENGLISH NATURE (NATURE CONSERVANCY COUNCIL FOR ENGLAND)

The Library, Information and Marketing Team, English Nature (Nature Conservancy Council for England), Northminster House, Peterborough PE1 1UA

☎(01733) 455094 (bibliographic enquiries; loans), (01733) 455100 (general nature conservation enquiries)

Fax (01733) 568834 library), (01733) 455103 (general enquiries)

e-mail: library.en.nh@gtnet.gov.uk; enquiries@english-nature.org.uk

url: http://www.english-nature.org.uk

Team Manager J B Creedy BSc

Librarian/Records Manager Ms I Chivers BA(Hons) DipLib MIInfSc

Librarian (Services) M J Rush MA ALA

Enquiry Service Manager G R Seamons BSc DipLib

ENGLISH-SPEAKING UNION

Page Memorial Library, English-Speaking Union, Dartmouth House, 37 Charles Street, London W1X 8AB

☎020 7493 3328

Fax 020 7495 6108

e-mail: library@esu.org.uk

Librarian/Information Officer Ms A K Wathern BA(Hons) DipLib

EQUAL OPPORTUNITIES COMMISSION

Information Centre, Equal Opportunities Commission, Overseas House, Quay Street, Manchester M3 3HN

☎0161 838 8343 (enquiries), 0161 838 8324 (administration)

Fax 0161 834 0805

e-mail: info@eoc.org.uk

Assistant Librarian Ms J Foster BA ALA

Information Officer Ms M Bryan BA DipLib

FOREIGN AND COMMONWEALTH OFFICE

Main Library, Foreign and Commonwealth Office, King Charles Street, London SW1A 2AH
☎020 7270 3925 (enquiries); 020 7270 3683 (administration)
Fax 020 7270 3270/3015
Librarian Mrs J Herring BA ALA DipLib

Departmental library
Legal Library, Foreign and Commonwealth Office, Room K168, King Charles Street,
London SW1A 2AH
☎020 7270 3050 (enquiries); 020 7270 3082 (administration)
Fax 020 7270 2767
Legal Librarian Mrs S Halls BA ALA

FORESTRY COMMISSION

Library, Forestry Commission, Forest Research Station, Alice Holt Lodge, Wrecclesham,
Farnham, Surrey GU10 4LH
☎(01420) 22255. (01420) 526216 (direct line)
Fax (01420) 23653
e-mail: library@forestry.gov.uk
Librarian Miss C A Oldham BA MA DipLib ALA (e-mail: c.oldham@forestry.gov.uk)

FRESHWATER BIOLOGICAL ASSOCIATION

Library, Freshwater Biological Association, Ferry House, Far Sawrey, Ambleside, Cumbria
LA22 0LP
☎(015394) 42468
Fax (015394) 46914
e-mail: ifelibrary@ife.ac.uk
Librarian I McCulloch BA(Hons) DipLIS MIInfSc (e-mail: i.mcculloch@ife.ac.uk)
Assistant Librarian Ms C Williams BSc DipLIS (e-mail: c.williams@ife.ac.uk)

GEOLOGICAL SOCIETY

Library, Geological Society, Burlington House, Piccadilly, London W1V 0JU
☎020 7734 5673
Fax 020 7439 3470
e-mail: library@geolsoc.org.uk
Librarian Miss S Meredith

GERMAN HISTORICAL INSTITUTE LONDON

Library, German Historical Institute London, 17 Bloomsbury Square, London WC1A 2LP
☎020 7303 2019/2022 (enquiries), 020 7309 2020 (administration)
Fax 020 7404 5573
e-mail: library-ghil@ghil.co.uk
Librarians Ms A-M Klauk, Mr C Schönberger

GOETHE-INSTITUT LONDON

Library, Goethe-Institut London, 50 Princes Gate, Exhibition Road, London SW7 2PH
☎020 7596 4040 (brief enquiries), 020 7596 4044 (information service)
Fax 020 7594 0230
e-mail: library@london.goethe.org
url: http://www.goethe.de/gr/lon/enibib/htm
Head Librarian Ms M Daum DiplBibl (e-mail: daum@london.goethe.org)

GOETHE-INSTITUT MANCHESTER

Library, Goethe-Institut Manchester, 4th Floor, Churchgate House, 56 Oxford Street, Manchester M1 6EU
☎0161 237 1078 (enquiries), 0161 237 1077 (administration)
Fax 0161 237 1079
e-mail: goethemanbibl@dial.pipex.com
Librarians Ms M Williams BA MSc, Ms D Brown MA Mphil

GUILDFORD INSTITUTE

Library, Guildford Institute of the University of Surrey, Ward Street, Guildford, Surrey GU1 4LH
☎(01483) 562142
Librarian Mrs E C Miles BA AMA

HEALTH AND SAFETY EXECUTIVE

Information Services, Health and Safety Executive, Broad Lane, Sheffield S3 7HQ
☎0114 289 2330
Fax 0114 289 2333
e-mail: point.publicenquiry@hse.gov.uk
url: http://www.open.gov.uk/hse/feedback.htm (use this address for general requests for information on health and safety at work)
Head of Information Services Ms M Riley (e-mail: melinda.riley@hse.gov.uk)
Manager, Centralized Services Miss J M Matkin BSc
Manager, Site Services Mrs A Heaney BA DipLib

Information centres

A   Information Centre, Health and Safety Executive, Rose Court, 2 Southwark Bridge Road, London SE1 9HS
☎020 7717 6104
Fax 020 7717 6134
Site Manager Vacant

B   Information Centre, Health and Safety Executive, Offshore Safety Division, Lord Cullen House, Fraser Place, Aberdeen AB9 1UB
☎(01224) 252643
Fax (01224) 252525
Site Manager Mrs M Kerr BA ALA

C   Information Centre, Nuclear Safety Division, Health and Safety Executive, St Peter's House, Balliol Road, Bootle, Merseyside L20 2LZ
☎0151 951 4042
Fax 0151 951 4004
Site Manager Mrs K McNichol MA ALA

D   Information Centre, Health and Safety Executive, Magdalen House, Stanley Precinct, Bootle, Merseyside L20 3QY
☎0151 951 4382
Fax 0151 951 3674
Site Manager Mrs H Evans BA ALA

E   Information Centre, Health and Safety Executive, Broad Lane, Sheffield S3 7HQ
☎0114 289 2330
Fax 0114 289 2333
Site Manager Mrs L Heritage BA

(General requests for information on health and safety at work should be referred to the Public Information Network at the main address above, or to the HSE Infoline on 0541 545500)

HEALTH EDUCATION AUTHORITY

Health Education Authority, Trevelyan House, 30 Great Peter Street, London SW1P 2BY
☎020 7413 1995 (enquiry desk); 020 7222 5300 (switchboard)
Fax 020 7413 1834
e-mail: hpic.enquiry@hea.org.uk
Head of Information Ms C Herman BA(Hons) PGDip (020 7413 1866)

HEALTH EDUCATION BOARD FOR SCOTLAND

Health Promotion Library Scotland, Health Education Board for Scotland, The Priory,
Canaan Lane, Edinburgh EH10 4SG
☎(0645) 125442 (enquiries - Scotland only), 0131 536 5595 (administration), textphone
0131 536 5593
Fax 0131 536 5502
e-mail: library.enquiries@hebs.scot.nhs.uk
url: http://www.hebs.scot.nhs.uk
Library Services Manager Ms M Forrest MA(Hons) MSc DipLib ALA MIInfSc FSA(Scot)
Librarian D M Mackay MA(Hons) DipLIS ALA

HIGH COMMISSION OF INDIA

Library, High Commission of India, Aldwych, London WC2B 4NA
☎020 7836 8484 ext 115
Fax 020 7836 4331
Librarian Miss M S Travis
(Staff library only)

HIGHGATE LITERARY AND SCIENTIFIC INSTITUTION

Library, Highgate Literary and Scientific Institution, 11 South Grove, Highgate, London N6
6BS
☎020 8340 3343
Fax 020 8340 5632
Librarian R Walker BA (e-mail: robert@hlsi.demon.co.uk)
(Public access allowed for reference)

HISPANIC AND LUSO-BRAZILIAN COUNCIL

Canning House Library, Hispanic and Luso-Brazilian Council, 2 Belgrave Square, London
SW1X 8PJ
☎020 7235 2303
Fax 020 7235 3587
e-mail: canninghouse@compuserve.com
url: http://www.canninghouse.com
Librarian Ms C Suárez BA MA
Assistant Librarian Ms F Lee MA MSc

HM CUSTOMS AND EXCISE

Library, HM Customs and Excise, 1st Floor, Ralli Quays East, 3 Stanley Street, Salford,
Lancs M60 9LA
☎0161 827 0444/5
e-mail: dparke.c&e.ralli@gtnet.gov
Chief Librarian Vacant (0161 827 0450)

Branch/department library
Library, HM Customs and Excise, 2nd Floor, New Kings Beam House, 22 Upper Ground,
London SE1 9PJ
☎020 7865 5668/9
e-mail: cz53@cityscape.co.uk
Librarian Ms L Goodey (020 7865 5671)

HM TREASURY AND CABINET OFFICE

Library and Information Service, HM Treasury and Cabinet Office, Treasury Chambers,
Parliament Street, London SW1P 3AG
☎020 7270 5290 (enquiries)
Fax 020 7270 5681
e-mail: library@hm-treasury.gov.uk
url: http://www.hm-treasury.gov.uk/
Chief Librarian Miss J E Clayton BA ALA

HMS SULTAN

Library, HMS Sultan, Military Road, Gosport, Hants PO12 3BY
☎023 9254 2678
Fax 023 9254 2555
e-mail: sultanlibrary@gtnet.gov.uk
Librarian J R C Quibell BA ALA
(Visits by arrangement)

HOME OFFICE

Information Services Group, Home Office, Communication Directorate, Queen Anne's Gate,
London SW1H 9AT
☎020 7273 3398 (enquiries)
Fax 020 7273 3957
url: http://www.homeoffice.gov.uk
Assistant Director, Information Services (Head of ISG) P D Griffiths BA FIInfSc ALA
Library Manager N Owens BA DipLib (020 7273 2763)

Site library
Prison Service Headquarters Library, Home Office, Room 224, Abell House, John Islip
Street, London SW1P 4LH
☎020 7217 5548/5253
Fax 020 7217 5209

HORTICULTURE RESEARCH INTERNATIONAL

Library, Horticulture Research International, East Malling, West Malling, Kent ME19 6BJ
☎(01732) 843833
Fax (01732) 849067
Librarian Ms Sarah M Loat BA ALA (e-mail: sarah.loat@hri.ac.uk)

HOUSE OF COMMONS

Department of the Library, House of Commons, ., London SW1A 0AA
☎020 7219 4272
Fax 020 7219 5839
e-mail: hcinfo@parliament.uk
url: http://www.parliament.uk
Librarian of the House of Commons Miss J B Tanfield BSc(Econ)

(There are specialist sections which deal with enquiries from Members of Parliament only. Outside enquirers should approach the Department's public interface, the House of Commons Information Office (address as above) 020 7219 4272 (5 lines)) Head of Information Office C M Sear BA DipLib

HOUSE OF LORDS

Library, House of Lords, London SW1A 0PW
☎020 7219 5242 (enquiries), 020 7219 3240 (administration)
Fax 020 7219 6396
e-mail: hllibrary@parliament.uk
Librarian D L Jones MA FSA ALA

HULTON GETTY PICTURE COLLECTION

Hulton Getty Picture Collection, Unique House, 21-31 Woodfield Road, London W9 2BA
☎020 7266 2662
Fax 020 7266 3154
e-mail: info@getty-images.com
General Manager M Butson
Managing Director Mrs S Kemp
Head of Sales and Marketing C Finlay
(The Hulton Getty Picture Collection is part of Getty Images)

IGER (INSTITUTE OF GRASSLAND AND ENVIRONMENTAL RESEARCH)

Stapledon Library and Information Service, IGER (Institute of Grassland and Environmental Research), Plas Gogerddan, Aberystwyth SY23 3EB
☎(01970) 823053 (library desk)
Fax (01970) 828357
e-mail: igerlib-wpbs@bbsrc.ac.uk
url: http://www.iger.bbsrc.ac.uk
Institute Librarian & Web Manager Ms C Moss-Gibbons BLib(Hons) PGCE

IMPERIAL CANCER RESEARCH FUND

Stoller Fund Library, Imperial Cancer Research Fund, PO Box 123, Lincoln's Inn Fields, London WC2A 3PX
☎020 7269 3206 (enquiries), 020 7269 3290 (administration)
Fax 020 7269 3084
e-mail: lib_info@icrf.icnet.uk
Head of Library & Information Services Ms J Chester BA ALA

IMPERIAL WAR MUSEUM

Department of Printed Books, Imperial War Museum, Lambeth Road, London SE1 6HZ
☎020 7416 5342
Fax 020 7416 5374
e-mail: books@iwm.org.uk
Keeper of Printed Books R Golland
Head of Public Services C J V Hunt (020 7416 5341)
Head of Acquisitions, Cataloguing and Computing Ms M Wilkinson (020 7416 5348)
(Coverage of 20th-century conflicts involving Great Britain and Commonwealth countries – military, civilian and social historical aspects)

INDEPENDENT TELEVISION COMMISSION

Library, Independent Television Commission, 33 Foley Street, London W1P 7LB
☎020 7306 7763 (enquiries)
Fax 020 7306 7750
e-mail: library@itc.org.uk
url: http://www.itc.org.uk
Librarian B I MacDonald MA ALA (020 7306 7766)
Deputy Librarian Jan Kacperek BA DipLib (020 7306 7765)

INLAND REVENUE

Library, Inland Revenue, Room 28, Somerset House, Strand, London WC2R 1LB
☎020 7438 6648
Fax 020 7438 7562
Library Team Leader F Higginson
(By appointment only)

INSTITUT FRANÇAIS

La Mediathèque, Institut Français, 17 Queensberry Place, London SW7 2DT
☎020 7838 2144 (enquiries), 020 7838 2152 (administration)
Fax 020 7838 2145
e-mail: library@mail.ambafrance.org.uk
Head Librarian Ms O Grandet

Children's Library, 32 Harrington Road, London SW7 3HD
☎020 7838 2157

INSTITUT FRANÇAIS D'ÉCOSSE

Library, Institut Français D'Écosse, 13 Randolph Crescent, Edinburgh EH3 7TT
☎0131 225 5366
Fax 0131 220 0648
e-mail: 106337.1403@compuserve.com
Librarian Ms A-M Usher

INSTITUTE OF ACTUARIES

Library, Institute of Actuaries, Napier House, 4 Worcester Street, Oxford OX1 2AW
☎(01865) 268200
Fax (01865) 268211
e-mail: libraries@actuaries.org.uk
url: http://www.actuaries.org.uk
Librarian Ms S Grover MA ALA
Deputy Librarian Ms F J McNeil BA ALA

INSTITUTE OF ARABLE CROPS RESEARCH – ROTHAMSTED LIBRARY

Institute of Arable Crops Research – Rothamsted Library, Rothamsted Experimental Station, Harpenden, Herts AL5 2JQ
☎(01582) 763133
Fax (01582) 760981
url: http://www.res.bbsrc.ac.uk/library/index.htm
Librarian Mrs S E Allsopp BA ALA DipLib (e-mail: liz.allsopp@bbsrc.ac.uk)

INSTITUTE OF CHARTERED ACCOUNTANTS IN ENGLAND AND WALES

Library, Institute of Chartered Accountants in England and Wales, Chartered Accountants'
Hall, PO Box 433, Moorgate, London EC2P 2BJ
☎020 7920 8620
Fax 020 7920 8621
e-mail: library@icaew.co.uk
url: http://www.icaew.co.uk
Librarian Ms S P Moore BA(Hons)Lib ALA
Deputy Librarian Ms A Dennis BA(Hons) DipLib ALA
(The Library is for members of the ICAEW and ICAEW registered students.)

INSTITUTE OF CHARTERED SECRETARIES AND ADMINISTRATORS

Information Centre, Institute of Chartered Secretaries and Administrators, 16 Park
Crescent, London W1N 4AH
☎020 7580 4741*
Fax 020 7612 7034
e-mail: icsa@dial.pipex.com
url: http://www.icsa.org.uk/icsa/
Information Centre Manager Miss M Nolan FCIS
(*Enquiries should be sent by letter or fax)

INSTITUTE OF CONTEMPORARY HISTORY AND WIENER LIBRARY

Library, Institute of Contemporary History and Wiener Library, 4 Devonshire Street, London
W1N 2BH
☎020 7636 7247
Fax 020 7436 6428
e-mail: lib@wl.u-net.com
Senior Librarian C B Clarke MA DipLib
Director Prof D Cesarani
Deputy Director B Barkow
Education Officer Dr J Reilly

INSTITUTE OF DIRECTORS

Business Library, Institute of Directors, 116 Pall Mall, London SW1Y 5ED
☎020 7451 3100
Fax 020 7321 0145
e-mail: businessinfo@iod.org.uk
Head of Business Services Ms P Bater BA DipLib ALA

INSTITUTE OF HYDROLOGY

Library, Institute of Hydrology, Maclean Building, Crowmarsh Gifford, Wallingford, Oxon
OX10 8BB
☎(01491) 692266
Fax (01491) 692424
e-mail: library@mail.nwl.ac.uk
Librarian Mrs S B Wharton BA ALA MIInfSc

THE INSTITUTE OF LOGISTICS AND TRANSPORT

Library (London), The Institute of Logistics and Transport, 80 Portland Place, London W1N 4DP
☎020 7467 9406 (library), 020 7467 9400 (administration)
Fax 020 7467 9440 (FAO Librarian)
url: http://www.iolt.org.uk
Librarian Ms K Isaksen BA(Hons) ALA DipLib (e-mail: ki@iolt.org.uk)

Library (Corby), The Institute of Logistics and Transport, PO Box 5787, Corby, Northants NN17 4XQ
☎(01536) 740112 (library), (01536) 740100 (administration)
Fax (01506) 740102
url: http://www.iolt.org.uk
Librarian Ms A McGregor (e-mail: angela.mcgregor@iolt.org.uk)

(The Chartered Institute of Transport and the Institute of Logistics merged on 1 June 1999 to form The Institute of Logistics and Transport)

INSTITUTE OF MANAGEMENT

Management Information Centre, Institute of Management, Management House, Cottingham Road, Corby, Northants NN17 1TT
☎(01536) 204222
Fax (01536) 401013
e-mail: mic.enquiries@imgt.org.uk
url: http://www.inst-mgt.org.uk
Head of Information Services R Norton BA FLA

INSTITUTE OF MATERIALS

Institute of Materials, 1 Carlton House Terrace, London SW1Y 5DB
☎020 7451 7360 (enquiries), 020 7451 7300 (switchboard)
Fax 020 7451 7349
Information Officer Ms H Kaune BA(Hons) DipLib (e-mail: Hilda_Kaune@materials.org.uk)

INSTITUTE OF OCCUPATIONAL MEDICINE

Library, Institute of Occupational Medicine, Roxburgh Place, Edinburgh EH8 9SU
☎0131 667 5131
Fax 0131 667 0136
e-mail: iom@iomhq.org.uk
Scientific Information Officer Ms A Boyle MA(Hons) MSc ALA

INSTITUTE OF PERSONNEL AND DEVELOPMENT

Library and Information Services, Institute of Personnel and Development, IPD House, Camp Road, London SW19 4UX
☎020 8263 3355 (enquiries), 020 8263 3410 (administration)
Fax 020 8263 3400
e-mail: lis@ipd.co.uk
url: http://www.ipd.co.uk
Manager of Library and Information Services Ms B Salmon

INSTITUTE OF PETROLEUM

Library and Information Service, Institute of Petroleum, 61 New Cavendish Street, London W1M 8AR

☎020 7467 7112/3/4/5 (enquiries), 020 7467 7111 (administration)
Fax 020 7255 1472
e-mail: lis@petroleum.co.uk
url: http://www.petroleum.co.uk
Head of Library and Information Service Mrs C M Cosgrove BSc(Hons) BA ALA
MInstPet
Senior Information Officer C L Baker BA(Hons) MInstPet

INSTITUTE OF PSYCHO-ANALYSIS
Library, Institute of Psycho-Analysis, 112a Shirland Road, Maida Vale, London W9 2EQ
☎020 7563 6900
Fax 020 7323 5312
e-mail: 106027.3726@compuserve.com
Library Executive Officer Ms J Duncan BA

INSTITUTE OF TERRESTRIAL ECOLOGY
Library, Institute of Terrestrial Ecology, Edinburgh Research Station, Bush Estate, Penicuik,
Midlothian EH26 0QB
☎0131 445 4343
Fax 0131 445 3943
url: http://www.nmw.ac.uk/ite/lib/html
Librarian Miss S Scobie MA DipLib (e-mail: s.scobie@ite.ac.uk)

Research station libraries
A   Library, Institute of Terrestrial Ecology, Monks Wood, Abbots Ripton, Huntingdon,
     Cambridgeshire PE17 2LS
     ☎(01487) 773381
     Fax (01487) 773467
     Librarian N Simmons (e-mail: n.simmons@ite.ac.uk)
B   Library, Institute of Terrestrial Ecology, Merlewood Research Station, Windermere
     Road, Grange-over-Sands, Cumbria LA11 6JU
     ☎(01539) 532264
     Fax (01539) 534705
     Librarian C Cook (e-mail: c.cook@ite.ac.uk)
C   Library, Institute of Terrestrial Ecology, Banchory Research Station, Hill of Brathens,
     Glassel, Banchory, Kincardineshire AB31 4BY
     ☎(01330) 823434
     Fax (01330) 823303
     Librarian Mrs R Ratcliffe (e-mail: r.ratcliffe@ite.ac.uk)
D   Library, Institute of Terrestrial Ecology, Furzebrook Research Station, Wareham,
     Dorset BH20 5AS
     ☎(01929) 551518
     Fax (01929) 551087
     Librarian Mrs I M Chester (e-mail: i.chester@ite.ac.uk)

INSTITUTION OF CHEMICAL ENGINEERS
Library and Information Services, Institution of Chemical Engineers, Davis Building, 165-
189 Railway Terrace, Rugby, Warwicks CV21 3HQ
☎(01788) 578214
Fax (01788) 560833
e-mail: library@icheme.org.uk
url: http://www.icheme.org.uk
Information Officer Miss T Farthing BA(Hons)

INSTITUTION OF CIVIL ENGINEERS

Library, Institution of Civil Engineers, Great George Street, Westminster, London
SW1P 3AA
☎020 7222 7722
Fax 020 7976 7610
e-mail: library@ice.org.uk
url: http://www.ice.org.uk
Librarian M M Chrimes BA MLS ALA

INSTITUTION OF ELECTRICAL ENGINEERS

Library, Institution of Electrical Engineers, Savoy Place, London WC2R 0BL
☎020 7344 5461 (enquiries & administration), 020 7344 5451 (management)
Fax 020 7497 3557
e-mail: libdesk@iee.org.uk
url: http://www.iee.org.uk/Library/
Library Manager J Coupland BA MIInfSc (020 7344 5451; e-mail: jcoupland@iee.org.uk)
Deputy Librarian Ms H Sparks BA ALA (020 7240 1874 ext 2208; e-mail:
hsparks@iee.org.uk)
(Also includes the British Computer Society Library and Institution of Manufacturing
Engineers Library)

INSTITUTION OF MECHANICAL ENGINEERS

Information and Library Service, Institution of Mechanical Engineers, 1 Birdcage Walk,
London SW1H 9JJ
☎020 7973 1266/1267/1274
Fax 020 7222 8762
e-mail: ils@imeche.org.uk
url: http://www.imeche.org.uk
Information and Library Service Manager J Ollerton ALA MIInfSc MIMgt
Senior Information Officer E Gooday BA MIInfSc ALA
Senior Librarian/Archivist K Moore MA DipLib
Information Officers Ms N Joyce BA ALA, Ms L Ray BA(Hons)
Librarian M Claxton BSc

INSTITUTION OF MINING AND METALLURGY

Library, Institution of Mining and Metallurgy, 77 Hallam Street, London W1N 5LR
☎020 7580 3802
Fax 020 7436 5388
e-mail: instmm@cix.compulink.co.uk
url: http://www.imm.org.uk
Head, Library and Information Services M McGarr BSc MIInfSc

THE INSTITUTION OF OCCUPATIONAL SAFETY AND HEALTH

Technical Enquiry and Information Service, The Institution of Occupational Safety and
Health, The Grange, Highfield Drive, Wigston, Leicestershire LE18 1NN
☎0116 257 3100
Fax 0116 257 3101
url: http://www.iosh.co.uk
Information Officer Ms A Wells

INSTITUTO CERVANTES

Library, Instituto Cervantes, 102 Eaton Square, London SW1W 9AN
☎020 7235 0324
Fax 020 7235 0329
e-mail: biblon@cervantes.es
url: http://www.cervantes.es
Head Librarian Ms M Azorin

Branch libraries
A Library, Instituto Cervantes, 58 Northumberland Road,
   Ballsbridge, Dublin 4
   ☎(00 353 1) 668 2024
   Fax (00 353 1) 668 8416
   e-mail: cervante@indigo.ie
   Head Librarian Ms Isabel Medina
B Library, Instituto Cervantes, 322-330 (Unit 8), Deansgate,
   Campfield Avenue Arcade, Manchester M3 4FN
   ☎0161 661 4210
   Fax 0161 661 4203
   e-mail: bibman@cervantes.es
   Librarian J M Fernandez

INTERNATIONAL INSTITUTE FOR STRATEGIC STUDIES

Library, International Institute for Strategic Studies, 23 Tavistock Street, London
WC2E 7NQ
☎020 7379 7676
Fax 020 7836 3108
e-mail: library@iiss.org.uk
url: http://www.isn.ethz.ch/iiss/
Chief Librarian Ms H J Oakley BA MA DipInf ALA

INTERNATIONAL LABOUR OFFICE

Library, International Labour Office, Millbank Tower, 21-24 Millbank, London SW1P 4QP
☎020 7828 6401
Fax 020 7233 5925
e-mail: ipu@ilo-london.org.uk
Manager, Publications/Information Unit N Evans
(Library available by appointment, 10.00–16.30 Mon–Fri. Closed 1–2 for lunch)

INTERNATIONAL MARITIME ORGANIZATION

Library, International Maritime Organization, 4 Albert Embankment, London SE1 7SR
☎020 7735 7611
Fax 020 7587 3236
url: http://www.imo.org
Librarian Ms M Harvey (e-mail: marianneharvey@imo.org)

ISLE OF MAN GOVERNMENT OFFICE

Tynwald Library, Isle of Man Government Office, Legislative Buildings, Isle of Man
Government Office, Bucks Road, Douglas, Isle of Man IM1 3PW
☎(01624) 685520
Fax (01624) 685522

e-mail: library@isle-of-man.org.uk
Librarian G C Haywood ALA

ITALIAN INSTITUTE
Library, Italian Institute, 39 Belgrave Square, London SW1X 8NX
☎020 7396 4406 (direct), 020 7235 1461 (switchboard)
Fax 020 7235 4618
e-mail: ici@italcultur.org.uk
url: http://www.italcultur.org.uk
Librarian Ms M D'Angelo

ITRI LTD (FORMERLY INTERNATIONAL TIN RESEARCH INSTITUTE)
Library, ITRI Ltd (formerly International Tin Research Institute), Kingston Lane, Uxbridge, Middlesex UB8 3PJ
☎(01895) 272406
Fax (01895) 251841
e-mail: postmaster@itri.co.uk
url: http://www.itri.co.uk
Librarian Dr L A Hobbs BTech(Hons) PhD DipLib MRSC CChem

JOINT SERVICES COMMAND AND STAFF COLLEGE
Library, Joint Services Command and Staff College, Broad Lane, Bracknell, Berkshire RG12 9DD
☎(01344) 454593 ext 7347 (enquiries), ext 7241 (administration)
Fax (01344) 303510
Librarian C M Hobson ALA

THE KENNEL CLUB
Library, The Kennel Club, 1-5 Clarges Street, Piccadilly, London W1Y 8AB
☎020 7518 1009
Fax 020 7518 1058
e-mail: thekennelclub@compuserve.com
url: http://www.the-kennel-club.org.uk/library/library.htm
Library and Collections Manager Ms B Walker BA ALA
(Open Tuesdays, Wednesdays and Thursdays, 9.30 am–4.30 pm)

KING'S FUND
Library and Information Service, King's Fund, 11-13 Cavendish Square, London W1M 0AN
☎020 7307 2568/9 (enquiries)
Fax 020 7307 2805
e-mail: library@kingsfund.org.uk
url: http://www.kingsfund.org.uk
Library and Information Service Manager Ms L Cawthra MA DipLib ALA

LABOUR PARTY
Information Resource Centre, Labour Party, Millbank Tower, Millbank, London SW1P 4GT
☎020 7802 1330
Fax 020 7802 1555
Information Officer Ms F Harrison BA

LAMBETH PALACE LIBRARY

Lambeth Palace Library, London SE1 7JU
☎020 7898 1400
Fax 020 7928 7932
Librarian and Archivist R J Palmer PhD ALA

LAW COMMISSION

Library, Law Commission, Conquest House, 37/38 John Street, Theobalds Road, London WC1N 2BQ
☎020 7453 1241 (enquiries), 020 7453 1242 (administration)
Fax 020 7453 1297
e-mail: library.lawcomm@gtnet.gov.uk
url: http://www.open.gov.uk/lawcomm/homepage.htm
Librarian Mrs J J King BLib ALA

LAW SOCIETY

Library, Law Society, Law Society's Hall, 113 Chancery Lane, London WC2A 1PL
☎0870 606 2511 (enquiries), 020 7320 5699 (administration)
Fax 020 7831 1687
e-mail: lib-enq@lawsociety.org.uk
Librarian and Head of Information Services Mrs L Quiney MSc DipLib ALA

THE LIBRARY AND MUSEUM OF FREEMASONRY

The Library and Museum of Freemasonry, Freemasons' Hall, Great Queen Street, London WC2B 5AZ
☎020 7395 9251
Fax 020 7404 7418
e-mail: ugle@compuserve.com
Director Ms D Clements
Deputy Librarian and Curator J F Ashby (020 7395 9254)
Assistant Librarian Mrs K Jowett (020 7395 9258)
(Telephone in advance. Visits by arrangement.)

THE LIBRARY ASSOCIATION

Information Services, The Library Association, 7 Ridgmount Street, London WC1E 7AE
☎020 7636 7543
Fax 020 7436 7218
e-mail: info@la-hq.org.uk
url: http://www.la-hq.org.uk
Head of Information Services Ms H Berry BA DipLib ALA MCIT
Information Manager, Members' Information Centre Ms B Stratton BA DipLib MSc ALA

LIBRARY FOR IRANIAN STUDIES

Library for Iranian Studies, The Woodlands Hall, Crown Street, London W3 8SA
☎020 8993 6384
Fax 020 8752 1300
Librarian Dr M Ajoudani

THE LINEN HALL LIBRARY

The Linen Hall Library, 17 Donegall Square North, Belfast BT1 5GD
☎028 9032 1707

Fax 028 9043 8586
e-mail: info@linenhall.com
Librarian J C Gray BA DLIS
(Previously known as the Belfast Library and Society for Promoting Knowledge)

LINNEAN SOCIETY OF LONDON
Library, Linnean Society of London, Burlington House, Piccadilly, London W1V 0LQ
☎020 7434 4479
Fax 020 7287 9364
e-mail: gina@linnean.demon.co.uk
Librarian G Douglas BSc FLS

LITERARY AND PHILOSOPHICAL SOCIETY OF NEWCASTLE UPON TYNE
Library, Literary and Philosophical Society of Newcastle upon Tyne, 23 Westgate Road,
Newcastle upon Tyne NE1 1SE
☎0191 232 0192
Fax 0191 261 2885
e-mail: litphil.library@btInternet.com
Librarian Mrs E A Pescod

LONDON CHAMBER OF COMMERCE AND INDUSTRY
Information Centre, London Chamber of Commerce and Industry, 33 Queen Street, London
EC4R 1AP
☎020 7248 4444
Fax 020 7489 0391
e-mail: info@londonchamber.co.uk
Research Manager Ms M Ewins

LONDON LIBRARY
London Library, 14 St James's Square, London SW1Y 4LG
☎020 7930 7705
Fax 020 7766 4766
e-mail: membership@londonlibrary.co.uk
url: http://www.londonlibrary.co.uk
Librarian A S Bell MA FSA
Deputy Librarian Ms I T P A Lynn BA ALA

LONDON METROPOLITAN ARCHIVES
Library, London Metropolitan Archives, 40 Northampton Road, London EC1R 0HB
☎020 7332 3820; Minicom: 020 7278 8703
Fax 020 7833 9136
e-mail: lma@ms.corpoflondon.gov.uk
Senior Librarian M Scott MA ALA

LONDON RESEARCH CENTRE
Research Library, London Research Centre, 81 Black Prince Road, London SE1 7SZ
☎020 7787 5666 (enquiries), 020 7787 5661 (administration)
Fax 020 7787 5674/5
e-mail: rlinfo@london-research.gov.uk

url: http://www.london-research.gov.uk
Director of Research Library Ms A Davies BA(Hons) ALA

LONDON TRANSPORT MUSEUM

Library, London Transport Museum, 39 Wellington Street, Covent Garden, London WC2E 7BB
☎020 7379 6344
Fax 020 7565 7252
Librarian Ms P Austin ALA (e-mail: patriciaa@ltmuseum.co.uk)
(Readers by appointment Mondays and Tuesdays only)

MANX NATIONAL HERITAGE

Library, Manx National Heritage, Kingswood Grove, Douglas, Isle of Man IM1 3LY
☎(01624) 648000
Fax (01624) 648001
e-mail: enquiries@mnh.gov.im
Librarian/Archivist R M C Sims BA DAA DPESS
Assistant Librarian A Franklin ALA
Assistant Archivist Ms W Thirkettle BA DAS

MARX MEMORIAL LIBRARY

Marx Memorial Library, 37A Clerkenwell Green, London EC1R 0DU
☎020 7253 1485
Fax 020 7253 1485
Librarian Ms T Newland BA MSc

MARYLEBONE CRICKET CLUB

Library, Marylebone Cricket Club, Lord's Ground, St John's Wood, London NW8 8QN
☎020 7289 1611
Fax 020 7432 1062
Curator S Green MA

METEOROLOGICAL OFFICE

National Meteorological Library and Archives, Meteorological Office, London Road, Bracknell, Berks RG12 2SZ
☎(01344) 854841 (enquiries)
Fax (01344) 854840
e-mail: metlib@meto.gov.uk
url: (Library) http://www.meto.gov.uk/sec1/sec1pg7.html; (Met Office) http://www.meto.gov.uk/home.html
Manager A Heasman
(Open to the public)

MINISTRY OF AGRICULTURE, FISHERIES AND FOOD

Whitehall Place Library, Ministry of Agriculture, Fisheries and Food, Whitehall Place, London SW1A 2HH
☎020 7270 8000
Fax 020 7270 8419
e-mail: w.library@inf.maff.gov.uk
Librarian Mrs C Smith BA(Hons) ALA (020 7270 8429)

(General collection on temperate agriculture. Visitors must give 24 hours' notice.)

Nobel House Library, Ministry of Agriculture, Fisheries and Food, Nobel House, 17 Smith Square, London SW1P 3JR
☎020 7238 6575
Fax 020 7238 6609
e-mail: n.library@inf.maff.gov.uk
Librarian Mrs J Carpenter BA DipLib DipBIT ALA (020 7238 6571)
(Specializes in food and environmental issues. Visitors must give 24 hours' notice.)

MAFF Helpline
☎0645 33 55 77 (09.00–17.00 Mon-Fri) (e-mail: helpline@inf.maff.gov.uk)
All calls charged at local call rate
(Provides an enquiry service to businesses and the general public who need access to information or specialist contacts relating to the work of MAFF)

MINISTRY OF DEFENCE
HQ Library Services, Ministry of Defence, Whitehall Library, 3-5 Great Scotland Yard, London SW1A 2HW
☎020 7218 4445 (general enquiries), 020 7218 4184 (administration)
Fax 020 7218 5413
e-mail: whitehall.lib.mod@gtnet.gov.uk
Chief Librarian R H Searle MPhil ALA

Site libraries
A   Abbey Wood Information and Library Service, Ministry of Defence, Library Building, MOD Abbey Wood #75, PO Box 702, Bristol BS34 8JH
      ☎0117 913 0727
      Fax 0117 913 0943
      Senior Librarian C C W Watson BA ALA
B   Library, Ministry of Defence, Kentigern House, 65 Brown Street, Glasgow G2 8EX
      ☎0141 224 2500
      Fax 0141 224 2257
      e-mail: library@khinf.demon.co.uk
      Librarian Ms M J Gair BA(Hons) DipLib ALA

MORRAB LIBRARY
Morrab Library, Morrab Gardens, Penzance, Cornwall TR18 4DA
☎(01736) 364474
Librarian Mrs A Read
(Available on payment of an annual subscription or a daily fee)

MUSEUM OF LONDON
Library, Museum of London, London Wall, London EC2Y 5HN
☎020 7600 3699
Fax 020 7600 1058
e-mail: info@museumoflondon.org.uk
url: http://www.museumoflondon.org.uk
Library Officer Ms S Brooks MA
(Readers by appointment only)

MUSEUM OF WELSH LIFE (AMGUEDDFA WERIN CYMRU)

Library, Museum of Welsh Life (Amgueddfa Werin Cymru), St Fagans, Cardiff CF5 6XB
☎029 2057 3446
Fax 029 2057 3490
Librarian N L Walker MA DipLib ALA

NATIONAL ARMY MUSEUM

Library, National Army Museum, Royal Hospital Road, London SW3 4HT
☎020 7730 0717 ext 2222 (enquiries), ext 2215 (administration)
Fax 020 7823 6573
e-mail: info@national-army-museum.ac.uk
url: http://www.national-army-museum.ac.uk
Head of Department of Printed Books M B Ball MA AMA
Head of Archives, Photographs, Film and Sound P B Boyden BA PhD
Head of Fine and Decorative Art Miss J M Spencer-Smith MA AMA

NATIONAL ART LIBRARY

National Art Library, Victoria and Albert Museum, South Kensington, London SW7 2RL
☎020 7938 8315 (enquiries), 020 7938 8304 (administration)
Fax 020 7938 8275
e-mail: enquiries@nal.vam.ac.uk
url: http://www.nal.vam.ac.uk/
Chief Librarian J van der Wateren MA DipLib HonFRIBA FLA FRSA

Site library
Archive of Art and Design, National Art Library, 23 Blythe Road, West Kensington, London
W14 0QF
☎020 7603 1514
Fax 020 7602 6907
Assistant Archivist Ms E Salmon

NATIONAL ASSEMBLY FOR WALES

Library, National Assembly for Wales, Cathays Park, Cardiff CF10 3NQ
☎029 2092 3683
Fax 029 2082 3122
e-mail: wolib.cp@gtnet.gov.uk
Chief Librarian D N Allum BA ALA

NATIONAL CHILDREN'S BUREAU

Library and Information Service, National Children's Bureau, 8 Wakley Street, London
EC1V 7QE
☎020 7843 6008 (enquiry line)
Fax 020 7843 6007
url: http://www.ncb.org.uk
Head of Library & Information Ms N Hilliard BA ALA

THE NATIONAL GALLERY

Libraries and Archive, The National Gallery, Trafalgar Square, London WC2N 5DN
☎020 7839 3321
Fax 020 7753 8179

Head of Libraries and Archive Ms E Hector MA ALA (e-mail:
elspeth.hector@ng-London.org.uk)
(Readers by appointment only)

NATIONAL INSTITUTE FOR MEDICAL RESEARCH (MEDICAL RESEARCH COUNCIL)

Library, National Institute for Medical Research (Medical Research Council), The Ridgeway,
Mill Hill, London NW7 1AA
☎020 8959 3666
Fax 020 8913 8534
e-mail: library@nimr.mrc.ac.uk
Librarian R J Moore BA ALA MIInfSc MIBiol

NATIONAL INSTITUTE OF ADULT CONTINUING EDUCATION (NIACE)

Library, National Institute of Adult Continuing Education (NIACE), 21 De Montfort Street,
Leicester LE1 7GE
☎0116 204 4200
Fax 0116 204 4253
e-mail: information@niace.org.uk
Senior Information Officer Ms L McGill (0116 204 4227; e-mail: louise@niace.org.uk)

NATIONAL INSTITUTE OF ECONOMIC AND SOCIAL RESEARCH

Library, National Institute of Economic and Social Research, 2 Dean Trench Street, Smith
Square, London SW1P 3HE
☎020 7654 7665
Fax 020 7654 1900
e-mail: library@niesr.ac.uk
Librarian Miss C Schofield BA DipLib (020 7654 1907; e-mail: claire@niesr.ac.uk)

NATIONAL LIBRARY FOR THE BLIND

National Library for the Blind, Far Cromwell Road, Bredbury, Stockport, Cheshire SK6 2SG
☎0161 355 2000
Fax 0161 355 2098
e-mail: enquiries@nlbuk.org.uk
url: http://www.nlbuk.org
Chief Executive M M Bennett
Development Librarian R Willis-Fear

NATIONAL LIBRARY OF SCOTLAND

National Library of Scotland, George IV Bridge, Edinburgh EH1 1EW
☎0131 226 4531
Fax 0131 622 4803
e-mail: enquiries@nls.uk
url: http://www.nls.uk
Librarian I D McGowan BA

Branch/regional libraries
A   Lending Services, National Library of Scotland, 33 Salisbury Place, Edinburgh
         EH9 1SL

☎0131 226 4531
Fax 0131 466 3814 (UK)
B   Map Library, National Library of Scotland, 33 Salisbury Place, Edinburgh EH9 1SL
☎0131 226 4531
Fax 0131 466 3812
C   Scottish Science Library, National Library of Scotland, 33 Salisbury Place,
Edinburgh EH9 1SL
☎0131 226 4531 (Business Information Help Desk 0131 667 9554)
Fax 0131 466 3810

NATIONAL LIBRARY OF WALES: LLYFRGELL GENEDLAETHOL CYMRU

National Library of Wales: Llyfrgell Genedlaethol Cymru, Aberystwyth, Ceredigion
SY23 3BU
☎(01970) 632800
Fax (01970) 615709
e-mail: holi@llgc.org.uk
url: http://www.llgc.org.uk/
Librarian A M W Green MA DipLib ALA

NATIONAL MARITIME MUSEUM

Caird Library, National Maritime Museum, Greenwich, London SE10 9NF
☎020 8312 6528/6673
Fax 020 8312 6632
e-mail: library@nmm.ac.uk
url: http://www.nmm.ac.uk
Library Resources Manager Ms R Mackenzie BSc MSc
Assistant Librarian Ms A Robinson Blib
Library Assistants Ms C Biggs, Ms S Bennett

NATIONAL MONUMENTS RECORD

Library, National Monuments Record, National Monuments Record Centre, Kemble Drive,
Swindon, Wilts SN2 2GZ
☎(01793) 414600
Fax (01793) 414606
e-mail: info@rchme.co.uk
url: http://www.english-heritage.org.uk
Librarian F Gilmour (01793) 414632
Information Officer P Randell/M Hogg

London Search Room and Library, National Monuments Record, 55 Blandford Street,
London W1H 3AF
☎020 7208 8200
Fax 020 7224 5333
e-mail: london@rchme.co.uk
(For architectural information on Greater London)

NATIONAL MUSEUMS & GALLERIES OF WALES

Library, National Museums & Galleries of Wales, Cathays Park, Cardiff CF10 3NP
☎029 2057 3202
Fax 029 2037 3214
Librarian J R Kenyon BA ALA FSA FRHistS FSA(Scot)

NATIONAL MUSEUMS OF SCOTLAND

Library, National Museums of Scotland, Chambers Street, Edinburgh EH1 1JF
☎0131 247 4137 (enquiries), 0131 247 4153 (administration)
Fax 0131 247 4311
e-mail: library@nms.ac.uk
url: http://www.nms.ac.uk
Head of Library Ms E Rowan MSc
Depute Librarians A Martin MA DipLib, Ms C Whittaker MA
(Amalgamated collections of Royal Museum of Scotland and the former Museum of
Antiquities libraries now based on the Chambers Street site)

Other library
Library, National Museums of Scotland, Scottish United Services Museum, The Castle,
Edinburgh EH1 2NG
☎0131 225 7534 ext 204
Curatorial Assistant Mrs E Philip

NATIONAL PHYSICAL LABORATORY

Main Library, National Physical Laboratory, Queen's Road, Teddington, Middlesex TW11
0LW
☎020 8943 6054
Fax 020 8943 6458
e-mail: enquiry@npl.co.uk
url: http://www.npl.co.uk
Head of Communication & Information Services and Press Officer Mrs R S Osborne
ALA

NATIONAL PORTRAIT GALLERY

Heinz Archive and Library, National Portrait Gallery, 2 St Martin's Place, London WC2H
0HE
☎020 7306 0055 ext 257
Fax 020 7306 0056
url: http://www.npg.org.uk
Head of Archive and Library R K Francis BSc(Hons) MA ALA
Librarian Ms A Leak BA(Hons) MA
(Readers by appointment only)

NATIONAL RAILWAY MUSEUM

Library and Archive, National Railway Museum, Leeman Road, York YO26 4XJ
☎(01904) 621261 (switchboard); (01904) 686235 (for appointments)
Fax (01904) 611112
e-mail: nrm.library@nmsi.ac.uk
url: http://www.nmsi.ac.uk/nrm
Librarian C P Atkins BSc (01904 686208; e-mail: p.atkins@nmsi.ac.uk)

NATIONAL TRUST

National Trust Archives, National Trust, 36 Queen Anne's Gate, London SW1H 9AS
☎020 7447 6462
Fax 020 7222 5097
Archivist and Records Manager Ms J Harley BA DAA
(Corporate archives available to researchers by appointment only and at the discretion of
the National Trust)

National Trust Photographic Library, National Trust, 36 Queen Anne's Gate, London
SW1H 9AS
☎020 7447 6788/9
Senior Picture Researcher R Morris

NATIONAL UNION OF TEACHERS

Library and Information Unit, National Union of Teachers, Hamilton House, Mabledon
Place, London WC1H 9BD
☎020 7380 4713
Fax 020 7387 8458
url: http://www.teachers.org.uk
Information Officer Ms J Friedlander BA ALA (e-mail: janet.f@geo2.poptel.org.uk)

NATIONAL YOUTH AGENCY

Information Centre, National Youth Agency, 17-23 Albion Street, Leicester LE1 6GD
☎0116 285 6789 (enquiries & administration)
Fax 0116 247 1500
e-mail: nya@nya.org.uk
url: http://www.nya.org.uk
Library Officer Ms J Poultney BA (e-mail: jow@nya.org.uk)
(Information collection on young people, the youth service and youth affairs. Provides a
postal loan and enquiry answering service. Personal visitors welcome, by appointment)

NATURAL HISTORY MUSEUM

Library, Natural History Museum, Cromwell Road, London SW7 5BD
☎020 7938 9191, 020 7938 8977 (library management)
Fax 020 7938 9290
e-mail: library@nhm.ac.uk
url: http://www.nhm.ac.uk
Head of Library and Information Services R Lester BSc PhD FIInfSc FLS
(The Library is divided into five specialist sections at South Kensington: General & Zoology
(020 7938 9191); Botany (020 7938 8928); Entomology (020 7938 9491) and Earth
Sciences (020 7938 9207). There is an out-station library: The Library, The Walter
Rothschild Museum, Akeman Street, Tring, Herts HP23 6AP (01442 824181), which con-
tains the collection of works on ornithology.)

NORTHERN IRELAND ASSEMBLY

Library, Northern Ireland Assembly, Parliament Buildings, Stormont, Belfast BT4 3XX
☎028 9052 1250
Fax 028 9052 1715
Librarian G D Woodman BA DipLib ALA (028 9052 1256)
Assistant Librarian Mrs R Menary BA ALA

NOTTINGHAM SUBSCRIPTION LIBRARY LTD

Nottingham Subscription Library Ltd, Bromley House, Angel Row, Nottingham NG1 6HL
☎0115 947 3134
Chief Librarian Mrs J V Wilson BA ALA
(Available to the public for reference purposes only, by prior appointment)

OCCUPATIONAL PENSIONS REGULATORY AUTHORITY (OPRA)

Library, Occupational Pensions Regulatory Authority (Opra), Invicta House, Trafalgar Place, Brighton, East Sussex BN1 4DW

☎(01273) 627686

Fax (01273) 627630

Information Officer Mrs J Godfrey BA(Hons) AIIS BIALL (e-mail: jan.godfrey@opra.gov.uk)

(The Library is not open to the public.)

OFFER (OFFICE OF ELECTRICITY REGULATION)

Library and Information Centre, OFFER (Office of Electricity Regulation), Hagley House, Hagley Road, Birmingham B16 8QG

☎0121 456 6377/8

Fax 0121 456 6376

e-mail: enquiries@offer.gov.uk

Librarian G Campbell BA MIInfSc

OFFICE FOR NATIONAL STATISTICS

National Statistics Information and Library Service, Office for National Statistics, 1 Drummond Gate, London SW1V 2QQ

☎020 7533 6262 (enquiries), 020 7533 6266 (administration)

Fax 020 7533 6261

e-mail: info@ons.gov.uk

Chief Librarian J Birch BLib ALA (020 7533 6250; e-mail: john.birch@ons.gov.uk)

(This library is open to the public. Includes most major government statistical series.)

Site library

A   National Statistics Information and Library Service, Office for National Statistics, Room 1.001, Government Buildings, Cardiff Road, Newport, South Wales NP9 1XG

     ☎(01633) 812973 (enquiries), (01633) 812399 (administration)

     Fax (01633) 812599

     e-mail: library@ons.gov.uk

     Librarian I W Bushnell BA ALA

     (Library open to the public. Specializes in micro-economic data)

B   National Statistics Information and Library Service, Office for National Statistics, Segensworth Road, Titchfield, Fareham, Hants PO15 5PR

     ☎(01329) 813606

     Fax (01329) 813406

     Librarian W Anderson BA ALA

     (This library is not open to the public.)

OFFICE OF FAIR TRADING

Library, Office of Fair Trading, Room 501, Field House, 15-25 Bream's Buildings, London EC4A 1PR

☎020 7211 8938/9

Fax 020 7211 8940

Public Liaison Unit (consumer information line) e-mail: enquiries@oft.gov.uk

url: http://www.oft.gov.uk

Librarian M Shrive BA ALA

OFFICE OF THE RAIL REGULATOR

Office of the Rail Regulator, 1 Waterhouse Square, 138-142 Holborn, London EC1N 2TQ
☎020 7282 2001
Fax 020 7282 2045
e-mail: orr@dial.pipex.com
url: http://www.rail-reg.gov.uk
Librarian Ms S MacSwan BA MSc

OFGAS (OFFICE OF GAS SUPPLY)

Library, OFGAS (Office of Gas Supply), 130 Wilton Road, London SW1V 1LQ
☎020 7932 1602/3/4
Fax 020 7932 1600
e-mail: library@ofgas.gov.uk
url: http://www.ofgas.gov.uk
Librarian Ms B Scott MSc ALA
Assistant Librarian Ms I Ghumra BA(Hons)

OFTEL (OFFICE OF TELECOMMUNICATIONS)

Research and Intelligence Unit, OFTEL (Office of Telecommunications), 50 Ludgate Hill,
London EC4M 7JJ
☎020 7634 8761
Fax 020 7634 8946
e-mail: infocent-oftel@gtnet.gov.uk
url: http://www.oftel.gov.uk
Head of Research and Intelligence Unit Ms K Peart BA(Hons) MA (020 7634 8862)

OFWAT (OFFICE OF WATER SERVICES)

Library and Information Services, OFWAT (Office of Water Services), Centre City Tower,
7 Hill Street, Birmingham B5 4UA
☎0121 625 1361 (general enquiries)
Fax 0121 625 1362
e-mail: enquiries@ofwat.gtnet.gov.uk
url: http://www.open.gov.uk/ofwat/
Librarian and Information Services Manager Miss J W Fisher BSc ALA (0121 625 1361)

THE OMNIBUS SOCIETY

The John F. Parke Memorial Library, The Omnibus Society, Museum of Iron,
Coalbrookdale, Ironbridge, Shropshire
Librarian A Mills (01922 631867)
(Manned by volunteers, the library is currently open to casual callers on the 1st, 3rd and 5th
Wednesdays of the month (09.30–16.30), although other weekday appointments can be
made by prior arrangement.)

OVERSEAS DEVELOPMENT INSTITUTE

Library, Overseas Development Institute, Portland House, Stag Place, London SW1E 5DP
☎020 7393 1600 (enquiries), 020 7393 1643 (direct)
Fax 020 7393 1699
e-mail: library@odi.org.uk
url: http://www.oneworld.org/odi
Librarian/Information Centre Manager Ms K C Kwafo-Akoto MA DipLib FLA
(Limited access to public by appointment only. 10–5 Mon–Fri.)

PARTNERSHIP HOUSE MISSION STUDIES LIBRARY

Partnership House Mission Studies Library, 157 Waterloo Road, London SE1 8XA
☎020 7928 8681
Fax 020 7928 3627
Principal Librarian C E Rowe BA ALA (e-mail: c.rowe@mailbox.ulcc.ac.uk)

PIRA INTERNATIONAL

Information Centre, PIRA International, Randalls Road, Leatherhead, Surrey KT22 7RU
☎(01372) 802050
Fax (01372) 802239
e-mail: infocentre@pira.co.uk
url: http://pira.co.uk/infocentre/
Commercial Director, Information, Training & Publishing Group Mrs M Rushton

PLUNKETT FOUNDATION

Library, Plunkett Foundation, 23 Hanborough Business Park, Long Hanborough, Oxon OX8 8LH
☎(01993) 883636
Fax (01993) 883576
e-mail: info@plunkett.co.uk
url: http://www.plunkett.co.uk
Information Services Manager Ms K Targett BA(Hons)
(Focus on history and practice of cooperatives)

PLYMOUTH MARINE LABORATORY/MARINE BIOLOGICAL ASSOCIATION

National Marine Biological Library, Plymouth Marine Laboratory/Marine Biological Association, Citadel Hill, Plymouth, Devon PL1 2PB
☎(01752) 633266
Fax (01752) 633102
e-mail: nmbl@pml.ac.uk
Head of Library and Information Services Miss L Noble BSc MIInfSc (01752 633282; e-mail: lno@wpo.nerc.ac.uk)

PLYMOUTH PROPRIETARY LIBRARY

Plymouth Proprietary Library, Alton Terrace, 111 North Hill, Plymouth, Devon PL4 8JY
☎(01752) 660515
Librarian Miss C M Blackman

POETRY LIBRARY

Poetry Library, Royal Festival Hall, London SE1 8XX
☎020 7921 0943/0664
Fax 020 7921 0939
e-mail: poetrylibrary@rfh.org.uk
url: http://www.poetrylibrary.org.uk
Librarian Ms M Enright BA DipLib
(Opening hours 11am-8pm 6 days a week; closed on Mondays)

POLICE STAFF COLLEGE

National Police Library, Police Staff College, NPT Bramshill, Bramshill, Hook, Hants RG27 0JW

☎(01256) 602372 (enquiries), (01256) 602100 (main switchboard)
Fax (01256) 602285
e-mail: library@npt.bramshill.ac.uk
Librarian Mrs S E King ALA

POLISH LIBRARY
Polish Library, 238-246 King Street, London W6 0RF
☎020 8741 0474
Fax 020 8746 3798
e-mail: polish.library@mailbox.ulcc.ac.uk
Librarian Dr Z Jagodzinski PhD
Deputy Librarian Mrs J Szmidt MA

THE PORTICO LIBRARY AND GALLERY
The Portico Library and Gallery, 57 Mosley Street, Manchester M2 3HY
☎0161 236 6785
Librarian Miss E Marigliano BA
(Tours by arrangement. Nineteenth-century stock available for scholarly research. Gallery open to the public.)

PROUDMAN OCEANOGRAPHIC LABORATORY
Library, Proudman Oceanographic Laboratory, Bidston Observatory, Birkenhead, Merseyside L43 7RA
☎0151 653 8633 ext 265
Fax 0151 653 6269
url: http://www.pol.ac.uk
Librarian Ms J Martin BA MSc ALA (e-mail: jul@ccms.ac.uk)

PUBLIC HEALTH LABORATORY SERVICE
Central Library, Public Health Laboratory Service, Central Public Health Laboratory, 61 Colindale Avenue, London NW9 5HT
☎020 8200 4400 ext 4616 (enquiries), ext 4617 (Chief Librarian)
Fax 020 8200 7875
e-mail: phlslib@demon.co.uk
Chief Librarian Miss M A Clennett BA ALA MIInfSc
Deputy Librarian D J Keech MSc DipLib ALA MIInfSc (e-mail: d.keech@phls.co.uk)

PUBLIC RECORD OFFICE
Library, Public Record Office, Ruskin Avenue, Kew, Richmond, Surrey TW9 4DU
☎020 8876 3444 ext 2458 (general library enquiries)
Fax 020 8878 8905
Librarian Mrs A Munro Cameron MA(Hons) DipLib (020 8392 5278; e-mail: aileen.cameron@pro.gov.uk)

RADIOCOMMUNICATIONS AGENCY
Information and Library Service, Radiocommunications Agency, 9th Floor, South Quay Three, 189 Marsh Wall, London E14 9SX
☎020 7211 0502/0505
Fax 020 7211 0507
e-mail: library.ra@gtnet.gov.uk
url: http://www.open.gov.uk/radiocom/
Head of Information and Publicity Ms J Fraser BA(Hons) DipLib ALA

Information and Library Service Manager P Hamilton BA(Hons) DipLib ALA

RELIGIOUS SOCIETY OF FRIENDS (QUAKERS)

Library, Religious Society of Friends (Quakers), Friends House, 173-177 Euston Road, London NW1 2BJ
☎020 7663 1135
Fax 020 7663 1001
e-mail: library@quaker.org.uk
Librarian M J Thomas BA DipArchStud

THE RESEARCH COUNCILS

Joint Library and Information Service, The Research Councils, Polaris House, North Star Avenue, Swindon, Wiltshire SN2 1SZ
☎(01793) 442103 (enquiries)
Fax (01793) 442042
e-mail: jils@pparc.ac.uk or library@pparc.ac.uk
url: http://www.pparc.ac.uk/jils/
Senior Librarian Ms I Howard BA ALA (01793 442008; e-mail: howardi@pparc.ac.uk)

Library serves the following research councils based at this site:
Biotechnology and Biological Sciences Research Council (BBSRC) (01793 413200; Fax 01793 413201)
Engineering and Physical Sciences Research Council (EPSRC) (01793 444000; Fax 01793 444010)
Natural Environment Research Council (NERC) (01793 411500; Fax 01793 411501
Particle Physics and Astronomy Research Council (PPARC) (01793 442000; Fax 01793 442002)
Economic and Social Sciences Research Council (ESRC) (01793 413000; Fax 01793 413001) (some enquiries answered on behalf of ESRC)

ROYAL ACADEMY OF ARTS

Library, Royal Academy of Arts, Burlington House, Piccadilly, London W1V 0DS
☎020 7300 5737 (enquiries), 020 7300 5740 (administration)
Fax 020 7300 5765
url: http://www.royal.academy.org.uk
Cables: Royacad, London
Librarian N L Savage BA
Schools Librarian A M Waterton (e-mail: adamw@royalacademy.org.uk)

ROYAL AERONAUTICAL SOCIETY

Library, Royal Aeronautical Society, 4 Hamilton Place, London W1V 0BQ
☎020 7499 3515 (enquiries), ext 233/234 (administration)
Fax 020 7629 4009
e-mail: library@raes.org.uk
Technical Manager A W L Nayler MAIAA MRAeS (e-mail: arnold.nayler@raes.org.uk)
Deputy Librarian B Riddle (e-mail: brian.riddle@raes.org.uk)

ROYAL AIR FORCE COLLEGE

Library, Royal Air Force College, Cranwell, Sleaford, Lincs NG34 8HB
☎(01400) 261201 ext 6329
Fax (01400) 261201 ext 6266
College Librarian & Archivist Mrs J M Buckberry ALA

ROYAL AIR FORCE MUSEUM

Department of Research and Information Services, Royal Air Force Museum, Hendon, London NW9 5LL
☎020 8205 2266
Fax 020 8200 1751
e-mail: info@rafmuseum.org.uk
url: http://www.rafmuseum.org.uk
Senior Keeper P J V Elliott MA BSc MIInfSc
(Prior appointment necessary)

ROYAL ASTRONOMICAL SOCIETY

Library, Royal Astronomical Society, Burlington House, Piccadilly, London W1V 0NL
☎020 7734 3307 (main line), 020 7734 4582 (direct)
Fax 020 7494 0166
e-mail: info@ras.org.uk
url: http://www.ras.org.uk/ras/
Chief Librarian P D Hingley RD BA ALA (e-mail: pdh@ras.org.uk)
Assistant Librarian Miss M I Chibnall BA ALA (e-mail: mic@ras.org.uk)
(Enquiries in writing preferred, access by appointment)

ROYAL BOTANIC GARDEN, EDINBURGH

Library, Royal Botanic Garden, Edinburgh, 20A Inverleith Row, Edinburgh EH3 5LR
☎0131 248 2853 (enquiries), 0131 248 2850 (administration)
Fax 0131 248 2901
e-mail: library@rbge.org.uk
url: http://www.rbge.org.uk
Chief Librarian Mrs H J Hutcheon BSc ALA MIInfSc

ROYAL BOTANIC GARDENS, KEW

Library and Archives, Royal Botanic Gardens, Kew, Richmond, Surrey TW9 3AE
☎020 8332 5414
Fax 020 8332 5430
e-mail: library@rbgkew.org.uk
Head of Library & Archives Vacant
Deputy Librarian J Flanagan ALA

ROYAL COLLEGE OF PHYSICIANS AND SURGEONS OF GLASGOW

Library, Royal College of Physicians and Surgeons of Glasgow, 232-242 St Vincent Street, Glasgow G2 5RJ
☎0141 227 3204 (enquiries), 0141 221 6072 (administration)
Fax 0141 221 1804
Librarian J Beaton MA(Hons) DipLib ALA (e-mail: james.beaton@rcpsglasg.ac.uk)
Archivist Mrs C Parry BA(Hons) DAA FETC (0141 221 9643; e-mail: carol.parry@rcpsglasg.ac.uk)
Library Assistant Mrs A Forrest (e-mail: anna.forrest@rcpsglasg.ac.uk)

ROYAL COLLEGE OF PHYSICIANS OF EDINBURGH

Library, Royal College of Physicians of Edinburgh, 9 Queen Street, Edinburgh EH2 1JQ
☎0131 225 7324
Fax 0131 220 3939

e-mail: library@rcpe.ac.uk
Librarian I A Milne MLib ALA MIInfSc

ROYAL COLLEGE OF PHYSICIANS OF LONDON

Library, Royal College of Physicians of London, 11 St Andrew's Place, Regent's Park,
London NW1 4LE
☎020 7935 1174 ext 312/3
Fax 020 7487 5218
Minicom 020 7486 5687 e-mail: info@rcplondon.ac.uk
url: http://www.rcplondon.ac.uk/docs/info/library/home.htm
Manager, Historical Resources G Davenport BA ALA
Manager, Information and Archives Vacant

ROYAL COLLEGE OF PSYCHIATRISTS

Library, Royal College of Psychiatrists, 17 Belgrave Square, London SW1X 8PG
☎020 7235 2351 ext 138/149
Fax 020 7245 1231
e-mail: library@rcpsych.ac.uk
url: http://www.rcpsych.ac.uk
Librarian Miss E M Nokes MA ALA
Honorary Librarian Dr I Pullen

ROYAL COLLEGE OF SURGEONS OF ENGLAND

Library, Royal College of Surgeons of England, 35-43 Lincoln's Inn Fields, London
WC2A 3PN
☎020 7973 2138 (enquiries), 020 7405 3474 (switchboard)
Fax 020 7405 4438
e-mail: library@rcseng.ac.uk
Librarian Mrs T Knight MA MA DipLib ALA

Lumley Study Centre, Royal College of Surgeons of England, 35-43 Lincoln's Inn Fields,
London WC2A 3PN
☎020 7973 2109 (direct), 020 7405 3474 (switchboard)
Fax 020 7405 4438
e-mail: lumley@rcseng.ac.uk
url: http://www.rcseng.ac.uk
Librarian Mrs L Jones MSc ALA

ROYAL COLLEGE OF VETERINARY SURGEONS

Wellcome Library, Royal College of Veterinary Surgeons, Belgravia House, 62-64
Horseferry Road, London SW1P 2AF
☎020 7222 2021
Fax 020 7222 2004
e-mail: library@rcvs.org.uk
url: http://www.rcvs.org.uk
Head of Library and Information Services T Roper BA DipLib MIInfSc ALA (e-mail:
t.roper@rcvs.org.uk)
Assistant Librarian (Reader Services and Collection Development) Ms J Harris BA
ALA (e-mail: j.harris@rcvs.org.uk)
Librarian (Systems) Ms V Carbines BA (e-mail: v.carbines@rcvs.org.uk)

ROYAL COMMISSION ON THE ANCIENT AND HISTORICAL MONUMENTS OF WALES

National Monuments Record of Wales, Royal Commission on the Ancient and Historical Monuments of Wales, Crown Building, Plas Crug, Aberystwyth, Ceredigion SY23 1NJ
☎(01970) 621200
Fax (01970) 627701
e-mail: nmr.wales@rcahmw.org.uk
url: http://www.rcahmw.org.uk
Secretary P R White BA FSA
Head of NMR Reader Services Mrs H Malaws BLib MIFA

ROYAL ENGINEERS LIBRARY

Royal Engineers Library, Brompton Barracks, Chatham, Kent ME4 4UG
☎(01634) 822416
Fax (01634) 822419
Librarian Mrs M Magnuson

ROYAL ENTOMOLOGICAL SOCIETY

Library, Royal Entomological Society, 41 Queen's Gate, London SW7 5HR
☎020 7584 8361
Fax 020 7581 8505
e-mail: reg@royensoc.demon.co.uk
url: http://www.royensoc.demon.co.uk
Librarian Ms B I Pedersen BA(Hons) ALA

ROYAL GEOGRAPHICAL SOCIETY (WITH THE INSTITUTE OF BRITISH GEOGRAPHERS)

Library, Royal Geographical Society (with the Institute of British Geographers), Kensington Gore, London SW7 2AR
☎020 7591 3040
Fax 020 7591 3001
e-mail: library@rgs.org
url: http://www.rgs.org
Librarian Miss R M Rowe MA(Cantab) MA(Lough) ALA DPA
Deputy Librarian Miss J C Turner BA(Hons)
Library Assistant Ms Y Sarrington BA(Hons) DipLib

ROYAL HORTICULTURAL SOCIETY

The Lindley Library, Royal Horticultural Society, 80 Vincent Square, London SW1P 2PE
☎020 7821 3050
Fax 020 7828 3022
e-mail: library_enquiries@rhs.org.uk
Librarian and Archivist Dr B Elliott

ROYAL INSTITUTE OF BRITISH ARCHITECTS

British Architectural Library, Royal Institute of British Architects, 66 Portland Place, London W1N 4AD
☎020 7307 3707 (24-hr recorded information service); 020 7580 5533 (switchboard)
Fax 020 7631 1802
Members' information line: 0906 302 4444; public information line (calls 50p per min): (0906) 302 0400

e-mail: bal@inst.riba.org
url: http://www.riba.net/
Director Ms R H Kamen BA MAMat MLS FLA FRSA

Branch library
British Architectural Library Drawings Collection, Royal Institute of British Architects, 21 Portman Square, London W1H 9HF
☎020 7580 5533
Fax 020 7486 3797
Assistant Director, Special Collections and Curator, Drawings Collection C Hind MA DipLib ALA

ROYAL INSTITUTE OF INTERNATIONAL AFFAIRS
Library, Royal Institute of International Affairs, Chatham House, 10 St James's Square, London SW1Y 4LE
☎020 7957 5723 or 020 7314 2783 (enquiries)
Fax 020 7957 5710
e-mail: libenquire@riia.org
url: http://www.riia.org
Librarian Ms C Hume BA DipLib ALA MIInfSc (020 7957 5720; e-mail: chume@riia.org)
Deputy Librarian Mrs M Bone BSc (020 7314 2775; e-mail: mbone@riia.org)

ROYAL INSTITUTION OF GREAT BRITAIN
Library, Royal Institution of Great Britain, 21 Albemarle Street, London W1X 4BS
☎020 7670 2939
Fax 020 7629 3569
e-mail: ril@ri.ac.uk
Director of Collections Dr F James (020 7670 2924; e-mail: fjames@ri.ac.uk)

ROYAL INSTITUTION OF NAVAL ARCHITECTS
Library, Royal Institution of Naval Architects, 10 Upper Belgrave Street, London SW1X 8BQ
☎020 7235 4622
Fax 020 7259 5912
e-mail: hq@rina.org.uk
url: http://www.rina.org.uk
Technical Information Officer D Culnane

ROYAL MILITARY ACADEMY SANDHURST
Central Library, Royal Military Academy Sandhurst, Camberley, Surrey GU15 4PQ
☎(01276) 63344 ext 2367
Fax (01276) 412538
e-mail: rmas.library@dial.pipex.com
Senior Librarian A A Orgill MA DipLib ALA

ROYAL NATIONAL INSTITUTE FOR DEAF PEOPLE
RNID Library, Royal National Institute for Deaf People, 330-332 Gray's Inn Road, London WC1X 8EE
☎020 7915 1553 (Voice and Minicom; enquiries & administration)
Fax 020 7915 1443
e-mail: rnidlib@ucl.ac.uk
url: http://www.ucl.ac.uk/library/RNID
Librarian Ms M Plackett ALA

ROYAL NATIONAL INSTITUTE FOR THE BLIND

Research Library, Royal National Institute for the Blind, 224 Great Portland Street, London
W1N 6AA
☎020 7391 2052
Fax 020 7388 0891
e-mail: library@rnib.org.uk
Librarian J B Roland BA DipLib ALA
Library and Information Officer A M Walker BA(Hons)
Library and Information Assistant S Jones BA(Hons)

A   RNIB Braille Library (Contact Customer Services Dept)
B   RNIB Cassette Library (Contact Customer Services Dept)
C   RNIB Talking Books Library, Wembley (Contact 020 7903 6666)

Library Services, Royal National Institute for the Blind, PO Box 173, Peterborough
PE2 6WS
☎(01733) 370777
Fax (01733) 371555
Library Services Manager J Crampton ALA

ROYAL PHARMACEUTICAL SOCIETY OF GREAT BRITAIN

Library, Royal Pharmaceutical Society of Great Britain, 1 Lambeth High Street, London
SE1 7JN
☎020 7735 9141
Fax 020 7793 0232
e-mail: library@rpsgb.org.uk
url: http://www.rpsgb.org.uk
Head of Information Centre R T Allcorn BSc MIInfSc
Librarian R Morrison BLib
Assistant Librarian Miss A S Walker BA(Hons) ALA

ROYAL PHOTOGRAPHIC SOCIETY

Library, Royal Photographic Society, The Octagon, Milsom Street, Bath, Avon BA1 1DN
☎(01225) 462841 ext 217-220
Fax /Answerphone (Library) (01225) 469880
e-mail: collection@rps.org
url: http://www.rps.org
Curator Ms P G Roberts BA(Hons) DipLib FRSA (e-mail: pam@collection.rps.org)
Part-time Librarian Ms G Thompson BA ALA
(Prior appointment essential for members and non-members)

ROYAL SOCIETY

Library, Royal Society, 6 Carlton House Terrace, London SW1Y 5AG
☎020 7451 2606
Fax 020 7930 2170
e-mail: library@royalsoc.ac.uk
url: http://www.royalsoc.ac.uk
Head of Library and Information Services Ms M C Nixon BA MA DipLib ALA

ROYAL SOCIETY FOR THE PREVENTION OF ACCIDENTS

Information Centre, Royal Society for the Prevention of Accidents, Edgbaston Park, 353 Bristol Road, Birmingham B5 7ST

☎0121 248 2063/6

Fax 0121 248 2001

e-mail: infocentre@rospa.org.uk

url: http://www.rospa.org.uk

Information Services Manager Ms P Siddall BSc MSc ALA MIInfSc (0121 248 2065; e-mail: psiddall@rospa.org.uk)

Information Officer (Statistics) Ms D Hooper BA(Hons) (0121 248 2064; e-mail: d.hooper@rospa.org.uk)

Information Officer (Databases) Ms L Kirwan BSocSc MA (0121 248 2063; e-mail: lkirwan@rospa.org.uk)

ROYAL SOCIETY OF CHEMISTRY

Library and Information Centre, Royal Society of Chemistry, Burlington House, Piccadilly, London W1V 0BN

☎020 7437 8656

Fax 020 7287 9798

e-mail: library@rsc.org

url: http://www.rsc.org/library

Librarian P O'N Hoey BSc MBCS FIInfSc

ROYAL SOCIETY OF MEDICINE

Library, Royal Society of Medicine, 1 Wimpole Street, London W1M 8AE

☎020 7290 2940 (enquiries), 020 7290 2931 (administration)

Fax 020 7290 2939 (requests), 020 7290 2976 (administration)

e-mail: library@roysocmed.ac.uk

url: http://www.roysocmed.ac.uk

Director of Information Services I Snowley BA ALA

ROYAL STATISTICAL SOCIETY

Science Library, Royal Statistical Society, D M S Watson Building, University College London, Gower Street, London WC1E 6BT

☎020 7387 7050 ext 2628

Fax 020 7380 7373/7727

Librarian D Chatarji BSc MPhil DipLib

ROYAL TOWN PLANNING INSTITUTE

Library, Royal Town Planning Institute, 26 Portland Place, London W1N 4BE

☎020 7636 9107

Fax 020 7323 1587

e-mail: online@rtpi.org.uk

url: http://www.rtpi.org.uk

Librarian Ms P Dobby BA ALA

RSA

Library, RSA, 8 John Adam Street, London WC2N 6EZ

☎020 7930 5115

Fax 020 7839 5805

e-mail: library@rsa-uk.demon.co.uk
Archivist Ms S Bennett
(Access by appointment)

ST DEINIOL'S RESIDENTIAL LIBRARY

St Deiniol's Residential Library, Hawarden, Deeside, Flintshire CH5 3DF
☎(01244) 532350
Fax (01244) 520643
e-mail: deiniol.visitors@btinternet.com
url: http://www.btinternet.com/~st.deiniols/homepage.htm
Warden Rev. P B Francis MTheol
Librarian: Miss P J Williams BA DipLib
(This is a residential library focusing mainly on Arts/Humanities with approximately 200,000 volumes, plus 50,000 pamphlets and over 250,000 manuscript items. Modern residential accommodation is available for 48 people at modest charges. Any students and scholars are welcome.)

SCIENCE FICTION FOUNDATION COLLECTION

Science Fiction Foundation Collection, University of Liverpool Library, PO Box 123, Liverpool L69 3DA
☎0151 794 2696 (library)
Fax 0151 794 2681
url: http://www.liv.ac.uk/~asawyer/sffchome.html
Librarian/Administrator A Sawyer MPhil ALA (0151 794 2733; e-mail: asawyer@liverpool.ac.uk)

SCIENCE MUSEUM LIBRARY

Science Museum Library, Imperial College Road, London SW7 5NH
☎020 7938 8234
Fax 020 7938 9714
e-mail: smlinfo@nmsi.ac.uk
url: http://www.nmsi.ac.uk/library/
Head of Library Ms P Dingley BA ALA (020 7938 8202)
(A national library for the history and public understanding of science and technology. Open free to the public. Enquiries accepted in person, by letter or by telephone. Some services are run jointly with Imperial College, Central Libraries.)

SCOTTISH BOOK TRUST

Children's Reference Library, Scottish Book Trust, 137 Dundee Street, Edinburgh EH11 1BG
☎0131 229 3663
Fax 0131 228 4293
Children's Librarian Mrs C Young

SCOTTISH ENTERPRISE

BIC, Scottish Enterprise, 120 Bothwell Street, Glasgow G2 7JP
☎0141 248 2700 (main), 0141 228 2268 (direct line)
Fax 0141 228 2589
url: http://www.scotent.co.uk
Manager Ms G Rogers MA DipLib (e-mail: gail.rogers@scotent.co.uk)

SCOTTISH NATURAL HERITAGE

Library Services, Scottish Natural Heritage, 2 Anderson Place, Edinburgh EH6 5NP
☎0131 446 2479 (enquiries), 0131 446 2478 (library management)
Fax 0131 446 2405
e-mail: ils@rasdsnh.demon.co.uk
Library Manager Miss A Coupe ALA

THE SCOTTISH OFFICE

Library and Information Services, The Scottish Office, K Spur, Saughton House,
Broomhouse Drive, Edinburgh EH11 3XD
☎0131 556 8400 (switchboard)
Fax 0131 244 4548
Head of Library and Information Services Vacant (0131 244 8159, Room X1/10,
Saughton House)
Reader Services Librarian B V Bourner MA MA(InfStud) DipEdTech ALA MIInfSc ACIB
(0131 244 4548; e-mail: brian.bourner@scotland.gov.uk)
Bibliographic Services Librarian Miss E M Macdonald BA ALA (0131 244 4546; e-mail:
morag.macdonald@scotland.gov.uk)
Electronic Publishing Unit Librarian Vacant (0131 244 4540)

SIGNET LIBRARY

Signet Library, Parliament Square, Edinburgh EH1 1RF
☎0131 225 4923
Fax 0131 220 4016
e-mail: signet.lib@dial.pipex.com
Librarian Ms A R Walker BA ALA

SOCIÉTÉ JERSIAISE

Lord Coutanche Library, Société Jersiaise, 7 Pier Road, St Helier, Jersey, Channel Islands
JE2 4XW
☎(01534) 730538 (enquiries), (01534) 633392 (administration)
Fax (01534) 888262
e-mail: library@societe-jersiaise.org
url: http://www.societe-jersiaise.org
Librarian Ms M M Billot BA DipLib

SOCIETY FOR COOPERATION IN RUSSIAN AND SOVIET STUDIES

Library, Society for Cooperation in Russian and Soviet Studies, 320 Brixton Road, London
SW9 6AB
☎020 7274 2282
Fax 020 7274 3230
Librarian/Information Officer Ms J Rosen BA(Hons) DipLib

SOCIETY OF ANTIQUARIES OF LONDON

Library, Society of Antiquaries of London, Burlington House, Piccadilly, London W1V 0HS
☎020 7479 7084
Fax 020 7287 6967
e-mail: library@sal.org.uk
url: http://www.dspace.dial.pipex.com/soc.antiq.lond
Librarian E B Nurse MA FSA ALA

SOCIETY OF GENEALOGISTS

Library, Society of Genealogists, 14 Charterhouse Buildings, Goswell Road, London
EC1M 7BA
☎020 7250 0291
Fax 020 7250 1800
e-mail: info@sog.org.uk
url: http://www.sog.org.uk
Librarian Ms S Gibbons BA ALA

SOUTHAMPTON OCEANOGRAPHY CENTRE

National Oceanographic Library, Southampton Oceanography Centre, University of
Southampton, Waterfront Campus, European Way, Southampton SO14 3ZH
☎023 8059 6111 (marine information and advisory service), 023 8059 6116 (general)
Fax 023 8059 6115
url: http://www.soc.soton
Head of Information Mrs P Simpson (e-mail: pauline.simpson@soc.soton.ac.uk)

SUPREME COURT LIBRARY

Supreme Court Library, Royal Courts of Justice, Queens Building, Strand, London
WC2A 2LL
☎020 7936 6587 (enquiries), 020 7936 6552 (administration)
Fax 020 7936 6661
Supreme Court Librarian Mrs S Phillips BL FLA

TATE GALLERY

Library, Tate Gallery, Millbank, London SW1P 4RG
☎020 7887 8838
Fax 020 7887 8901
e-mail: library@tate.org.uk
Librarian Ms M Duff BA DipEd DipNZLS
(Readers by appointment only)

TAVISTOCK AND PORTMAN NHS TRUST

Tavistock Library, Tavistock and Portman NHS Trust, 120 Belsize Lane, London NW3 5BA
☎020 7447 3776 (direct line)
Fax 020 7447 3734
e-mail: info@tavilib.demon.co.uk
Librarian Mrs M L Walker ALA

THE THEATRE MUSEUM

The Theatre Museum Research Department, The Theatre Museum, 1E Tavistock Street,
London WC2E 7PA
☎020 7836 7891
Fax 020 7836 5148
url: http://www.vam.ac.uk
Head of Library and Information Services Ms C Hudson BA ALA

TPS CONSULT LTD

The Information Centre, TPS Consult Ltd, The Lansdowne Building, Lansdowne Road,
Croydon, Surrey CR0 2BX
☎020 8256 4516

Fax 020 8256 4698
Information Centre Manager G Ziynettin (e-mail: ziynettin.gursel@tarmacps.co.uk)

TRADES UNION CONGRESS
TUC Library Collections, University of North London Learning Centre, 236-250 Holloway Road, London N7 6PP
☎020 7753 3184
Fax 020 7753 3191
url: http://www.unl.ac.uk; (TUC Library): http://www.nemo.unl.ac.uk/library/tuc/tucmain.shtml
Enquiries Officer Ms C Coates MA ALA (e-mail: ccoates@unl.ac.uk)

UNITED NATIONS INFORMATION CENTRE
Library, United Nations Information Centre, Millbank Tower (21st Floor), 21/24 Millbank, London SW1P 4QH
☎020 7630 1981
Fax 020 7976 6478
e-mail: info@uniclondon.org
Librarian Ms A Mcleod BSc

UNITED STATES INFORMATION SERVICE
Information Resource Center, United States Information Service, American Embassy, 55/56 Upper Brook Street, London W1A 2LH
☎(0891) 633456 (10am–12 noon, enquiries), 020 7499 9000 ext 2643 (administration)
Fax 020 7629 8288
e-mail: reflond@usia.gov
url: http://www.usembassy.org.uk
Director Ms K Bateman MA DipLib

VETERINARY LABORATORIES AGENCY
Library, Veterinary Laboratories Agency, New Haw, Addlestone, Surrey KT15 3NB
☎(01932) 357314 (enquiries), (01932) 357603 (administration)
Fax (01932) 357608
Acting Senior Librarian Mrs H Hulse BA(Hons)
Librarian i/c Vacant

WELLCOME INSTITUTE FOR THE HISTORY OF MEDICINE
Library, Wellcome Institute for the History of Medicine, 183 Euston Road, London NW1 2BE
☎020 7611 8582 (enquiries)
Fax 020 7611 8369
e-mail: library@wellcome.ac.uk
url: http://www.wellcome.ac.uk/library
Librarian D Pearson BA MA DipLib ALA
Head of Public Services Ms W Fish BA DipLib

WESTMINSTER ABBEY
Muniment Room and Library, Westminster Abbey, London SW1P 3PA
☎020 7222 5152 ext 228
Fax 020 7222 6391
Librarian Dr T A Trowles DPhil

WILLIAM SALT LIBRARY

William Salt Library, 19 Eastgate Street, Stafford ST16 2LZ
☎(01785) 278372
Fax (01785) 278414
e-mail: william.salt.library@staffordshire.gv.uk
url: http://www.staffordshire.gov.uk/archives/salt.htm
Librarian & Head of Archive Services Ms T Randall BA DAS

DR WILLIAMS'S LIBRARY

Dr Williams's Library, 14 Gordon Square, London WC1H 0AG
☎020 7387 3727
Fax 020 7388 1142
e-mail: 101340.2541@compuserve.com
Director of Dr Williams's Trust and Library D L Wykes BSc PhD
(The Congregational Library at 15 Gordon Square is administered by Dr Williams's Library.
Other details are the same)

YORK MINSTER

Library, York Minster, Dean's Park, York YO1 7JD
☎(01904) 625308
Fax (01904) 611119
Librarian Canon J Toy MA PhD
Archivist Mrs L Hampson BA MA
Assistant Librarian Mrs D Mortimer MA ALA

ZOOLOGICAL SOCIETY OF LONDON

Library, Zoological Society of London, Regent's Park, London NW1 4RY
☎020 7449 6293
Fax 020 7586 5743
Librarian Ms A Sylph MSc MIInfSc (e-mail: a.sylph@ucl.ac.uk)

Selected Academic, National and Special Libraries in the Republic of Ireland

AN CHOMHAIRLE LEABHARLANNA (LIBRARY COUNCIL)

Research Library, An Chomhairle Leabharlanna (Library Council), 53/54 Upper Mount Street, Dublin 2, Republic of Ireland
☎(00 353 1) 676 1167/676 1963
Fax (00 353 1) 676 6721
e-mail: libcounc@iol.ie
url: http://www.iol.ie/~libcounc
Research & Information Officer A Bevan MLib ALA

ARCHBISHOP MARSH'S LIBRARY

Archbishop Marsh's Library, St Patrick's Close, Dublin 8 Republic of Ireland
☎(00 353 1) 454 3511 (enquiries & administration)
Fax (00 353 1) 454 3511
e-mail: marshlib@iol.ie
url: http://www.kst.dit.ie/marsh
Keeper Dr M McCarthy
(Archbishop Marsh's Library includes a book conservation bindery and a print, drawing, water-colour, map and flat paper conservation service in the Delmas Conservation Bindery (00 353 1 454 4609))

CENTRAL CATHOLIC LIBRARY

Central Catholic Library, 74 Merrion Square, Dublin 2, Republic of Ireland
☎(00 353 1) 676 1264 (enquiries & administration)
Librarian Ms T Whitington MA DLIS ALA

CHESTER BEATTY LIBRARY

Chester Beatty Library, The Clocktower Building, Dublin Castle, Dublin 2, Republic of Ireland
☎(00 353 1) 269 2386
Fax (00 353 1) 283 0983
e-mail: info@cbl/oe
url: http://www.cbl.ie
Director and Librarian Dr M Ryan (e-mail: mryan@cbl.ie)
(The library is closing to the public in July 1999. Reopening is scheduled for early 2000; please check website for further information.)

DUBLIN CITY UNIVERSITY

Library, Dublin City University, Dublin 9, Republic of Ireland
☎(00 353 1) 704 5418 (enquiries); (00 353 1) 704 5212 (administration)
Fax (00 353 1) 704 5010
url: http://www.dcu.ie/~library/
Director of Library Services P Sheehan (e-mail: paul.sheehan@dcu.ie)

DUBLIN INSTITUTE OF TECHNOLOGY

Central Services Unit, Dublin Institute of Technology, Rathmines Road, Dublin 6, Republic of Ireland
☎(00 353 1) 402 7800 (enquiries), 7801 (administration)
Fax (00 353 1) 402 7802
e-mail: csu.library@dit.ie
url: http://www.dit.ie/library
Head of Library Services P Sheehan BA DipLib LLB (00 353 1 402 7803; e-mail: paul.sheehan@dit.ie)

Senior Librarian, Collection Development Ms A McSweeney BA DLIS MLIS (00 353 1 402 7804; e-mail: ann.mcsweeney@dit.ie)
Senior Librarian, Systems Development Ms U Gavin BA DLIS MLIS (00 353 1 402 7805; e-mail: ursula.gavin@dit.ie)
Faculty Librarian Ms Y Desmond BA DLIS (00 353 1 402 7807; e-mail: yvonne.desmond@dit.ie)

Library, Dublin Institute of Technology, Aungier Street, Dublin 2, Republic of Ireland
☎(00 353 1) 402 3068/9
Fax (00 353 1) 402 3289
e-mail: ast.library@dit.ie
Faculty Librarian Ms A Ambrose BA DLIS (00 353 1 402 3067; e-mail: anne.ambrose@dit.ie)

Library, Dublin Institute of Technology, Bolton Street, Dublin 1, Republic of Ireland
☎(00 353 1) 402 3681
Fax (00 353 1) 402 3995
e-mail: bst.library@dit.ie
Faculty Librarian P Cahalane BA DipLib (00 353 1 402 3682; e-mail: peter.cahalane@dit.ie)

Library, Dublin Institute of Technology, Cathal Brugha Street, Dublin 1, Republic of Ireland
☎(00 353 1) 402 4423/4 (enquiries & administration)
Fax (00 353 1) 402 4499
e-mail: cbs.library@dit.ie
Faculty Librarian B Gillespie BA DipLib (00 353 1 402 4361; e-mail: brian.gillespie@dit.ie)

Library, Dublin Institute of Technology, Kevin Street, Dublin 8, Republic of Ireland
☎(00 353 1) 402 4894 (general enquiries)
Fax (00 353 1) 402 4651
e-mail: kst.library@dit.ie
Faculty Librarian Ms M H Davis BSc(Hons) MLIS MIInfSc (00 353 1 402 4631; e-mail: mary.davis@dit.ie)

Library, Dublin Institute of Technology, 40-45 Mountjoy Square, Dublin 1, Republic of Ireland
☎(00 353 1) 402 4108
Fax (00 353 1) 402 4290
e-mail: mjs.library@dit.ie
Faculty Librarian Ms A Wrigley BA DLIS (00 353 1 402 4128; e-mail: ann.wrigley@dit.ie)

Library, Dublin Institute of Technology, Rathmines House, 143-149 Lower Rathmines Road, Dublin 6 Republic of Ireland
☎(00 353 1) 402 3461
Fax (00 353 1) 402 3499
e-mail: rmh.library@dit.ie
Faculty Librarian Ms A Wrigley BA DLIS (00 353 1 402 4128; e-mail: ann.wrigley@dit.ie)
Librarian Ms A O'Brien BA DLIS (00 353 1 402 3462; e-mail: aoife.obrien@dit.ie)

ECONOMIC AND SOCIAL RESEARCH INSTITUTE
Library, Economic and Social Research Institute, 4 Burlington Road, Dublin 4, Republic of Ireland
☎(00 353 1) 667 1525
Fax (00 353 1) 668 6231
url: http://www.esri.ie
Acting Librarian Ms S Burns BSocSc (e-mail: sarah.burns@esri.ie)

ENTERPRISE IRELAND

Library, Enterprise Ireland, Glasnevin, Dublin 9, Republic of Ireland
☎(00 353 1) 808 2335
Fax (00 353 1) 837 8854
e-mail: infodesk@forbairt.ie
Head of Information Services Department Ms J McCluskey ALA

NATIONAL ARCHIVES

National Archives, Bishop Street, Dublin 8, Republic of Ireland
☎(00 353 1) 407 2300
Fax (00 353 1) 407 2333
e-mail: mail@nationalarchives.ie
url: http://www.nationalarchives.ie
Director Dr D Craig
(Formed by the amalgamation of the Public Record Office of Ireland and the State Paper Office.)

NATIONAL GALLERY OF IRELAND

Art Reference Library, National Gallery of Ireland, Merrion Square West, Dublin 2, Republic of Ireland
☎(00 353 1) 661 5133; ext 159 (librarian); ext 102 (library office)
Fax (00 353 1) 661 5372
Librarian Ms C Cannon BA MPhil MA ALA
(The library is not open to the public whilst being renovated – projected re-opening is in late 1999.)

NATIONAL LIBRARY OF IRELAND

National Library of Ireland, Kildare Street, Dublin 2, Republic of Ireland
☎(00 353 1) 603 0200
Fax (00 353 1) 676 6690
e-mail: info@nli.ie
Director B O'Donoghue

NATIONAL UNIVERSITY OF IRELAND, GALWAY

James Hardiman Library, National University of Ireland, Galway, University Road, Galway, Republic of Ireland
☎(00 353 91) 524411 ext 2540 (enquiries); (00 353 91) 524809 (administration)
Fax (00 353 91) 522394; (00 353 91) 750528 (interlibrary loans)
e-mail: library@nuigalway.ie
Chief Librarian Ms M Reddan DipLib DipSyAn FLAI ALA (00 353 91 524809; e-mail: marie.reddan@nuigalway.ie)
Sub-Librarians
Systems Administrator P Corrigan BA DipLIS (00 353 91 524809 ext 2497; e-mail: peter.corrigan@nuigalway.ie)
Reader Services B Finan BA HDipEd (00 353 91 524809 ext 2738; e-mail: bernard.finan@nuigalway.ie)
Technical Services Vacant
Information Services Ms M Doyle MA HDipEd DipLibTr (00 353 91 524809 ext 3359; e-mail: maeve.doyle@nuigalway.ie)

Branch libraries
A   Medical Library, National University of Ireland, Galway, Clinical Sciences Institute,

---

University Road, Galway, Republic of Ireland
☎(00 353 91) 524411 ext 2791
Fax (00 353 91) 750517
Medical Librarian T Collins BSc HDipEd DipLib DipSyAn FLA MIInfSc (e-mail:
tim.collins@nuigalway.ie)

B Nursing Library, National University of Ireland, Galway, University College Hospital,
University Road, Galway, Republic of Ireland
☎(00 353 91) 524222 ext 4361
Fax (00 353 91) 527214
Nursing Librarian Ms M Ó hAodha BA DipLIS (e-mail: maire.ohaodha@nuigalway.ie)

NATIONAL UNIVERSITY OF IRELAND, MAYNOOTH AND ST PATRICK'S COLLEGE MAYNOOTH

The Library, National University of Ireland, Maynooth and St Patrick's College Maynooth, Co
Kildare, Republic of Ireland
(John Paul II and Russell Libraries)
☎(00 353 1) 708 3884
Fax (00 353 1) 628 6008
e-mail: reader.services@may.ie
url: http://www.may.ie/library/index.htm
Librarian Dr T Kabdebo PhD FLA OM
Deputy Librarian Ms A Neligan BA HDipEd ALA
Sub-Librarian Ms V Seymour BA(Mod) ALA

OIREACHTAS LIBRARY

Oireachtas Library, Leinster House, Kildare Street, Dublin 2, Republic of Ireland
☎(00 353 1) 618 3412
Fax (00 353 1) 618 4109
Chief Librarian M Corcoran

REPRESENTATIVE CHURCH BODY

Library, Representative Church Body, Braemor Park, Churchtown, Dublin 14, Republic of
Ireland
☎(00 353 1) 492 3979
Fax (00 353 1) 492 4770
e-mail: library@ireland.anglican.org
url: http://www.ireland.anglican.org/
Librarian & Archivist Dr R Refaussé BA PhD

ROYAL COLLEGE OF SURGEONS IN IRELAND

The Mercer Library, Royal College of Surgeons in Ireland, Mercer Street Lower, Dublin 2,
Republic of Ireland
☎(00 353 1) 402 2409 (enquiries); 402 2411 (administration)
Fax (00 353 1) 402 2457
e-mail: library@rcsi.ie
Librarian Miss B M Doran BA MBA DipLibr ALAI (e-mail: bdoran@rcsi.ie)

Branch library
RCSI Library, Royal College of Surgeons in Ireland, Beamont Hospital, Beaumont Road,
Dublin 9 Republic of Ireland
☎(00 353 1) 809 2531
Fax (00 353 1) 836 7396

Librarian Ms G McCabe BA DLIS (e-mail: gmccabe@rcsi.ie)

ROYAL DUBLIN SOCIETY
Library, Royal Dublin Society, Ballsbridge, Dublin 4, Republic of Ireland
☎(00 353 1) 668 0866
Fax (00 353 1) 660 4014
Librarian Ms M Kelleher BA(Hons) DipLibInfS (00 353 1 668 0866 ext 386; e-mail: mary.kelleher@rds.ie)

ROYAL IRISH ACADEMY
Library, Royal Irish Academy, 19 Dawson Street, Dublin 2, Republic of Ireland
☎(00 353 1) 676 2570/676 4222
Fax (00 353 1) 676 2346
e-mail: library@ria.ie
Librarian Mrs S O'Rafferty BA HDipEd DLIS (e-mail: s.orafferty@ria.ie)
Deputy Librarian Ms B Cunningham MA DipLib (e-mail: b.cunningham@ria.ie)

TEAGASC
Library, TEAGASC, 19 Sandymount Avenue, Dublin 4, Republic of Ireland
☎(00 353 1) 637 6000
Fax (00 353 1) 668 8023
e-mail: library@hq.teagasc.ie
Librarian Ms D Brennan BA DipLIS

Research libraries

A   Library, TEAGASC, Moore Park Research Centre, Fermoy, Co Cork, Republic of Ireland
    ☎(00 353 25) 42222
    Fax (00 353 25) 42340
    Librarian Ms S Keating (e-mail: skeating@moorepark.teagasc.ie)
B   Library, TEAGASC, National Food Centre, Dunsrea, Castleknock, Dublin 15, Republic of Ireland
    ☎(00 353 1) 805 9500
    Fax (00 353 1) 805 9550
    e-mail: xxx@nfc.teagasc.ie
    Librarian Vacant
C   Library, TEAGASC, Johnstown Castle Research Centre, Wexford, Republic of Ireland
    ☎(00 353 53) 42888
    Fax (00 353 53) 42004
    e-mail: xxx@jcastle.teagasc.ie
    Librarian Ms S Lacey
D   Library, TEAGASC, Oak Park Research Centre, Carlow, Republic of Ireland
    ☎(00 353 503) 70200
    Fax (00 353 503) 42423
    e-mail: xxx@oakpark.teagasc.ie
    Librarian Vacant
E   Library, TEAGASC, Grange Research Centre, Dunsany, Co Meath, Republic of Ireland
    ☎(00 353 46) 25214
    Fax (00 353 46) 26154
    e-mail: xxx@grange.teagasc.ie
    Librarian Ms A Gilsenan
F   Library, TEAGASC, Kinsealy Research Centre, Malahide Road, Dublin 17, Republic of Ireland

☎(00 353 1) 846 0644
Fax (00 353 1) 846 0524
e-mail: xxx@kinsealy.teagasc.ie

TRINITY COLLEGE DUBLIN

Library, Trinity College Dublin, College Street, Dublin 2, Republic of Ireland
☎(00 353 1) 608 1127 (general enquiries); (00 353 1) 608 1661 (Librarian's office)
Fax (00 353 1) 671 9003
e-mail: library@tcd.ie
url: http://www.tcd.ie/library/
Librarian and College Archivist W G Simpson BA MA ALA FRSA (e-mail: wsimpson@tcd.ie)
Deputy Librarian D R H Adams BA DipLib (e-mail: radams@tcd.ie)

Departmental libraries

A   Medical Library, Trinity College Dublin, St James's Hospital, James's Street, Dublin 8,
        Republic of Ireland
        ☎(00 353 1) 454 3922
        Fax (00 353 1) 453 6087
        Site Librarian Ms T Pope BA DipLib (e-mail: thelma.pope@tcd.ie)
B   Occupational Therapy Library, Trinity College Dublin, School of Occupational Therapy,
        Rochestown Avenue, Dun Laoghaire, Co Dublin, Republic of Ireland
        ☎(00 353 1) 284 9687 (afternoons only in term time)
        Fax (00 353 1) 285 5531
        Site Librarian Ms J Moss

UNIVERSITY COLLEGE CORK

The Boole Library, University College Cork, Cork, Republic of Ireland
☎(00 353 21) 902281/902851
Fax (00 353 21) 903119
e-mail: library@ucc.ie
Librarian J Fitzgerald BA MPhil DLIS

Branch/department library

Medical Library, University College Cork, Cork University Hospital, Wilton, Cork City, Republic
of Ireland
☎(00 353 21) 902976/343688
Fax (00-353 21) 345826
Assistant Librarian N McSweeney BA DipLib(Wales) (e-mail: n.mcsweeney@ucc.ie)

UNIVERSITY COLLEGE DUBLIN

Library, University College Dublin, Belfield, Dublin 4, Republic of Ireland
☎(00 353 1) 706 7583 (enquiries); (00 353 1) 706 7694 (administration)
Fax (00 353 1) 283 7667
e-mail: library@ucd.ie
url: http://www.ucd.ie/~library/
Chief Librarian S Phillips BA ALA ALAI (e-mail: sean.phillips@ucd.ie)
Deputy Librarian Miss P Corrigan BA DipLib ALAI (e-mail: pauline.corrigan@ucd.ie)

Site libraries

A   Architecture Library, University College Dublin, Richview, Clonskeagh, Dublin 14,
        Republic of Ireland
        ☎(00 353 1) 706 2741
        Fax (00 353 1) 283 0329

    Librarian i/c Ms J Barrett BMus DipLib (e-mail: julia.barrett@ucd.ie)

B   Medical Library, University College Dublin, Earlsfort Terrace, Dublin 2, Republic of Ireland

    ☎(00 353 1) 706 7471

    Fax (00 353 1) 475 4568

    Librarian i/c Miss S Murphy BA DipLib (e-mail: sheila.murphy@ucd.ie)

C   Veterinary Library, University College Dublin, Ballsbridge, Dublin 4 Republic of Ireland

    ☎(00 353 1) 668 7988

    Fax (00 353 1) 668 9732

    Librarian i/c Ms A Hastings BA DipLib (e-mail: angela.hastings@ucd.ie)

D   Library and Business Information Centre, University College Dublin, Michael Smurfit Graduate School of Business, Blackrock, Co Dublin, Republic of Ireland

    ☎(00 353 1) 706 8920

    Fax (00 353 1) 283 1991

    Librarian i/c Mr J Steele BA DipLib MLIS FLAI (e-mail: steele_j@blackrock.ucd.ie)

UNIVERSITY OF LIMERICK

Library and Information Services, University of Limerick, Limerick, Republic of Ireland

☎(00 353 61) 202166 (enquiries); 202165 (administration)

Fax (00 353 61) 213090

url: http://www.ul.ie

Manager, Library and Information Services Ms L Mitchell MA DipLib DipComp

Schools and Departments of Information and Library Studies

ABERDEEN

School of Information and Media, The Robert Gordon University, Garthdee Road, Aberdeen AB10 7QE

☎(01224) 263900 (administration & enquiries)

Fax (01224) 263939

e-mail: sim@rgu.ac.uk

url: http://www.rgu.ac.uk/schools/~sim/sim.htm

Head of School Ian M Johnson BA FLA MIMgt MIInfSc (e-mail: i.m.johnson@rgu.ac.uk)

ABERYSTWYTH

Department of Information and Library Studies, University of Wales, Aberystwyth, Llanbadarn Fawr, Aberystwyth, Ceredigion SY23 3AS

☎(01970) 622155

Fax (01970) 622190

e-mail: dils@aber.ac.uk

url: http://www.dil.aber.ac.uk/index.htm

Head of Department Gwilym Huws BA ALA

BIRMINGHAM

School of Information Studies, University of Central England in Birmingham, Franchise Street, Perry Barr, Birmingham B42 2SU

☎0121 331 5625 (enquiries & administration)

Fax 0121 331 5675

url: http://www.uce.ac.uk/cis/

Head of School Dr Graham Matthews BA DipLib ALA (e-mail: graham.matthews@uce.ac.uk)

BRIGHTON

The School of Information Management, University of Brighton, Watts Building, Lewes Road, Moulsecoomb, Brighton, Sussex BN2 4GJ

☎(01273) 643500

Fax (01273) 642405

url: http://www.it.bton.ac.uk

Head of School Dr Peter G B Enser BA(Econ) MTech MBCS MIInfSc (e-mail: p.g.b.enser@bton.ac.uk)

BRISTOL

Graduate School of Education, University of Bristol, 8–10 Berkeley Square, Clifton, Bristol BS8 1HH

☎0117 928 7149

Fax 0117 925 4975

url: http://www.bris.ac.uk/Publications/PGProspectus/ss_028.htm

Course Contact for MSc in Information and Library Management Prof E J Thomas MA MSc PhD (0117 928 7138; e-mail: e.j.thomas@bristol.ac.uk)

DUBLIN

Department of Library and Information Studies, University College Dublin, Belfield, Dublin 4, Republic of Ireland

☎(00 353 1) 706 7055 (administration); (00 353 1) 706 7080 (voice mail)

Fax (00 353 1) 706 1161

e-mail: noreen.hayes@ucd.ie

url: http://www.ucd.ie/~lis

Head of Department Prof Mary A Burke BSc MSc PhD (e-mail: mary.burke@ucd.ie)

EDINBURGH

Napier University

Department of Print Media, Publishing and Communication, Napier University, Craighouse Campus, Craighouse Road, Edinburgh EH10 5LG

☎0131 455 6150

Fax 0131 455 6193

url: http://www.pmpc.napier.ac.uk

Head of Department Dr S Lodge MA

Course Leader for BA(Hons)/Librarianship and Information Studies Dr Alistair Duff BA(Hons) MPhil MSc ALA MIInfSc (e-mail: a.duff@napier.ac.uk)

Deputy Course Leader David Craig BA ALA

Student Tutor Dr Chris Atton MA(Hons) DipLib TCert FLA

Queen Margaret University College

Faculty of Arts, Information Management Section, Queen Margaret University College, Clerwood Terrace, Edinburgh EH12 8TS

☎0131 317 3502

Fax 0131 316 4165

url: http://www.qmced.ac.uk

Senior Lecturer James E Herring MA MA(Lib) (0131 317 3508; e-mail: j.herring@mail.qmced.ac.uk)

GLASGOW

Department of Information Science, Strathclyde University, Livingstone Tower, 26 Richmond Street, Glasgow G1 1XH

☎0141 548 3700

Fax 0141 553 1393

e-mail: secretary@dis.strath.ac.uk

url: http://www.dis.strath.ac.uk/

Head of Department Forbes Gibb BA FIInfSc ALA

LEEDS

School of Information Management, Leeds Metropolitan University, The Grange, Beckett Park, Leeds LS6 3QS

☎0113 283 2600 ext 7421 (course enquiries); ext 3242 (school office)

Fax 0113 283 3182

url: http://www.lmu.ac.uk/ies

Head of School John Blake MSc MBCS CStat (e-mail: j.blake@lmu.ac.uk)

LIVERPOOL

Information Management, The Liverpool Business School, Liverpool John Moores University, 98 Mount Pleasant, Liverpool L3 5UZ

☎0151 231 3815 (switchboard); 0151 231 3861 (Business School); 0151 231 3801 (under-graduate programme); 0151 231 3857 (postgraduate programme)

Fax 0151 707 0423

e-mail: d.liston@livjm.ac.uk

url: http://www.livjm.ac.uk/bus

Head of Information Management Doug Haynes MA BSc (0151 231 3592; e mail: d.l.haynes@livjm.ac.uk)

Information and Library Management Leader Glyn Rowland MA (0151 231 3596; e-mail: g.rowland@livjm.ac.uk)

LONDON

City University

Department of Information Science, City University, Northampton Square, London EC1V 0HB
☎020 7477 8382
Fax 020 7477 8584
e-mail: dis@city.ac.uk
url: http://web.is.city.ac.uk/
Head of Department Dr David A R Nicholas MPhil ALA (020 7477 8383; e-mail:
nicky@is.city.ac.uk)
Course Director, Diploma in Pharmaceutical Information Management Dr David Bawden
BSc MSc PhD FIInfSc (0171 477 8390; e-mail: dab@is.city.ac.uk)
Course Director, Electronic Publishing Mrs Susan Jones BA MSc MBCS (020 7477 8398;
e-mail: s.jones@is.city.ac.uk)
Course Director, Information Science and Technology Dr Penny Yates-Mercer BSc MSc
PhD FIInfSc MInstAM (020 7477 8382; e-mail: paym@is.city.ac.uk)
Course Director, Information Science Dr Ian Rowlands BSc MSc MIInfSc (020 7477 8382;
e-mail: ir@iscity.ac.uk)

Thames Valley University

Centre for Information Management, Thames Valley University, St Mary's Road, Ealing,
London W5 5RF
☎020 8579 5000 (switchboard); 020 8231 2198 (department)
Fax 020 8231 2987
url: http://www.tvu.ac.uk
Coordinator, Centre for Information Management Colin Askew BA MSc (e-mail:
colin.askew@tvu.ac.uk)

University College London

School of Library, Archive and Information Studies, University College London, Gower Street,
London WC1E 6BT
☎020 7380 7204
Fax 020 7383 0557
e-mail: o.manager@ucl.ac.uk
url: http://www.ucl.ac.uk/SLAIS/slais.htm
Director of School Prof I C McIlwaine BA PhD FLA

University of North London

School of Law, Governance and Information Management, University of North London,
Ladbroke House, 62–66 Highbury Grove, London N5 2AD
☎020 7753 5031 (enquiries & administration)
Fax 020 7753 5763
e-mail: m.doyle@unl.ac.uk; c.pedulla@unl.ac.uk (for MA course queries)
url: http://www.unl.ac.uk
Head of School Leslie Sheinman
Senior Lecturer (with responsibility for placements, professional liaison and international links
in Information Management) Tony Beard BA CertEd DipLib ALA

LOUGHBOROUGH

Department of Information Science, Loughborough University, Ashby Road, Loughborough,
Leics LE11 3TU
☎(01509) 223052

Fax (01509) 223053
e-mail: dis@lboro.ac.uk
url: http://www.lboro.ac.uk/departments/dis/
Head of Department Prof Cliff McKnight BTech PhD CPsychol AFBPS (e-mail:
c.mcknight@lboro.ac.uk)
Director of LISU (Library & Information Statistics Unit) Dr J Eric Davies MA PhD FLA
FIInfSc MIMgt FinstAM FRSA (01509 223071; fax 01509 223072; e-mail:
J.E.Davies@lboro.ac.uk)
**Project Head (Computers in Teaching Initiative Centre for Library and Information
Studies)** Prof Cliff McKnight

MANCHESTER

Department of Information and Communications, Manchester Metropolitan University, Geoffrey
Manton Building, Rosamond Street West, off Oxford Road, Manchester M15 6LL
☎0161 247 6144
Fax 0161 247 6351
e-mail: infcomms-hums@mmu.ac.uk
url: http://www.mmu.ac.uk/h-ss/dic/
Head of Department R J Hartley BSc MLib ALA MIInfSc
**Professor of Information Management and Director of the Centre for Research in Library
and Information Management (CERLIM)** Prof Peter Brophy JP BSc FLA FIInfSc FRSA

NEWCASTLE UPON TYNE

Department of Information Studies, University of Northumbria at Newcastle, Lipman Building,
Sandyford Road, Newcastle upon Tyne NE1 8ST
☎0191 227 4917
Fax 0191 227 3671
e-mail: il.admin@unn.ac.uk
url: http://www.ilm.unn.ac.uk/
Head of Department Prof Joan M Day BA MA ALA MIInfSc FRSA

SHEFFIELD

Department of Information Studies, University of Sheffield, Western Bank, Sheffield S10 2TN
☎0114 222 2630 (dept/administration)
Fax 0114 278 0300
e-mail: dis@sheffield.ac.uk
url: http://www.shef.ac.uk/~is/home.html
Head of Department Prof Micheline Beaulieu MA PhD FIInfSc (0114 222 2640; e-mail:
m.beaulieu@sheffield.ac.uk)

Name index

All page numbers from 3 to 147 refer to public libraries or public library authorities; page numbers from 201 to 353 refer to academic institutions and special libraries.
Numbers in italic relate to Children's Youth and Schools Library Services section (pages 151–97)

Subject index

The following is an index of known specialist libraries, but does not reflect specialist collections in general libraries. Please refer to the name index for page numbers, or consult the main sequence.

Aeronautics *see also* **Engineering**
Civil Aviation Authority
Imperial College of Science, Technology and Medicine
Royal Aeronautical Society
Royal Air Force College

Agriculture, Horticulture and Botany
Cranfield University
De Montfort University
Forestry Commission
Harper Adams Agricultural College
Horticulture Research International
IGER
Institute of Arable Crops Research, Rothamsted Library
Ministry of Agriculture, Fisheries and Food
Nottingham University
Oxford University
Queen's University of Belfast
Royal Botanic Garden, Edinburgh
Royal Botanic Gardens, Kew
Royal Horticultural Society
Scottish Agricultural College
The Scottish Office
Writtle College

Archaeology *see also* **History**
National Monuments Record
Royal Commission on the Ancient and Historical Monuments of Wales
Scottish Office
University College, London

Architecture
Royal Institute of British Architects
Royal Town Planning Institute
South Bank University
University College Dublin

Art and Design
Birmingham University
Bristol University
Camberwell College of Arts (London Institute)
Central St Martin's College of Art and Design (London Institute)
Chelsea College of Art and Design (London Institute)
Courtauld Institute of Art
Coventry University
Cumbria College of Art and Design
Dartington College of Arts
De Montfort University
Edinburgh College of Art
Falmouth College of Arts
Glasgow School of Art
Hertfordshire University
Hulton Getty Picture Collection
Kent Institute of Art and Design
London College of Fashion (London Institute)
London College of Printing (London Institute)
London University
Loughborough University
National Art Library
The National Gallery
National Gallery of Ireland
National Portrait Gallery
Norwich School of Art and Design
Nottingham University
Portico Library and Gallery
Ravensbourne College of Design and Communication
Royal Academy of Arts
Royal College of Art
RSA
Southampton University
Surrey Institute of Art and Design
St Deiniol's Residential Library
Tate Gallery
Theatre Museum
University of Ulster, Belfast
Wimbledon School of Art

Business, Industry and Management *see also* **Economics**
BG plc
BTG International Ltd
Business Information Source
CCLRC
Chartered Institute of Management Accountants
Chartered Insurance Institute
City Business Library (City of London Libraries)
Competition Commission
Confederation of British Industry
Cranfield University

Support Groups
Royal National Institute for Deaf People
Royal National Institute for the Blind

Theology and Religion
Central Catholic Library
Exeter University
Lambeth Palace Library
London School of Jewish Studies
National Library of Ireland, Maynooth and St
    Patrick's College, Maynooth
Orchard Learning Resources Centre
Partnership House Mission Studies Library
Religious Society of Friends
Representative Church Body
St Deiniol's Residential Library
St Mary's, Strawberry Hill
Spurgeon's College
Westminster Abbey
Westminster College
Dr Williams's Library
York Minster

Transport
Department of the Environment, Transport
    and the Regions
Imperial College of Science, Technology and
    Medicine
Institute of Logistics and Transport
International Maritime Organization
London Transport Museum
National Maritime Museum
National Railway Museum
Office of the Rail Regulator
Omnibus Society

Veterinary Science
Bristol University
Edinburgh University
The Kennel Club
Liverpool University
London University
Royal College of Veterinary Surgeons
Royal Veterinary College
University College Dublin
Veterinary Laboratories Agency

Eighth edition
Walford's Guide to Reference Material
Volume 1: Science and Technology

MARILYN MULLAY AND PRISCILLA SCHLICKE, EDITORS

'Walford is more indispensable than ever'
Indexer

'As always, Walford is international in scope and much more comprehensive than comparable works ... this is an outstanding resource for any academic or large public library.'
American Reference Books

This edition has been completely revised and updated. It contains selective and evaluative entries to guide the enquirer to the best source of reference in each subject area, be it journal article, CD-ROM, online database, bibliography, encyclopaedia, monograph or directory. It features full critical annotations and reviewers' comments and comprehensive author–title and subject indexes. Contents include:

- mathematics
- physics
- earth sciences
- anthropology
- natural history
- zoology
- medicine
- transport vehicles
- household management
- chemical industry
- industries, trades and crafts

- astronomy and surveying
- chemistry
- palaeontology
- biology
- botany
- patents and inventions
- engineering
- agriculture and livestock
- communication
- manufactures
- building industry.

Marilyn Mullay MA ALA is Senior Librarian at the Edinburgh School of Agriculture.
Priscilla Schlicke BA DipLib ALA was until 1994 Senior Lecturer in the School of Librarianship and Information Studies at Robert Gordon University, Aberdeen.

8th edn; 1999; c800pp; hardback; 1-85604-341-X; c£135.00

A Guide to World Language Dictionaries

ANDREW DALBY

Sadly, most of the world's 5000 or more languages will be dead before anyone has had the time or energy to compile a full dictionary giving meanings, nuances, etymologies, etc. However, this unique new work looks worldwide at those languages for which in-depth research dictionaries do exist. It provides the first evaluative and critical bibliography of the dictionaries of 276 languages from Abkhaz to Zulu.

Organized in alphabetical order by language, the Guide appraises the main dictionaries, assessing the special value of each, its strengths and weaknesses and how different dictionaries complement one another. It includes comprehensive bibliographical details including up-to-date information on new editions and supplements and on the progress of multi-volume dictionary projects. There is also cross referencing to language families and comparative dictionaries. Its approach is unique as it:

- gives detailed and critical annotation
- selects those dictionaries that are of long-term research use
- explores inside the dictionaries, approaching them as a user
- shows the script, transliteration and alphabetical order where needed
- traces history and publication dates fully
- includes dictionaries of slang, colloquialisms and dialects
- indicates the best source of word histories.

This is an indispensable guide for dictionary users and researchers who want to know the range of information sources available and how to use them. It is also essential as a tool to enable librarians and linguists to assess the strengths of their own reference collections, for enquiry desk work related to languages and foreign language study, and as a guide for library users.

1998; 480pp; hardback; 1-85604-251-0; £59.95